MICHAEL ARMSTRONG

Lady Clarissa escaping from Lady Dowling's Drawing Room

THE LIFE & ADVENTURES OF
MICHAEL ARMSTRONG
THE FACTORY BOY

Mrs Fanny Trollope

NONSUCH

First published 1840
Copyright © in this edition Nonsuch Publishing, 2007

Nonsuch Publishing
Cirencester Road, Chalford, Stroud, Gloucestershire, GL6 8PE

Nonsuch Publishing (Ireland)
73 Lower Leeson Street, Dublin 2, Ireland

www.nonsuch-publishing.com

Nonsuch Publishing is an imprint of NPI Media Group

For comments or suggestions, please email the editor of this series at:
classics@tempus-publishing.com

British Library Cataloguing in Publication Data.
A catalogue record for this book is available from the British Library.

ISBN 978 1 84588 214 3

Typesetting and origination by NPI Media Group
Printed in Great Britain by Oaklands Book Services

CONTENTS

INTRODUCTION TO THE MODERN EDITION

FRANCES MILTON TROLLOPE WAS BORN on 10 March 1780. She was the daughter of the Reverend William Milton, the son of a Bristol tradesman who had risen above the status of his father through a privileged education at Winchester and Oxford, and Mary Gresley, the daughter of a prosperous Bristol family who could, and did, boast of Norman ancestry. Frances would have, nevertheless, grown up well aware of her inferiority to those around her in both the Bristol and Hampshire society of her youth, although her father's position as a clergyman gave them entry to the society enjoyed by the local gentry. In contrast to her relatively comfortable childhood, Frances was to experience much financial hardship throughout her adult life, which was not to abate until her own success as a writer was achieved at the age of fifty-two. With these struggles she developed a keen concern for the poor, and a wish to help attack the social ills that abounded in Victorian England. This was to be evident in much of her writing, in particular *The Life and Adventures of Michael Armstrong,* which explored the harsh realities of child factory workers in England. Her early life, however, could not have signalled what was to become later.

Fanny, as she preferred to be called, spent her first years in Stapleton, a village just north of the city of Bristol, where her parents had moved from Heckfield, Hampshire, in hope of greater opportunities than the parish living of just £120 that had been available there. Sadly, his wife's early death left William to bring up Fanny, her brother, Henry, and sister, Mary, alone, along with his own ageing father. The absence of a maternal presence in the young sisters' lives meant they grew up unaccustomed to the domestic skills usually acquired by girls in their day, and Fanny's attentions were thus permitted to stray to other pastimes. She began to read voraciously, and her love for this was later to become a characteristic of all the heroines in her own novels. The death of her mother was to affect her in other ways too; she was forced to become more independent and self-reliant than she would perhaps otherwise have been, something that must have given her the strength to make many of the difficult decisions she faced throughout her life.

After a few short years spent in Clifton, a fashionable spa town overlooking the docks of Bristol's city centre, Fanny's father, along with his new wife, moved the Milton family back to Heckfield in 1801. Although she always looked back on her time there with fond memories, when the opportunity to escape the boredom of rural life arose just two years later Fanny seized it eagerly, as Henry had obtained a position at the War Office in London and wished his two sisters to join him. Together, the three young Miltons set up a home for themselves in Russell Square, and began to make new acquaintances through Henry's work colleagues, enjoying dinner parties and theatre trips. It was in 1808 that Henry introduced Fanny to Thomas Anthony Trollope, and just a year later they were married. They moved into a house owned by Thomas Anthony on the same street in Russell Square, and Fanny settled happily into domestic life. A succession of six children soon followed; Thomas in 1810, Henry in 1811, Arthur in 1812, Anthony in 1815, Cecilia in 1816 and, lastly, Emily in 1818.

However, the Trollope family's early days of prosperity had gradually begun to decline by the time of Emily's birth; Thomas Anthony's legal practice was suffering from a lack of clients, and the inheritance he had been depending upon was lost when his childless uncle remarried after the death of his wife, and soon became a father to a son and heir. This left Fanny and her large family to rely upon the success of her husband's career, which was not to be forthcoming, and over the years their financial hardship steadily worsened to the point of despair. This situation drove Fanny to make some drastic decisions, the first of which was to take her family to America, in hope of greater opportunities and prosperity. Their principal venture, to set up a shop selling British goods, proved a failure, but Fanny's experiences inspired her to write a book, which was published on her return to England in 1832. *Domestic Manners of the Americans* met with instant success, and at fifty-two Fanny had become a celebrity, while at the same time singularly reviving the fortunes of her family.

Domestic Manners was to be followed by another forty books, of which *The Life and Adventures of Michael Armstrong* was one of her most ambitious and, at the time, controversial. The first 'industrial' novel to appear in England, it explored the plight of child factory workers, something Fanny was inspired to write about after reading an account of the life of Robert Blincoe, a workhouse orphan who was forced into child labour. She spent several weeks visiting factories in Manchester and Bradford to research the realities of life for the child workers, as well as speaking to those involved in the campaign for factory reform. The novel, which tells the story of a factory boy called Michael Armstrong, was published in 1840, and was the first novel by a woman to be released in monthly instalments. This was to ensure that it would reach as wide an audience as possible, including the working classes, something which courted controversy for its author. Many people at the time believed the book encouraged people to hate factory owners, and some even went as far as to suggest she should go to prison for writing it! However, the book also did much to shock the middle classes out of their complacency regarding factory conditions, and it is clear that her writing encouraged people to demand legal changes. The Factory Act of 1844 did just that, limiting child working hours to six-and-a-half-hour shifts. Other novels were produced in a similar vein, such as *Jonathan Jefferson Whitlaw*, about the evils of slavery, and *Jessie Philips*, which explored the Poor Laws. Regardless of some contemporary criticism, Fanny Trollope was certainly one of the most popular writers of her day, although this, inexplicably, did not guarantee her lasting renown, and her son Anthony went on to achieve far greater fame as a novelist. Despite this, her novels undoubtedly have much to offer to the modern reader; *The Life and Adventures of Michael Armstrong* is a fine example of her literary abilities, and one which cannot fail to revive a much-deserved interest in this remarkable woman.

I

Description of Dowling Lodge and its appurtenances—Of its master—
Of its mistress—And all the Masters and Misses Dowling—A large
dinner-party—A hot drawing-room, and the way to escape from it

N O TRAVELLER CAN RIDE OR drive within sight of Dowling Lodge, without being tempted to inquire, "Whose house is that?"

It forms, indeed, a very striking object on the right of the London road, as the hill rises gradually, and overlooks the town of Ashleigh, one of the busiest in Lancashire, to the left; for although the trees about the mansion are not yet of sufficient growth to make it picturesque, its lofty portico, well-proportioned wings, and commanding site, render it an ornament to the neighbourhood for miles around.

Those who are admitted to a nearer view of the house (and, for the convenience of the public, every Wednesday is set apart for its being shown), will find still more to admire, than such as see it only from a distance. It has its park and its pinery; conservatories, which cause the mercury in the thermometer, when paraded through them, to run up to the cocoa-ripening heat of the tropics, and ice-houses that would bring it down again to the temperature of Bhering's Straits. It has three drawing-rooms, two dining-rooms, a great library, all full of new books; as many bedrooms, dressing-rooms, and boudoirs, as a great man's house ought to have, and a study besides—Sir Matthew Dowling's own private study. This delightful little apartment is small, not more than twelve feet square; but nothing can be more agreeable and convenient. It opens by one door from the great hall of entrance, and by another communicates through a long stone-passage with the offices of the mansion; enabling the knight to receive, without interruption, not only his over-lookers (Sir Matthew being the proprietor of many cotton-mills), but his coachman, gardener, bailiff, and whomever else he might wish to transact business with.

Of the fitting up of this princely mansion, it is only necessary to say, that it is done in a spirit of emulative imitation, which renders it fully equal, in this respect, to the most finished private dwellings in Europe. The furniture is uniformly rich throughout: the picture-frames in the best style of art; Saxony carpets in the drawing-rooms, Turkey ditto in the dining-rooms, Brussels in the bedrooms, and indeed not a single inch of Kidderminster any where, except in the garrets.

I will not attempt to state the amount of Sir Matthew Dowling's wealth; Cocker himself would have found it a laborious task to make the calculation; and it is sufficient for the gratification of all reasonable curiosity to say, that throughout the whole line of that Golconda country, which, being the busiest of the manufacturing districts, is probably the richest in the world, there was not any one who could vie in wealth with him. In a word, he shone amidst his rich neighbours like a golden sun, surrounded by silver moons.

But Sir Matthew was a superior man in all ways. He was six feet two inches in height, and stout in proportion, with hands and feet that might have sufficed a giant. His intellectual gifts were also of no ordinary character. He liked well enough, perhaps, to stand pre-eminent in the commercial estimation of his neighbours; but so enlightened was his spirit, that he liked better still to shine before their eyes as a man of taste, a literary and accomplished gentleman, a speaker of modern languages, a critical French scholar, a playful votary of the muses himself, and a universal Mecænas to all who wielded a pen in their service. But beyond all else, Sir Matthew valued himself upon his reputation for the lighter graces of wit and gallantry: he sought to make himself into something of a delightful mixture between Killegrew and the Count de Gramont; and there was no receptacle of wit from Joe Miller downwards, no gallant memoirs in an intelligible tongue, that he did not study with assiduity and perseverance of the highest order.

He was often heard to declare, that he loved nothing so well as the promotion of mirth and light-heartedness among his fellow creatures;

THE LIFE & ADVENTURES OF MICHAEL ARMSTRONG

but tragedy and comedy often walk through the world hand in hand together, and their alliance may be traced without difficulty in the career of Sir Matthew Dowling.

The wife of this prosperous gentleman had also many admirable qualities. She was not one of the idle gossipers who delight in chattering about their own concerns to every one who will listen! she despised such weakness, and had never been heard to hint at her own parentage, or early history, to any one; rightly considering, that when such matters are unceasingly discussed, they may be exceedingly likely to prevent people's minding their own business, while devoting an undue share of attention to that of others.

Nevertheless, with nice and laudable discrimination, she took care that her neighbours should be well acquainted with all such facts respecting her as it concerned them to know. There was hardly an individual within ten miles who was not aware that Lady Dowling kept two carriages, six horses, one coachman, one postilion, five gardeners, two grooms, three footmen, one butler, and a page—not to mention two nurses, four nursery-maids and more ladies'-maids, housemaids, cook-maids, kitchen-maids, laundry-maids, still-room maids, dairy-maids, and the like, than any other lady in the country. Neither could any be ignorant that, except in the article of jewels, her wardrobe might vie with that of any duchess in the land, and all might see, moreover, that she was comely still, both in form and feature. She conversed with great ability on all subjects connected with fashionable life; and though some few carping critics thought that she was too apt to diversify the monotony of the English language, by indulging in some remarkable variations from its ordinary laws, nobody, or scarcely any body, attempted to deny that she was on the whole a very charming woman. Such was the testimony of her general acquaintance; those who knew her better were aware that her moral qualities outshone, as they always ought to do, all her external graces. She was a faithful and exceedingly fond wife, and doted upon all her children; no woman could more heartily detest every species of light flirting airs in females, and, being deeply sensible of the dangerous attractions of youth and beauty in her own sex, she studiously avoided bringing those of her family who might suffer thereby from coming in contact with any thing of the kind; so that the female portion of her establishment consisted of the ugliest set of neat and carefully dressed middle-aged women that ever were found assembled together.

The knight and his excellent lady were blessed with a very numerous progeny, certainly not less than eighteen or twenty; but, as they were rarely all at home together, it was at no time easy to count them.

Augustus, the eldest of the family, was a prodigiously fine young man, just returned from college. He had not indeed thought it necessary to take a degree, nor did Sir Matthew or her ladyship particularly wish it, both of them being of opinion that little distinction could be gained by the assumption of a title which was never used in society, and to which he conceived every Englishman to be eligible who could just read and write a little. But as, on all points that concerned the interest of his eldest son, Sir Matthew was too deeply interested to run any risk of blundering: he did not give his consent for the return of Augustus, without his having gone through this idle academic ceremony, till he had paid a visit to the rector of his parish, to elicit from him some information on the subject.

"May I ask, sir," said Sir Matthew abruptly, "what degree you took at the university?"

Mr Hetherington was a new incumbent, and might, perhaps, have been a little affronted at a question which, by the blunt manner of it, seemed almost to insinuate a doubt whether he had taken any degree at all; but, though a good man, and an excellent clergyman to boot, he had a strong taste for humour, and had already discovered that his neighbour at the great house was rich in more ways than one. It was, therefore, with the utmost civility that he answered, "My degree, Sir Matthew, was that of Master of Arts."

"And pray, sir, does it give you any title by which you can be distinguished as in any way a superior sort of person in society?"

"I am afraid not, Sir Matthew," was the reply.

"I thank you, sir, for your sincerity," rejoined the knight. "It was important that I should ascertain the truth on this point.—You are, then, never addressed in company as Mr Master of Arts, or any thing of that kind?"

"I have never yet, Sir Matthew, met with any one of sufficient politeness to do me that honour," replied Mr Hetherington gravely.

"And I suppose you have lived in respectable society?"

"Very decent society—very decent, Sir Matthew," replied Hetherington, whose mother was the daughter of a distinguished nobleman.

"Good morning, sir; I shall be happy to see you at Dowling Lodge— that is to say, sir, if your gown does not lead you to object to elegant amusements. I love science, Mr Hetherington, and am indeed devoted to every thing intellectual, but, notwithstanding this, I am a worshipper at the shrine of grace and wit, and could not exist among people who did not relish the lighter embellishments of society."

"I shall be happy, Sir Matthew, to share in your gayer hours, provided I am fortunate enough to find that you have no objection to profit by my graver ones," replied the clergyman.

Sir Matthew returned from this visit very well pleased with the new rector. Mr Augustus was immediately comforted by a letter, informing him that he might call in his accounts, and prepare to leave the university as soon as he pleased; and, within ten days after receiving it, the amiable young man was restored to the bosom of his family.

Next to this primal hope of the Dowling race, came three young ladies, between the ages of seventeen and twenty-one; the two eldest of them being as like as two peas, and the third like nothing on earth but herself. Then followed several young gentlemen, who were placed at different fashionable schools; for Sir Matthew, who was a man of very enlarged mind, declared it to be his opinion and his principle, that the patronage of such a fortune as his should be extended as widely as possible. After these young gentlemen came, one after the other, with the interval of about eleven months between them, ever so many little girls, who, for the present, were all educated at home, having a particularly clever French governess. All the rest were nice little children of different degrees of babyhood; the dear little girls being remarkable for their long plaited hair, short frocks, and furbelowed trousers, and the dear little boys for the manly bustle with which they wore their Scotch bonnets and plaided tunics, which, considering that neither Sir Matthew nor his lady had ever been in Scotland in their lives, showed

great enlargement of national feeling. Altogether, it was considered to
be the finest family ever seen.

It happened upon a broiling day about the middle of July, during
one of the hottest summers England had ever known, that Sir Matthew
and Lady Dowling "entertained a party of distinguished fashionables"
at dinner.

It may have been remarked by those who study such subjects, that
there is a difference between a dinner-party given at such a grand
mansion as that of Sir Matthew Dowling, and one at a dwelling of
perhaps not a quarter the size, where the owners are of a different order
of the aristocracy, having a longer pedigree, and a shorter purse. At both,
probably, the banquet will be a costly one, yet the one entertainment
will *come off* in a manner as unlike as possible to the other. There is so in
the usual way of wearing stiff new-made grandeur, not far unlike that of
wearing stiff new-made clothes. Neither the one nor the other sits easily.

At this splendid dinner at Dowling Lodge, the company consisted of
a selection from the neighbouring families, made on the most legitimate
principles of exclusiveness; no family being invited who did not drive
four horses at the races. To this there were indeed two exceptions.
The first was the Right Honourable Lady Clarissa Shrimpton; but this
distinguished lady, though she drove only one pony instead of four
horses, was considered by all the country round as the one thing needful
to render a party completely elegant. She was, indeed, neither young,
handsome, nor rich, but she was Lady Clarissa, and this was enough.

The other exception was to be found in the rotund person of Dr
Crockley, who having formerly been a celebrated quack, made a little
fortune, and taken out a diploma, had lately married a beauty, and settled
in the town of Ashleigh, where he was well pleased to pick up a few
guinea fees, both as a public evidence of his being a real M.D., and as
a private fund wherewith to indulge his still very tender passions by
buying finery for his pretty young wife.

This fat little gentleman was an especial favourite with Sir Matthew,
chiefly on account of his jocund humour and ready laugh; and also,
perhaps, because he had a pleasant way, peculiar to himself, of paying
compliments in the bluntest and most unstudied manner possible.

But, notwithstanding the presence of all these distinguished persons, the dinner moved on very slowly. Sir Matthew, indeed, was as brilliant as it was possible for any man to be under the circumstances, and Lady Clarissa, who did not scruple to declare that she was very partial to him, listened to all he said to her with as much attention at least as any lady could be expected to do, who was making one of sixteen at a dinner, where there were an equal number of dishes of hot meats reeking upon the table, and the thermometer standing at 87°. Dr Crockley, too, laughed repeatedly; but his laugh was like a Lucifer match that fails, just kindling and sputtering a little, but going out before it is able to communicate its light.

The very sight of the servants as they panted round the table, was quite enough to smother and stifle all inclination for enjoyment—their shoes creaked—their faces shone—ice became water—the salad looked as if it were stewed—the cucumbers seemed to have fainted away—the prodigious turbot smelt fishy, and its attendant lobster-sauce glowed not with a deeper tint, than did my Lady Dowling's cheeks as her nose caught the unfragrant gale. In short, it was a great dinner in the dog-days, and no more need be said of it.

Great was the inward satisfaction of every guest, when at last Lady Dowling rose, and gave signal that the party was to be divided in half. The languid ladies welcomed the coolness of the marble hall as they passed through it, and the gentlemen gazed eagerly at the butler as he brought forward a fresh supply of claret, and a reinforcement of ice. But the enjoyment of neither party lasted long; for Lady Dowling was too grand and too solemn not to marshal all her company into her fine drawing-room, where they were all ceremoniously deposited on satin sofas, amidst swelling pillows that might have defied the frosts of January; while seven or eight hot-looking children were commanded to walk round the circle and kiss every body.

Nor did the gentlemen fare much better; for scarcely had the drawing-room door closed after the ladies, before the shining bald head of Dr Crockley stretched itself up nearly to a level with the long-backed Sir Matthew's breast-pin, whilst, with a very ominous sort of growl, making itself heard before his lips opened, he first preluded, and then uttered the following speech.

"I don't like it, Sir Matthew.—I don't like this business at the Weavers' Arms."

"What business, Doctor?" replied his friend sharply.

"Why this meeting, Sir Matthew. I can't get the notion of a strike out of my head." Every chair was drawn towards the little doctor: nobody had heard a word of it. "Well, gentlemen, perhaps I am mistaken—perhaps there has been no meeting," resumed the friendly doctor. "God knows, I don't wish to spoil the enjoyment of this delightful hour; but at any rate, my good friends, it is as well for you to be on the look-out." Then lowering his voice, he muttered, as near to the ear of Sir Matthew as he could reach, "I know that your people are meeting, in doors and out of doors. But you are such a good, generous, kind-hearted creature, that I dare say we shall hear, before long, of your having done some d—d good-natured thing or other, and that perhaps will set all right; who knows?"

Sir Matthew gave an almost imperceptible nod, and pushed on the claret-jug; but the gaiety of the party had been effectually checked, and it was not long before the second richest man in company (Sir Matthew of course being the first) said, "I do think and believe, Sir Matthew, that my lady's coffee would do more to cool us than your wine." The opinion was not opposed, and, much earlier than usual, the gentlemen rose, and followed the ladies.

But this movement did not appear greatly to increase the enjoyment of either party. It was near nine o'clock, but the heat continued to be most oppressive, and the company being for the most part massive in all ways, their union produced more additional caloric than gaiety. The whole process seemed to have the power of turning the hours into molten lead as they passed, a portion of which appeared to drop, and weigh heavily on each individual head. In vain Sir Matthew made the circuit of the company, pausing in front either of the richest or handsomest ladies, as duty or inclination preponderated; in vain he uttered his newest puns and freshest bon-mots—not one of them had strength to laugh, beyond a little feeble "he, he!" and even that was evidently a painful effort.

Things were in this state, when Lady Clarissa Shrimpton suddenly rose from the silken couch amidst whose pillows she was imbedded, and, without explaining her intentions to my Lady Dowling, or any one else, darted through the open French-window, and out upon the well-shaven lawn.

Had it been possible that any one in the room could have been ignorant of the rank of Lady Clarissa, he must from that moment have felt an innate conviction that she was somebody; for nobody that was not somebody could have ventured upon so daring an escapade from such a solemn presence-chamber. The effect it produced was electric, Sir Matthew darted across the room with the eagerness of a man of gallantry and gaiety. He piqued himself upon being, of all the great men in the neighbourhood, the one upon whom Lady Clarissa bestowed the most attention. His estimate of the outward advantages of his extensive person was indeed not a low one; and, despite all his lady could do to crush such an odious idea, he was conscious that he was devoted to the fair sex, and flattered himself that the fair sex was not ungrateful. In fact, his general manner to ladies had a good deal of what in female slang is called *swaining*; but to Lady Clarissa it was certainly something more. Had she been simply Miss Shrimpton, it is probable that notwithstanding her great mental advantages, she would never have been exposed to the danger of this fascinating distinction, for she was nearly forty years old, had a sharp nose, and was deplorably thin. But Sir Matthew was not a man to be insensible to the charm of getting talked of in the neighbourhood about his devotion to Lady Clarissa, even had she been a skeleton with a Gorgon's head. There was, however, independently of her bewitching title, a charm in her conversation and character, to which the knight was peculiarly sensible. Her ladyship was celebrated for her devotion both to literature and art; and she permitted all the world to know, for indeed she never ceased to repeat it, that talent of every kind was to her an object of idolatry. Now Sir Matthew knew that he was full of talent—poetical talent, pictorial talent, epigrammatic talent, every kind of talent, and it was certainly very delightful to be appreciated by such a superior creature as Lady Clarissa. So strongly indeed did this intellectual sympathy between them occasionally manifest itself, that not even the sharp elbows and red-tipped nose of the noble lady, who, to borrow the phrase of an inimitable describer, was in every sense "*preter-blue perfect*," could render Lady Dowling quite easy respecting the nature of the friendship. Nor was it without something like a pang that she marked the sudden alacrity of movement with which Sir Matthew now strode across the floor to accompany Lady Clarissa in the extraordinary frolic which led her, in white satin shoes and a gauze dress to exchange the drawing-room for the garden, at nine o'clock in the evening.

But upon this occasion, as upon many others, Lady Dowling found consolation in the well-known fact, that Lady Clarissa rarely moved a step without being obsequiously attended by her humble companion, Miss Mogg. This young lady had been selected to fill her present enviable situation, principally from her appearance, though she was indeed by no means void of many other qualifications admirably suited to it. But in appearance she was a striking contrast to her tall and slender patroness; and, notwithstanding Lady Clarissa's mental superiority, she was not insensible to the advantage of having a foil that should set off the charms upon which she particularly prided herself. Lady Clarissa had a thin, narrow foot, and an ankle that resembled nothing so much as the leg of a Robin red-breast; the person of Miss Mogg was supported on shafts that told her Saxon origin, and feet that need not have shrunk from sustaining an ox. Lady Clarissa's slender waist might have been encircled by a ring of six inches diameter; a cestus of nearly double the span had often gone nigh to suffocate her plump companion. The throat of Lady Clarissa had not only all the flexile length of the swan's, but might even be said to resemble that of the stork in its proportions; while the head of Miss Mogg was separated from her shoulders by an interval so trifling, as hardly to be perceptible at all. The hair of her ladyship, though not very abundant, was as black as ink, and its straight nature enabled her to lay it in classic bands upon her forehead, furnishing a graceful foundation for the wreath of oak leaves with which, in judicious imitation of Domenichino's exquisite head of Sappho, she usually adorned herself when in full dress: while Miss Mogg, on the contrary, had a bushy abundance of flaxen curls, which gave a round fussy sort of contour to her face, that could not fail of setting off to advantage the severer outline of the noble lady; and, in a word, the contrast was altogether perfect.

To the great satisfaction of Lady Dowling, this round little personage arose, as usual, when her principal rose, and waddled to the window after her. Many people are apt to overlook and forget companions, and the poor toady is as much used to he trod upon as the despised reptile whose name she bears. But if the world in general be found guilty of this scorn towards what is too lowly to turn, and scorn again, more especially was our knight liable to the weakness.

As he now hastened to offer his hand to Lady Clarissa in order to assist her in stepping over the window-sill, he very nearly overturned Miss Mogg as he passed her; but heeding neither the resistance her plump person offered to his passing elbow, nor yet the timid "oh!" which spoke her alarm, he hurried onward, and, manfully seizing the hand whose touch was honour, walked out side by side with the titled lady upon the lawn.

II

A delightful ramble—Friendship and the muse—
An adventure—Danger and escape—Gratitude and benevolence

"ONLY SEE THAT! HOW VERY extraordinary!" exclaimed Lady Dowling, suddenly rising, and addressing herself to no one in particular.

"Oh! how delightful!" cried several ladies at once. "How clever Lady Clarissa is! Such a delicious refreshment!" "To be sure, it the only thing in the world to do on such an evening as this," exclaimed Miss Brotherton, who, as being the richest young lady in company, very properly thought she ought to speak first. "I am sure I shall follow her example;" and so saying, she rose and walked towards the window. Three of the most dauntless ladies in the party started up to follow her; which, strange as the manœuvre appeared to the full-dressed Lady Dowling, she did not oppose, greatly preferring that the garden party should be enlarged. But, though not by her, the adventurous fair ones were stopped before they accomplished their design, by a chorus of remonstrtnces from all the rest of the company, male and female.

"My dear Miss Brotherton, you will catch your death!" cried one.

"Oh! look at your satin shoes!" screamed another.

"What would Mr Tomkins say if he was here, Mrs Tomkins?" demanded a third.

"And your neck and shoulders, Miss Williamson!" whispered a fourth.

"And your blonde dress, Mrs Simpkins!" vociferated a fifth; with a vast deal more in the same strain. So that before the *sortie* was accomplished, every lady, save Miss Brotherton, yielded before the storm of reasons that pelted them on all sides. The rich young lady, however, stood firm: what young lady with two hundred thousand pounds would not?

"Mr Augustus Dowling," said she, still pursuing her way window-ward, but pausing ere she stepped out, "will you have the excessive kindness,—*vraiment j'ai honte*; but will you have the charity to look in the hall for my pink satin *mantelet*, trimmed with swansdown; without it I fear my poor little shoulders will be *arrosées*—'too rudely, alas!' with the dews of night."

Now the young lady's shoulders were really very pretty little shoulders, and, moreover, Mr Augustus Dowling, notwithstanding all his elegant *nonchalance*, perfectly well remembered that she had two hundred thousand pounds; so, before she had stamped with her little foot twice, in her impatience to join those who, from their gaiety, seemed to be so greatly enjoying the fresh air, he returned with the *mantelet*, and having, as usual, adjusted his glass in the corner of his eye to present his making any mistakes, placed it on her shoulders.

"Now, then!" she cried, "give me your arm. Is not this good fun?"

The young gentleman obeyed, declaring it was delightful, and in a moment they were beside Lady Clarissa and Sir Matthew; good Miss Mogg keeping a step or two behind.

"Nobody but your ladyship had wit enough to find out that there was more air to be got out of doors than in," said the heiress, venturing to pass her arm through that of her noble friend. But, upon this occasion, Lady Clarissa, though particularly intimate with Miss Brotherton, and seldom refusing to use her carriage and act as her chaperone to all the parties in the neighbourhood, seemed inclined to check her advances.

"My dear child," said she, "I am delighted to see you come out. I am sure you must have been half stifled, as well as myself. But you and Mr Augustus must wander away by yourselves, and you may take Mogg with you, if you like it, for I have just got into a discussion with Sir Matthew, that I would not break off for the world. So away with you, my dear, as fast as you can."

Lady Clarissa's will was of course law, even to the heiress, but it was not without a little toss of the head that she turned off to another walk;

nor was it without a considerable struggle between her inclination and
a sense of propriety, which, all things considered, really did her honour,
that she permitted poor Miss Mogg to obey the hint of her patroness,
and follow after.

"And so you really have not seen this gifted young man yet, Sir
Matthew?" resumed her ladyship, as soon as they were again alone. "You
have never yet seen this Osmund Norval?"

"No, my lady, I have not," replied the knight; "and to say the truth" he
added, venturing to press with his stout arm the slender one that rested
on it, "to say the truth, though I have heard a monstrous deal about him,
I was determined that I would have nothing to say to him, till I had
heard your opinion, my lady."

"How kind! how flattering, Sir Matthew! But you will let me bring
him to you now?"

"Will I?" (again pressing the lean arm.) "Fancy me saying no, when
you tell me to say yes! Ah! my lady, you know better than that, or I am
greatly mistaken."

"Oh! Sir Matthew, you are always so kind! What magnificent gardens
you have! By the way, I think I never tasted such a pine as that we had
to-day. I assure you, my brother, Lord Highlandloch, is celebrated for his
pines—quite celebrated. They are the finest in all Scotland, but I give
you my honour, I never saw one equal to it at his table."

"Oh! my lady, that is only your amiable condescension," replied Sir
Matthew, greatly touched by this preference. "But if you really can be
so polite as to think them good, I must entreat you just to let me knock
at the head-gardener's door, who lives close outside this gate. I don't let
him live inside, because of his children, Lady Clarissa. I know what birds
peck the worst—ha! ha! ha! However, you *must* just let me pass through
the gate to tell him to put up a brace for your ladyship. They shall be
well taken care of now, my lady, trust me for that; I never valued them
so much before, I promise you."

"You are too kind a thousand times!" said the lady, stretching out her
own hand to open the gate. "I will go with you; there is nothing I dote
upon like visiting a gardener. Could he not take us into the hot-houses,
Sir Matthew? You have no idea how I should enjoy it."

By no means displeased to show off the high-born lady upon his arm, even to the eyes of his gardener, the knight joyfully assented to the proposal.

"Macnab!" he cried, knocking as he passed the cottage-window, "Macnab! come here directly, and bring a knife and a basket with you; you must come directly—this very moment, and unlock the hothouses—her ladyship wishes to walk through them, and I must have one or two of the finest pines cut, and packed in a basket, to be put into Miss Brotherton's carriage: but mind, they are for Lady Clarissa Shrimpton; so you had better give them in charge to her ladyship's own man."

Mr Alexander Macnab promptly left the seeds he was sorting, and prepared himself, basket in hand, to follow his master. The knight and the lady left the cottage, arm-and-arm together; but before they again entered the garden, a fancy seized her lively ladyship, that a short ramble in the green lane outside it would be the most agreeable thing in the world.

"Dear me! what a poetical idea!" exclaimed Sir Matthew with enthusiasn "There's only one thing," he said, stopping short, "but that will spoil my pleasure altogether: I am so dreadfully afraid that your ladyship will take cold."

"Ask the gardener's wife to lend me one of her kerchiefs," said Lady Clarissa, laughing. "But it will only be to satisfy you, Sir Matthew, for there is no catching cold in such weather as this."

It was with something quite like tender anxiety that the knight stepped back, asked for and obtained a neat shawl, and himself wrapped it round the slender person of his amiable companion.

"Thank you! thank you a thousand times! But, dear Sir Matthew, I must not lose my pines by my frolic: will you give the gardener orders to get them without waiting for us? and perhaps you would let him put up a bunch of grapes, and a few peaches at the same time—it is no good to let him wait for us, Sir Matthew;—when you and I get into a chat together, we shall neither of us think of the pines again."

Quitting her highly-valued aristocratic arm for an instant, the flattered knight ran back and gave the necessary orders; and then, almost unconscious, in his full contentment, that his own gray head was as

bare as that of the oak-crowned nymph by his side, he returned to his
bewitching companion and led her gently onward over the mossy turf
that bordered the road.

The gardener and his wife stood together for a moment looking
after them. "Who would think now that she was one of the true old
gentlefolks, and Scotch to boot, to see her pair off that way with our
rogue of a spinner there? How, in God's name, can she choose to be so
free and friendly with such as he?" said the gardener.

"Just for the same reason as yourself, Sawny," replied his wife; "to get
all she can out of him."

"And that's true," replied Sawny, setting off upon his business. "I had
like to forget the pines, and the grapes, and the peaches. She's not so far
wrong after all; and yet 'tis a pity, too."

★   ★   ★   ★   ★

The evening was still oppressively sultry, and hardly a breath of air
disturbed either the leaves on the oaks beside the road, or those that
mimicked them so abominably on the lady's brow; but, nevertheless,
there was a freshness in the smell of the hedges and the grass, which
could not fail to be agreeable to any nerves that had endured the
steaming dinner, and the irksome drawing-room of Dowling Lodge.

The shady lane in which the knight and the lady were thus recreating
themselves, after skirting the extensive and lofty walls of the garden,
turned at right angles both to the right and the left at the corner of it.
The branch to the left followed the boundary of the garden, and led
to the stable-yard and back entrance to the house; that to the right
conducted to the factory, which was the source and head-spring of all
the wealth that flowed over, and irrigated with its fructifying stream,
meadows, parks, hot-beds and flower-gardens, till it made itself a
prodigious cistern in the depths and heights of Dowling Lodge.

When the strangely-matched pair came to this point, Sir Matthew
made a halt, till Lady Clarissa came to the end of a little poem, which the
protegé whom she was so desirous of introducing to her rich and (to use
her own words) "really very clever friend," had inscribed in her album.

Nothing could be more agreeable to her ladyship than this pause. In the first place it was the greatest possible relief to her lungs, for the lines she was reciting were much too full of deep feeling to be repeated without a painful effort, while walking; and in the second, the halt, accompanied as it was by a look of earnest attention from her apparently-delighted companion, furnished the most agreeable commentary in the world upon the poem itself, as well as on her manner of reciting it.

It said so plainly, "Stay!—move not!—lest a word, an intonation, a cadence, be lost to me!"

Lady Clarissa was really touched by it; and let Sawny the gardener, and his wife Janet, say or think what they would, neither peach nor pines had any thing to do with the gratification she at this moment experienced in the society of the great manufacturer.

His eyes were fixed on her face, and she bore the gaze, and returned it with that sort of courage and confidence, which genuine enthusiasm alone can give.

She had just finished a stanza when Sir Matthew ceased to move, and feeling that he did so under the influence of a spell, which she well knew would be more powerful still were it spoken when she were at rest—for Lady Clarissa was aware that she was exceedingly short-breathed—she repeated the last eight lines in a manner that showed she felt the pleasure she was producing—a pleasure, as she thought, like that occasionally caused by the repetition of some delicious phrase in a musical composition, reiterated as if to fill the soul wfth its sweetness.

"And should the eye for which I write
By sun-lit morn, or moon-lit night,
Drop on this record of my soul,
Which tells a part—ah! not the whole,
Of hopes that trembling, faltering, timid,
Now fire my cheek, now turn it livid,—
Should that soft eye but drop one tear,
I'd hug my chain, and call it dear!"

The tear asked for, almost came as she ceased.

"You feel it, dear Sir Matthew!" she said, in a voice of considerable emotion.

"I'd hug my chain, and call it dear!"—she again murmured, hanging on his arm with such an evident degree of weakness, as showed the slender form to be less powerful than the ardent spirit it enshrined.

"Let us turn hack," said Sir Matthew. "My dear friend," faintly ejaculated Lady Clarissa, "you are moved too strongly.—But—no, no! Sir Matthew! Believe me, it were far better for both of us that we should proceed.—Are we, either of us, my dear friend, in a state at this moment to meet the curious stare of idle eyes?—Come on, dear Sir Matthew!"—and she gently pulled him forward as she spoke—"this soft glade invites us."

Though perfectly determined to find some excuse for not leading his fascinating companion within sight of his grim-looking factory, which another turn in the lane at no great distance would have made very unpicturesquely visible, it was impossible at that moment not to yield to the gentle violence which carried him forward; and, in what Lady Clarissa felt to be very eloquent silence, he proceeded for a few steps farther. Considerably, however, before they had reached the dreaded turning, his good star shot a ray upon him in the shape of a very large cow, with a pair of enormous horns, that slowly turned the corner, and fronted them.

"Good heaven!" he exclaimed in an accent of great alarm.—"There is that horrid spotted cow! she is the worst beast in the whole parish. Turn back, dearest Lady Clarissa! turn back instantly."

"How kindly considerate!" returned Lady Clarissa. "But you little know the strength of your friend's mind, Sir Matthew. Were I alone, indeed, I might tremble and turn as pale as the veriest child that ever hid its face on a nurse's lap; but with you!"—and here the lady turned a very flattering glance on the athletic form of her protector—

"Heaven knows," replied Sir Matthew, once more pressing her lean arm, "Heaven knows that all which the strength of man could do to protect you, would not be left undone by me—but consider the dog!" he added, pointing to a little cur that always followed him; "its power of irritating an animal of this kind is quite estraordinary." And as he spoke, he whistled in a note which meant, as his dog Spite knew as well as he did, neither more nor less than—"At her, Spite!"

"If any thing can keep Spite quiet," resumed the knight, "it is whistling to him."

Obedient to the true meaning of the signal, however, the dog sprang forward, and of course there ensued the scene which always follows on such occasions. The dog yelped, and affected to spring at the nose of the cow, while she, somewhat accelerating her stately pace, threw up her tail, and bent down her head till her horns nearly touched the ground, offering so exact an image of "the cow with the crumpled horn," with whose portrait her ladyship's early studies had made her familiar, that her confidence in the prowess of Sir Matthew could sustain her no longer, and she rapidly uttered a succession of tremendous screams.

The purpose of the knight was accomplished, and he therefore indulged the fair lady by letting her scream on for at least a minute and a half, while he supported her with every appearance of the most pitying tenderness. Meanwhile, two little boys who were making their way from the factory homewards, across a field by the side of the lane, ran with terrified curiosity, and all the strength they had, to a gate, through which they could see the interesting spectacle of a fine full-dressed lady, screaming with all her might from between the sheltering arms of the magnificent Sir Matthew Dowling, and a little dog worrying an old half-starved cow.

"Come here, you young scamps!" cried the knight, on perceiving the two little heads peeping over the gate: "Don't you see whats going on? Clamber over the gate, can't you, and drive back that devil of a beast."

The youngest, but by far the stoutest and tallest of the two boys, instantly obeyed this command, and placing himself midway between the tormented cow and the fair creature, whose nerves her menacing attitude had so cruelly shaken, he stood manfully astride in the middle of the lane, flourished his ragged hat on high, and with a few lusty 'wough! woughs!" repeated at the top of his young voice, succeeded in turning the front of the enemy, which was presently seen to wheel round, and, by a sort of feeble, ambling little trot, speedily got out of sight round the corner.

"Now, then," said Sir Matthew, "let me lead you home, my dear lady!"

"Not till I have thanked my little deliverer," exclaimed Lady Clarissa, with very sentimental fervour. "Good heaven! what might have been my fate without him! I know—I feel, Sir Matthew, that you never could have borne to leave me, and what then could have stopped the fearful approach of that most vicious animal?—Death, or worse than death—dislocation of limb, disfigurement of feature! Oh, Sir Matthew, your heart, I know, will go side by side with mine. Tell me, what can I do—what can we both do, to reward the astonishing bravery of that noble little fellow?"

"Depend upon it, my lady, he will be delighted if you will give him sixpence."

"Sixpence!" cried her ladyship, turning extremely red,—but in a moment she recovered herself and said: "Oh! Sir Matthew! do I not know how dearly you love a jest? Men of wit and humour can rarely be grave for long together, even under circumstances that most keenly touch their feelings; did I not know you well, my friend, what should I not think of your proposal? But come, come—be serious for a moment longer: we have, it is true, escaped a tremendous danger, and it may well make us feel light at heart; but we will not laugh over it, till we have settled in what way that heroic child shall receive the meed he has earned. I shall not rest in peace, my friend, unless his destiny be as favourably influenced by me, as mine has probably been by him. Sir Matthew, you have great power, enormous wealth, a generous heart, a noble nature, and intellect, before which, if I mistake not, all difficulties will melt away like a mist before the sun. Of all this I am quite certain. There is but one IF in the business. IF you value me, Sir Matthew, as much as I think you do, that little boy now getting over the gate will be clothed, educated, fed, lodged by you. Do I deceive myself? or will the daily sight of him, by renewing the memory of this evening, rather cause you pleasure than pain?"

Sir Matthew Dowling clearly saw, that sending "the little blackguard to the devil," which was decidedly what his heart whispered to him, would, at this stage of the business, be inevitably sending her sentimental ladyship to at least an equal distance from himself; and this he had no inclination to do. She was the only Lady Somebody Something in the whole neighbourhood, and he was quite aware that he had already acquired more envy and hatred among his friends and neighbours, by the superior degree of intimacy he had contrived to achieve with her, than by all his successful struggles to outspend them all.

This pleasure was not to be given up for a trifle, especially at a moment when it seemed so very clear that it only depended on himself to make all the world perceive that they were dearer friends than ever; so, making a virtue of necessity, he looked in her face with one of his wittiest smiles, and cleverly taking the cue she had given, replied—"If you had *not* found out that I was jesting with you, Lady Clarissa, I never should have believed in your friendship more! Come here, my boy," he continued, raising his loud voice to a note that must have been heard as far as the factory, "come here, I say."

The little fellow, on hearing these imperative accents, which were not quite unknown to him, thought this was the first time he had been so greatly honoured as to have them addressed to himself, again let go the hand of his brother, by whose side he had begun to resume his progress homeward, and once more clambering over the gate, presented himself, cap in hand, before the illustrious pair.

"You are a happy little boy," said Lady Clarissa, "in having had the extraordinary good fortune of looking over yonder gate at the moment you did; and you are a brave little fellow into the bargain for not running away, as you certainly might have done, when you saw that dreadful beast. Oh! those tremendous horns, Sir Matthew! they haunt me still! I am quite sure it will be weeks before I lay my head on my pillow without dreaming of them. But you drove them away, my dear child, and as a reward for it, you shall be comfortably clothed and fed for the rest of your life. You will like that, won't you?"

"I should very much like never to go to work at the factory any more," replied the child; "but, please ma'am," he added the minute after, "I'd sooner you'd clothe and feed Teddy than me. He looked over the gate first, please ma'am."

"Did he, my dear? Then that is another reason why this good gentleman's favour should be shown to you; for if your brother saw my distress first, it was you who were the first to relieve it."

"That was only because Teddy is so lame, please ma'am," said the boy.

"Lame, is he?" repeated her ladyship, "Poor fellow! However, my little man, if I do not greatly mistake, you have this day made a friend by serving me, who will put you in a situation where, if you behave well, you will be able to assist all who belong to you."

The child opened a pair of remarkably large eyes, and fixing them on her face, said, "What! mother and all?"

"Yes, I should think so, my dear. He is a fine intelligent looking little fellow, is he not, Sir Matthew? But he does not look healthy. However, I dare say he will improve in that respect. Plenty of food generally cures all poor people's complaints, particularly when they are young. How old are you, my dear?"

"Nine last birthday," replied the boy.

"A tall little fellow for his age, though very thin, to be sure. And what is your name?"

"Michael Armstrong, ma'am."

"Michael Armstrong: I shall not forget it, I assure you; for truly do I believe that I should have been trampled in the dust by this time, if you had not been heart-strong as well as Armstrong. And what shall we do with him at first, Sir Matthew? Shall we take him home with us?"

"What! to your cottage, my dear lady?—Yes, certainly, if it will give you pleasure."

"My dearest Sir Matthew! there you are at your jestings again."

"Ha! ha! ha! Lady Clarissa, you begin to know me so well, that I shall never be able to cut my little dry jokes upon you," replied the knight laughing, as it seemed, most heartily, but inwardly cursing the audacious exaction of his fair friend, in attempting to make him pay the enormous price she hinted at, for permitting him to enjoy the honour and glory of flirting with her. The idea of being thus entrapped, and forced to adopt "*a bag of rags out of his own factory*" (for it was thus he inwardly designated little Michael), galled him for a moment so severely, that he was within an ace of exclaiming, "Confound you, and the beggar's brat together, you old fool!" But, most fortunately for all parties, he did no such thing; on the contrary, he happily remembered at that critical moment the important hints he had received from his excellent friend Dr Crockley, and instantly decided "that this absurd whim of her ladyship should be worked up into the d—d good-natured thing that was to set all right."

At the very same moment, as if to confirm his resolution, Lady Clarissa drew from her pocket a cambric pocket-handkerchief, something the worse for wear, perhaps, but most elaborately embroidered at each corner with the coronet of a countess. It was one of a dozen bequeathed to her a few years before by her thrifty and truly admirable mother, the late Countess of Highlandloch. This coincidence appeared to be the work of Providence.

"Give me your arm, my charming friend!" said the well-satisfied knight, with an air of tender gallantry, "and only remember, that all I shall do in this business, will proceed wholly from my devoted friendship to you. Follow us, little boy, and you shall learn what it is to have served Sir Matthew Dowling's most honoured friend."

Having said this, he began leading his fair companion back towards the house as rapidly as might be consistent with the delicate style in which she was shod.

"Please ma'am, may I go and tell Teddy?" said little Michael, walking after them.

"Teddy?—who is Teddy, my little man?" inquired Lady Clarissa, graciously smiling upon him; for her ladyship, at no time an ill-natured woman, was at this moment in the best of all possible humours with herself, and every body else. There had been various passages in what had passed between herself and Sir Matthew, during this most delightful walk, which convinced her that the knight, notwithstanding the homage he paid to her rank, could not wholly resist the fascinations of her person, talents, and manners;—and the conviction pleased her. But let not the character of this noble lady be for a moment misunderstood. Lucretia herself would hardly have shrunk with greater horror from an improper attachment. All she dreamed of in her intimacy with Sir Matthew Dowling, with the young poet, Osmund Norval, and with a few other gentlemen whom she was in the habit of meeting, was but that their admiring friendship should be animated by a lambent, innoxious flickering of the flame, which, after a peculiar theory of her own, she believed to pervade the universe, cheering the well-conducted by its mild platonic warmth, but scorching, burning, and destroying those who permitted it to exercise over them a too-sovereign sway and masterdom. That she had reached the age of forty, unsolicited in marriage by any suitor of any degree, she attributed, rightly enough perhaps, to the unfortunate disproportion between her fortune and her rank—but must she, therefore, live and die without the sweet consciousness of having been loved? Where was the law that enforced such cruelty? She knew it not; and accordingly had, for many years, and quite upon principle, made up her mind to permit as many gentlemen, of all ages, ranks, and conditions, to deserve "the soft impeachment," whether they owned it or not, as it was in her power to captivate. For most of these tender and really very innocent friendships, she was able to assign to herself some excellent cause—as poetical sympathy with one, botanical sympathy with another, philosophical religious sympathy with a third, and so on; but in the case of Sir Matthew Dowling, she sometimes felt a little puzzled herself.

It was not, however, that she was weak enough in the least degree to blame herself for wishing to be admired by a vulgar man. She had long ago given such feelings to the winds. From the time she quitted, on the death of her mother, the floods and the fells of her native land, to inhabit a pretty little cottage (the timely gift of an English godmother), which happened to be situated in the midst of a manufacturing district, she had been schooling her spirit to endure the change from poor lairds of a hundred descents, to rich manufacturers, who would have been, for the most part, quite as pleased had they been unable to trace one. Just at first, her Scotch pride rebelled a little; but an hour or two of quiet meditation on the subject, led her to perceive so clearly all she might lose, and all she might gain, by being or not being on friendly terms with her neighbours, that she made up her mind on the matter at once, and thenceforward feasted upon delicate cates, and battened in the fructifying sunshine of universal popularity, in a neighbourhood that might be safely described as the richest in the world.

But still this did not quite explain the terms she was upon with Sir Matthew Dowling, and she did feel sometimes conscious of taking more pains to please him than she quite knew why—unconscious that it arose from a latent wish to be distinguished by a man, celebrated for the warmth of his devotion to the fair sex. But for this, she must not be out of measure blamed, inasmuch as those who have reached the age for looking on upon the drama of life can many of them testify that in this she only yielded to a weakness very unaccountably common to the majority of the sex.

But poor little Michael Armstrong has been left unmercifully long, looking up in her ladyship's smiling face, as she inquired who Teddy was.

"Teddy is my brother, please ma'am," was his answer.

"Is he still waiting for you at the gate, my dear?" said the lady "I don't see him."

"He can't stand very well, ma'am, because he is lame," replied Michael. "I shouldn't wonder if he was set down, and gone to sleep."

"Gone to sleep!—why it is hardly bedtime yet, my dear, is it? However, I suppose he had better go to see, Sir Matthew?—Your brother," turning again to the child, "is younger than you are, I suppose, if he falls asleep on the grass like a baby. Is he old enough to go home by himself, and tell the great news that has happened to you?"

"Teddy is two years older than me—only he is always so tired," replied the boy.

"Well, then, just step back, and bid him run along home by himself, and tell all the family what a fine act you have done, and that Sir Matthew Dowling is going to take care of you all the rest of your life."

Michael now, for the first time, ventured to look steadily up into the face of the majestic Sir Matthew, and his little heart sank within him. It was quite evident from the child's speaking-countenance, that no pleasurable ideas were suggested, by the assurance that Sir Matthew would take care of him all the rest of his life. The knight saw this, and would for a moment have desired no better sport than wringing his neck round; nevertheless, he patted his head with astonishing condescension, and said, "It is quite true, my boy. For the sake of this charming lady, for whose happiness you must pray morning, noon, and night, I will undertake to provide for you. You may step back, if you will, and tell your brother so, who, if he be two years older than you, will be able to make your friends understand the good fortune that has happened to you."

"I have got no friends, please sir," said the boy.

"Where do you live then?"

"With mother, sir."

"Is not she your friend, my poor child?" demanded Lady Clarissa in an accent of great feeling.

"Please ma'am, she is my mother," answered Michael, while a slight flash mantled his pale cheek, and something like a tear twinkled in his eye.

"How very odd!" exclaimed Lady Clarissa. "Is she not kind to you, my boy?"

"Kind?" responded Michael, staring at her.

Do you love her, my little fellow?"

"Love her?" again echoed Michael.

"Whatever she is, she has not taught you good manners, my lad, or you would not answer her ladyship this way," said the knight rather indignantly.

The little boy was certainly very foolish, for, large as his eyes were, they could not contain the salt rheum which, for no reason in the world that the lady or gentleman could guess, first filled them and then ran down in two great big drops upon his cheeks.

"I dare say he is hungry," exclaimed Lady Clarissa with sudden animation. "How delightful, dearest Sir Matthew, to have found a little creature so greatly in want! Are you hungry, my dear? Tell the truth— don't be afraid."

"Not very," said the child.

"Poor little fellow!—it is quite evident, Sir Matthew, that he is exceedingly shy. Let us go back, shall we?—just as far as the gate, and give the message ourselves to that lazy fellow that he says is asleep under the hedge—and two years older than this one.—Only conceive!—I am delighted that *he* is not to be the object of your bounty, for there is nothing so detestable as idleness."

Sir Matthew had turned in compliance with the word and action which expressed her ladyship's desire that he should do so, and in another minute they reached the gate.

"Where is this brother of yours?—I don't see him," said Lady Clarissa, looking about.

"There he is, ma'am, if you please," replied Michael, once more climbing over the gate; and presently he was close under the flowery hedge, extending his two hands to raise a miserably sick-looking child, who was, in truth soundly sleeping there. In consequence of a few words whispered to him by little Michael, the boy came forward with a shuffling gait, his knees sloping inwards, and his legs frightfully emaciated; but the moment he reached the gate, Lady Clarissa exclaimed, "Good gracious! how beautiful!"

It was indeed a lovely face that was then turned up to meet her eye; and when, as if somewhat daunted by her earnest gaze, he removed his own from her countenance to that of Sir Matthew, the bright flash that lighted it up for a moment made it appear more beautiful still.

"And what is your name, my pretty boy?" said the lady.

"Edward Armstrong," was the reply.

"But, my dear child, you don't look well, and you ought not to go to sleep so, quite late in the evening, upon the grass. What makes you so very sleepy, my dear? Have you been at play?"

"No, ma'am," replied the boy, furtively glancing at Sir Mattthew, "I have been at work."

"At work! You can't have done much work, my poor little fellow, looking as you do."

"I have been at work since"—

"My dear Lady Clarissa, I really will not let you stay another moment," suddenly exclaimed Sir Matthew. "The heat is gone off and I am sure you will be quite chilled if you remain any longer out of doors."

"I believe you are right, my dear friend," said Lady Clarissa, with a glance of affectionate gratitude for this earnest zeal. "Let us go. Never can I forget the kindness you have shown me during this eventful walk, and heartless indeed must I be were I to refuse to acknowledge that it has made a deep impression on me."

For a moment Lady Clarissa held her coroneted handkerchief to her eyes, and then resumed. "Go home, little Edward—tell your mother, who, by the by, I trust is not harsh to you, that your brother Michael is rewarded for an act of bravery that probably saved the life of an earl's daughter—has been most generously and nobly adopted by her friend Sir Matthew Dowling, and that henceforward she need have no anxiety whatever on his account. Now, then, Sir Matthew, I am ready."

"Are we never to see Michael again?" said the lame boy, while a sudden expression of anguish passed across his beautiful features.

"Why not, child?" replied her ladyship rather sharply. "Do you suppose that Sir Matthew and I are going to hide him?"

"It is all very well then," returned Edward, limping away. "But be sure to go and tell mother all about it yourself to-morrow, Mike."

"Come along, little one!" said Lady Clarissa, moving off. "Follow this generous gentleman, and see the palace of a home which your bravery has won."

So saying, she moved on; the obsequious knight at her side, and the wondering Michael Armstrong after her.

On reaching the gate beside the gardener's house, Sir Matthew paused. He had been meditating, while seemingly listening in rapt attention to the lady's talk, on the effect which would be produced on the party they were about to rejoin, by the appearance of the ragged little companion they had brought back with them.

Had he been a ragged sailor-boy, or a ragged plough-boy, or even a ragged chimney-sweeper, there might by possibility have been excited some feeling of curiosity and interest; but a ragged factory-boy was of all created beings the one least likely to give birth to such emotions, among his friends and neighbours, or indeed to any other emotion fit to be exhibited in good society. So, merely saying to his fair friend, "Excuse me, my lady, for one moment," he once more knocked at the cottage-window, and called aloud for "Macnab!"

The obedient North Briton appeared immediately, and was about to forestall the inquiry he anticipated by assurances that her ladyship's pines, peaches, and grapes, had all been consigned to the care of her ladyship's own serving-man, when he was very literally struck dumb by his master saying—

"Macnab, take this lttle boy into the servants' hall, and tell the servants to take care of him—do you hear?—and he is to have a bed made for him, and—and supper, and breakfast—and all that; and to-morrow I will talk to Parsons about what must be done for him. Observe, Macnab, and take care, if you please, that all the servants about the place know it, that this boy is to be the object of the greatest benevolence."

"The greatest—what was you pleased to say, sir?" said the Scotch gardener, really and truly doubting his own ears.

"BENEVOLENCE, sir!" shouted the knight vehemently; "and woe to any one on my estate who dares to question or thwart my design!"

"How inspiring is this angelic goodness," exclaimed Lady Clarissa affectionately. "Ah, Sir Matthew! how few there are who know you as I know you!"

"Come along, my man," said the Scotchman, leading away Michael; and he said no more till he was quite sure that the knight and the lady had got far enough in their progress across the garden to be out of hearing, and then he added: "And now, my little fellow, tell me in God's name what all this means? Why, you look for all the world like one of the little ragamuffins out of the factory."

"I *am* one of the ragamuffins out of the factory," replied Michael.

"You are? and our master's going to make a house-pet of ye? Why, now, you'll be made the talk of the whole country. I should not have been one-half so much surprised if he had taken one of our sucking pigs into the drawing-room."

"Nor I, sir," said Michael timidly, but with half a smile.

"So, then, you don't understand it much better than I do, it seems? But what did he *say* it was for? He didn't take the Earl of Highlandloch's daughter among the infernal whirligigs, did he, and pick you out as a specimen to be kept in a glass case?"

"I hope he won't put me in a glass case, sir," said Michael, taking courage from the gardener's good-humour; "but why he brought me here at all, I don't very well understand. The lady said it was because I held up my hat, and cried 'Wough!' to Dame Knight's old cow: but of course she was only making fun."

"At any rate, he was making no fun, for he roared like a bull dog, didn't he? So his bidding I'll do, let it mean what it will; and if it brings you food and lodging, I don't suppose you'll break your heart for being taken out of the factory—shall you?"

"Not if he'll take Edward out too," said the boy.

"Edward out, too! Oh! Lord, oh! Lord, how many more? Did he cry 'Wough!' to the cow, too?"

"I wish he had!" said Michael, shaking his head very mysteriously.

★   ★   ★   ★   ★

Meanwhile Lady Clarissa and the gallant knight re-entered my Lady Dowling's drawing-room, amidst a perfect storm of questions, exclamations of admiration, wonder, fears for the lady's safety, and so forth.

Miss Brotherton, who always took more liberties than any one else, laughed immoderately; Lady Dowling looked the picture of conjugal woe; and good Miss Mogg bustled forward with her usual amiable attention, put a footstool under the lady's misused white satin shoes, took Mrs Janet Macnab's shawl off her shoulders, and whispered in her ear, that she was dreadfully afraid she must have caught cold.

But Lady Clarissa, with a lively action of both hands at once, not only drove Miss Mogg back, but every one else who attemptel to crowd round her, saying, "Give me space! give me space, I entreat you! I must have 'ample room and verge enough' to breathe. Such a series of adventures! Lady Dowling, you have no idea! Good heaven! I can hardly believe it myself. I have been in the greatest possible danger of losing my life—a beast—a monster—the most terrific animal certainly that nature ever permitted on the earth! You know, Mogg, I fear nothing—I have the spirit of my race within me. Who ever heard of a Highlandloch being afraid? But I give you my honour—I pledge my noble word to you all, that such a monster as that which I have escaped from this night, might have made the black Douglas fear!"

"Or the Earl of Warwick either, perhaps," said Miss Brotherton, for she had heard Sir Matthew utter the word "cow," in answer to the importunate inquiries of his eldest son.

"But what shall I say of Sir Matthew Dowling?" resumed Lady Clarissa with increased energy. "Such benevolence! such noble, disinterested conduct!—No, I cannot—I really have no strength left. Miss Brotherton, my dear, pray do order your carriage; my nerves are in disorder, so is my dress—in short, I long to get home, and meditate in solitude on my providential escape."

Here Lady Clarissa found it necessary to lie down upon a sofa, her faithful Mogg endeavouring in vain to pull her dress over her slender feet and ankles, for her ladyship was restless, feverish, and unable to remain in the same attitude for a minute together.

Ere ong, however, the carriage of the heiress was announced, and the languid Lady Clarissa exerted herself to reach it, with the aid of Miss Mogg's substantial arm on one side, and that of Sir Matthew Dowling on the other.

"Farewell, my friend!" she uttered with some effort, after taking her seat:"ere long I shall call upon you, and shall hope to see our interesting protegé looking very differently from what he did when we parted from him. Farewell! I do assure you I am almost fainting! Do ask—will you, dear Sir Matthew?—if the fruit, the pines particularly, are put in. I really think they will do me good, and I am sure I want it. Thank you! thank you! Adieu!"

III

*Introduction of Michael Armstrong into the family of Sir
Matthew Dowling—Conjectures concerning his parentage—
A confabulation between Sir Matthew and Mr Joseph Parsons*

WHEN MR MACNAB AND HIS little companion entered the kitchen,
in their way to the servants' hall, to which place of honour
the wondering Scotchman remembered he had been commanded to
conduct his charge, the first person they encountered was Mr Simkins,
the butler, whom some accidental wish or want had led to enter a
region but rarely honoured by the sunshine of his presence.

"Good morning, Macnab. What! empty-handed? I am afraid you have
forgotten the little basket of peaches I desired to have; and upon my word,
sir, if you leave it any longer, I shall not consider them worth presenting
to the lady for whom I desired to have them. Be pleased to recollect,
good Mr Sawney, that when every garden-wall is hung with ripe fruit, a
bottle of comfort will be rather too high a price for a dozen."

"Your discourse, Mr Simkins, is neither civil nor discreet in any way,"
replied the offended North Briton: "my word, sir, is as good as the bank,
either in England or Scotland; and it is beneath a gentleman, to say nothing
of your rank as a butler, Mr Simkins, to suspect that I should forget it."

"Well, well, the sooner the better, that's all. But who in God's name
have you got here?"

"That is more than I am able to tell you, sir," replied Macnab. "All I
know about him is a mystery. Sir Matthew, and a lady that was hardly
born to be so free in his company, came to the garden-house about an
hour ago, and Sir Matthew was as gay as a lark, and ambled and smirked;

while the Highlandloch's daughter, old fool, looked as well pleased as if she had been gallanted by the Duke of Argyle. Well, sir, he ordered a basket of the choicest and best for her ladyship, and it went against me, Mr Simkins, both ways—for first it ought to choke her, seeing who she is, and who he is, and next I thought upon my promise to you, sir. However, and nevertheless, Mr Simkins, I will keep my word with you, if it cost me a ton of coals more in the forcing."

"But what's all this to do with your ragged companion there? The child looks as if he was ready to drop. I'll bet a bottle you caught him thieving in the fruit-garden."

The boy's colour rose on hearing these words. He spoke not, however; but his large eyes were turned up to the face of his companion, and the fingers of his little hand pressed the hard palm that held them, almost convulsively. Sawney understood the appeal, and answered it: for though, like many other gentlemen, his code of honour was at some points a little loosened and enlarged, to fit and suit his individual circumstances, he felt the value of character as much as any man; and promptly replied, in good Scotch, which must, however, for sundry weighty reasons, be here translated into English: "No, no, Mr Butler! no such thing, I assure you; the lad's as honest as I am, for aught that I know to the contrary. But, to make a short story of a long one, my lady walked off up the lane, after borrowing a shawl from my wife, and your master with her, Mr Simkins, who but he—Well, I had picked the fruit, packed it, and delivered it over to my lady's man, and was just set down again to my seed-picking, when I heard Sir Matthew's big voice again halloaing to me, and when I came out, there stood the ill-sorted pair, arm in arm together, as before, and this ragged chap beside them."

"Well! and what then?" ejaculated the portly butler, impatiently. "What a long-winded man you are, Macnab."

"Hoot, man!" retorted Macnab, "if you want the story, you must just find patience to hear it. 'Take this boy to the servants' hall,' said Sir Matthew, quite upon the strut, 'and order supper and a bed for him.'"

"To the servants' hall?" repeated the indignant man of bottles, measuring the little fellow from head to foot with an eye, which, notwithstanding it was small and bloodshot, was eloquent of scorn.

Michael Armstrong's
Introduction to Dowling
Lodge

"To the servants' hall? Sir Matthew will inflict his own company upon us next, I suppose. Why, look at the cotton fluff mixed with his hair! He is neither more nor less than a factory-boy."

"To be sure he is," replied the gardener, shrugging his shoulders, "but it's no fault of mine, Mr Simkins; to the servants' hall I must take him right or wrong. Come along, boy."

"Stop one moment, if you please, Macnab. Let me step to Mrs Thompson's room, and speak one word to her about it. Sit down, sit down, will you, for one moment." And away hurried Mr Simkins, scattering dismay as he traversed the passages, by tittering as he passed along to footmen and housemaids, abigail and page, "Go to the kitchen, do, in God's name! go and see the company Sir Matthew has been ordering into the servants' hall!"

And away they flew, one after another, eager to see the wonder; so that by the time Mr Simkins himself returned to the kitchen, marshalling the housekeeper before him, at least half-a-dozen servants had assembled there, all of whom were gazing at little Michael, very much as if he had been caught in a forest, and conveyed thither to gratify their desire of studying natural history.

"Who is that dirty little boy, Macnab?" said the magnificent Mrs Thompson, advancing to the spot where the gardener was seated with his frightened charge standing beside him, and all the lookers-on making way for her as she passed.

"It is a factory-boy sent here by Sir Matthew, Mrs Thompson," replied Macnab, while, forestalling, it may be, the storm likely to follow the intelligence, he seemed to settle himself in the arm-chair either to enjoy the fun, or abide the tempest.

But he was, as it should seem, mistaken as to Mrs Thompson's feelings; for that lady, though usually considered by the subordinates as somewhat warm in temper, appeared on this occasion to be as mild as a lamb.

"A factory-boy, certainly," she replied with the dignity that was peculiar to her, "nobody is likely to doubt *that*, Mr Macnab; one might know his calling at half a mile's distance. The vulgar factory itself, with its millions of windows, is not more easily known than the things that crawl out of it, with their millions of cotton specks—that is not the main point of the question, Mr Macnab: it is not what the boy is, but who he is, and for what reason any one has dared to say that he was to sup in the servants' hall."

"Oh! dear me, ma'am," replied the gardener, endeavouring to look very grave, "that wasn't one half of it. To you, ma'am, it's my duty to repeat Sir Matthew's words exact, and this is what he said. 'Macnab,' or 'Mr Macnab,' for he calls me both at times, 'take this little boy,' says he, 'into the servants' hall, and tell every body there to take care of him— every body to take care of him'—that was it, Mrs Thompson, word for word. And then he went on: 'He is to have a bed,' says he, 'made up on purpose for him, and he is to be waited upon with supper and breakfast,' and a great deal more, that Mr Parsons is to make known to-morrow. But you have not heard all yet, ma'am," continued Macnab, raising his voice, on perceiving that the stately housekeeper was putting herself in act to speak. "Sir Matthew went on, raising his arm like one of his own steam-engines, 'Observe, Mr Macnab,' says he, "and take care that all the servants, little and great, know it, that *this boy is to be the object of the greatest benevolence.*' That's something new for you, Mrs Thompson isn't it?"

"Sir Matthew may settle about his benevolence with himself, when he is in his own pew at church," replied Mrs Thompson, with a very satirical sort of smile; "but most certainly it shall not be brought to dirty my premises; so let me hear no more about it, gardener, if you please." And with these words, she turned haughtily away.

"But, ma'am—Mrs Thompson, you had better stop if you please, for go I must, if that's your answer, and tell Sir Matthew of it."

If Mr Macnab had been a blacksmith instead of a gardener, he might have been less surprised at the phenomena which followed these words; for he would have known that white heat is stronger than red heat, though it does not look so fierce. He had fancied the housekeeper particularly calm and placable upon this occasion because, forsooth, she looked rather pale than red when she entered the kitchen; but no sooner had he uttered this threat of reporting her words to Sir Matthew, than the fact of her being in an exceedingly terrible rage became evident. Notwithstanding the usual dignified gentility of her manner, on which, indeed, when more self-possessed, she greatly prided herself, she clenched her fists, raised her arms on high, and from one of the most imposing housekeepers in the British domininions, suddenly assumed the aspect of an inspired fury.

"Tell!—You?—Sir Matthew?—Blackguard! Scoundrel!—base-born spinning spider! —I, that have lived with the Duke of Clarington!"

"'Tis two, too bad, and that's the fact!" exclaimed my Lady Dowling's own footman, who always sided with the principal person in company, which gave him very much the air of being a superior person himself; "and if I was Mrs Thompson, I'd throw my salary in the vulgar fellow's face, before I'd bear to have a factory-boy pushed into my company."

"And so I will, Mr Jennings, you may depend upon it," replied the incensed prime ministeress, somewhat softened: "so now, Mr Macnab, you may just take yourself off; and leave the brat in the kitchen, or take him away with you, as you like best."

"I have done my share of the *benevolent* job, so I will wish you good night, Mrs Thompson; and whether this little fellow eats his supper and breakfast in the kitchen or the hall, it will be much the same to him, I fancy." So saying, the gardener rose, and giving a sort of general nod to the company, left the kitchen.

Considering that there had been nothing very affectionate in the nature of the intercourse which had taken place between them, it was rather singular that the little Michael should feel as sorry as he did at the departure of Mr Macnab. But he did feel sorry, and when the door shut after him, he turned away, and hid his face with his uplifted arm.

Pride of place, and elevation of character, having been in a considerable degree satisfied by Mrs Thompson's energetic expression of her feelings, something like curiosity awoke within her to learn what the circumstances had been which had induced Sir Matthew Dowling to declare an intention of acting benevolently. For a moment she struggled against it, and again seemed about to leave the room; but as she turned her eyes upon the child, she seemed to feel that before one so very abject, no loss of importance could be feared, even if she did question him. So, with the air of a judge walking up the bench, she stalked onwards to the seat Mr Macnab had left, and placing her austere person in it, made a signal with her hand, that the kitchen-maid who had ventured to approach the little boy should stand back, and leave her space to examine him.

On one side of this space stood the lordly butler, with his arms folded, and a look of scorn upon his countenance that seemed to question the propriety of the measure Mrs Thompson had thought proper to adopt. On the other was the courtly Jennings, with an arm resting upon her chair, as if to give evidence that he was near at hand to support her. An extremely fat and very professional-looking cook came next, while my lady's own maid, with all time elegant superiority of attire which marks the station, held a scent-bottle to her nose, that the curiosity which led her to be a witness of this extraordinary scene, might be punished with as little suffering as possible. Two sprightly housemaids seemed to find something vastly amusing in the whole business, though their evident merriment was restrained by the solemnity of Mrs Thompson's manner.

"Look up in my face, little boy," said the housekeeper, as soon as she had seated herself and saw that those around her stood still, as if they had taken their places, and were prepared to listen.

Michael did not move; he was probably ashamed to show that he was weeping, before the face of a lady who spoke so very grandly.

The kitchen-maid gave him a nudge, but a gentle one, whispering at the same time—"Look up, my boy. What be you 'feard of? There's nobody as wants to hurt you here."

Thus encouraged, Michael let his arm drop by his side, and discovered a face that was indeed sallow, and by no means very plump, but with features and expression which, whatever Sir Matthew Dowling's men and maids might think of it, might have sufficed to make the fortune of an able painter.

"Whose child are you?" demanded the housekeeper. "Mother's," replied the boy.

"I suspected as much," rejoined the inquisitor, half aside to Mr. Jennings.

"And I beant no ways surprised to hear it, I promise you," he replied.

Mrs Thompson sighed deeply. "It is dreadful!" said she. Then, after taking a moment to recover herself, she resumed, "And where does the unhappy person live?"

"Please, ma'am, who?" said the puzzled boy.

"The—your mother, child.—Shame upon you for forcing me to name her!"

Michael gave a little shake of the head, which seemed to the merciful kitchen-maid to say, that he did not know what the great lady meant; but he presently replied, as if discreetly determined to mind only what he did understand, "Mother lives in Hoxley Lane, ma'am."

"The most deplorable situation in the whole parish! inhabited only by the *very* lowest!" observed the housekeeper, with another indignant sigh.

"So much the worse for she," muttered the kitchen-maid; but not loud enough to be heard by her in whose hands rested the appointment of kitchen-maids as well as cooks.

"And why does such as you come here?" resumed the housekeeper.

"Because the squire ordered t'other man to bring me," answered Michael.

"I suspect that the boy is a natural fool," observed Mrs Thompson, addressing the butler. "It is a sure fact, and a great dispensation—bad parents have almost always children out of shape, both mind and body. You may take my word for that, all of you," she added, looking round her; "and you will do well to teach it to your children after you."

"I'll be burnt if I don't think it very likely that it was his own father sent him here, and no one else," said Mr Jennings, chuckling.

"Fie! Jennings, fie!" returned Mrs Thompson, with a frown. "God in heaven only knows what may have been the cause of it—Not but what it does look strange, there's no denying that."

"Do you know any thing about your father, child?" said Mr Simkins in a magisterial tone.

"Father's in heaven," replied the child.

"Mercy on me! do you hear him? Is not that like mocking the Lord's prayer?" exclaimed the lady's-maid.

"No, it is not!" said Michael, while a flash of youthful indignation rushed into his face. "My father is in heaven along with God."

"I dare say he means that his father is dead," observed the butler with an air of great sagacity; "and if what has been jealoused at is correct," he added, winking his eye at Mr Jennings, "it is very natural that he should have been told to say so."

"That's very true," said the housekeeper, "and it may be, certainly, that the child knows nothing about it whatever, either one way or t'other—I think it's a good deal the most likely that he does not;—but, any how, it's a vary shocking business, and, as far as I am concerned, I'll neither make nor meddle in the matter.—Of course, the men-servants may do just as they like about taking notice of him—for here he is, and here he will bide, I dare say; but I recommend the maids to follow my example, and not to injure their characters, or to corrupt their morals by having any thing to do with the offspring of——It is more decent not to finish what I was going to say for your goods, young women,—and lucky it is that there is no need. You must all understand me without it."

Mrs Thompson then rose from her chair, and turning her eyes, and indeed her head, aside, to prevent herself from again seeing Michael, she walked with a degree of stateliness and majesty that few housekeepers ever attained, through the kitchen, along the passage, across the servants' hall, into the sacred shelter of her own parlour, where she gave way to emotions which rendered a glass of prime London Madeira absolutely necessary.

Meanwhile Michael remained in no very happy condition in the kitchen. He was very tired, very sleepy, very thirsty, very much longing to see his mother and brother, and very greatly puzzled as to himself.

But though accounted to be a brave little fellow for his age, he could not muster courage enough to ask any questions of those around him, and if he had, it would have been of no avail; for the very moment Mrs Thompson was out of sight, so many of the servants began talking together, that no sounds his voice could produce would have been heard.

Jokes and gibes about Sir Matthew, mingled with ridiculous anecdotes, and very cordial abuse of him and all his race, furnished the first subject, and filled the first chorus. Then followed some facetious observations from Mr Jennings concerning Mrs Thompson, and a few of her peculiarities; and it was in the midst of the giggling which these occasioned, that the kitchen-maid ventured to say—

"Well, now, you are all so keen, and so clever about her, that I wonder it don't come into your heads to find out that she spoke just like an old fool and no better, when she invented all that rigmarole about the boy. Master might be just the devil you says he is, and ten times worser too, for any thing I know about him; but the worser he is, the farther I'd be, if I was such a mighty good gentlewoman as she thinks herself, from giving such a bad father out of my own invention to any body—whether they comed out of the factory or not."

"I do think Molly's right," said one of the housemaids.—"What business has the old frump to find a father for him? Nobody asked her."

"That may be all very true, Rebecca," observed the lady's-maid, shaking her head very gravely. "I know well enough, that Mrs Thompson does not always wait for right and reason before she speaks—but that makes no difference as to our having any familiarity with this dirty little boy; for it certainly does appear plain enough, that his mother is very little better than she ought to be."

"Lord bless us! and how much better be you than you ought to be, I should like to know?" said the fat cook, who had her own reasons for not being at all partial to Mrs Wittington, her ladyship's waiting-maid.

"I!—You miserable lump of kitchen-stuff, that no man in his senses would ever deign to look upon twice! Do you dare to say that I'm no better than I ought to be?"

Now the cook was an Irishwoman and though she had famous black eyes, and teeth like an elephant, her principal claim to the coveted attentions of the other sex (setting aside the attractions which it is but fair to presume her profession gave her), arose from the ready sauciness of her tongue, which, in a brogue as strong as that of the Scotch gardener, and equally dangerous for the untaught to meddle with, was wont to rattle about her, right and left, sometimes scolding, but oftener making sport of all who crossed her humour.

Now this virtuous outbreak of Mrs Wittington, was too fair an opportunity to be lost; and accordingly, putting on as demure a look as her wicked eyes would let her, she replied, "You be better than you ought to be, be you? Well now, that's a trouble for your conscious, isn't it?—Is there nobody as can help her out of it?—Think what it is, gentlemen, to be so burdened, and she, poor soul, unable to confess to a priest, seeing she's a heretic!—Oh! she's better than she ought to be! and you've her own word for it too, and that's the reason you see why she's obliged, whether she will or no, to turn her back on this poor little fellow, just because he's fatherless. Isn't that a sore strait for a young lady's conscious?—Praise and glory to the Holy Virgin, and all the company of saints, now and for ever more, that I beant one bit better than I ought to be, and I hope you beant neither, Molly; and so just run to the larder, will you, girl, and bring out something for supper, fit for a hungry little boy, that havn't the misfortune to be so burdened in mind as pretty Mrs Wittington.—Oh! the poor soul! she's better than she ought to be!"

Molly, the kitchen-maid, did not wait for a second order; and if a capital dish of cold cutlets could have set little Michael's heart at rest, he might then have been a very happy fellow; but, in truth, he was longing for his own porridge, by his own mother's bedside; and except from the relief afforded by a copious draught of milk, he went to the bed prepared for him by his friend, the kitchen-maid, so little elated in spirit, and so little thankful for the extraordinary change which had befallen him, that, had his noble patroness been made aware of it, she would, beyond all doubt, have punished his ingratitude, by requesting Sir Matthew to turn him out of doors again; and, moreover, have for ever abandoned the generous idea of surrounding his young head, as she poetically expressed it, with a halo of immortality by means of getting Mr Osmund Norval to relate his adventure in verse.

Sir Matthew Dowling went to his bed also, hardly better pleased with what had occurred than little Michael. But there was this difference between them: little Michael said his prayers, which the great Sir Matthew did not; but, on the contrary, spent his last waking moment in cursing, with great fervour of spirit, the folly of the hidious old maid, who had entailed such a detestable burden upon him—the result of which, as a peace-offering to the whole body of operatives, was at any rate but problematical.

Nevertheless, when he awoke the next morning with his head quite cool, he felt disposed to think more of the hint given him by his friend and favourite Dr Crockley, and less of the inconvenience of having a few pounds to pay out of hundreds of thousands for a job, which, if well managed, might help, perhaps, to avert a monstrous deal of mischief.

With these thoughts working strongly in his ever-active brain, he rang his bell, and ordered that Joseph Parsons, his principal overlooker, should be sent for instantly, and shown into his study.

A short half-hour brought the master and man to a *tête-à-tête* in the snug little apartment described in the first chapter.

"Good morning, Parsons," said Sir Matthew.

The overlooker bowed his head respectfully,

"Have you heard any thing of this meeting at the Weavers' Arms. Parsons?" inquired Sir Matthew.

"As much as a man was likely to hear, Sir Matthew, who, as you will easily believe, was not intended to hear any thing," replied the confidential servant.

"And how much was that, Parsons? Sit down, Parsons—sit down, and let us hear all about it."

"I was a coming, sir, if you hadn't a sent for me," rejoined ths overlooker; "for to say truth, my mind misgives me, that there's mischief brewing."

"I have heard as much," said the master; "but it can hardly have gone very far yet, if such a sharp-sighted fellow as you only suspect."

"That's true, sir," said the man, with a grim smile, in acknowledgment of the compliment; "and I've not been idle, I promise you. But all I know for certain is, that the people, old and young, our own people I mean, have, one and all, taken dudgeon about that girl Stephens, that died the week before last, just after leaving the mill. She had been at work all day in the spinning-mill, and who was to guess that she was that low?"

"It was a d—d stupid thing though, Parsons, to have a girl go on working, and not know whether she was dying or not."

"And how is one to know, sir? I'll defy any man to find out, what with their tricks, and what with their real faintings."

"You won't tell me, Parsons, that if you set your wits to work, you can't tell whether they are shamming or not?"

"That's not the question, Sir Matthew, asking your pardon. There's no great difficulty in finding out whether they are in a real faint, or only making the most of being a little sickish from standing, and want of air. That's not the difficulty. The thing is to know, when they really take to the downright faintings, whether they are likely to live through it or not."

"And where is the great difficulty of that? You know Dr Crockley would come at a moment's warning at any time, and feel their pulses."

"And he does do it, sir. Bnt, in the first place, I doubt if any man can justly tell whether girls are likely to go on fainting, and up again, as lots and lots of 'em do for years, or drop down and die, as Nancy Stephens

did. That's one thing; and another is, that Dr Crockley is so fond of a
joke, that 'tis rarely one knows when he speaks earnest, and when he
does not. He *did* see Nancy Stephens, about a month ago, and all he
said was, 'she do look a little pale in the gills, to be sure, but a dance
would cure her, I have no doubt.' A dance! says I, doctor. And please to
tell me, says I, how the work is to get on, if the factory boys and girls
sets off dancing?"

"Maybe you haven't got a fiddle?" said he.

"Maybe I haven't," said I.

"Well, then,' says he, 'if it don't suit you to let them dance to the fiddle,
I'll bet ten to one you'll be after making 'em dance to *the strap*.' And
with that, if you'll believe me, sir, he set off capering, and making antics,
just as if there had been somebody behind a-strapping him. To be sure,
it was fit to make one die of laughing to see him; but that's not the way
you know, sir, to do one any good as to finding out the real condition
of the people."

Sir Matthew could not resist a hearty laugh at this characteristic trait
of his friend, but he concluded by acknowledging that Parsons was
quite right in saying that this way of doing business was more agreeable
than useful.

"However, Parsons," he continued, "we must not talk about that now,
for I have something else to say to you. It is quite plain that they are
getting again to their grumblings; and Crockley, who you now is up to
every thing, says that he'll bet his life they have got some new mischief
into their cursed heads. Now this must be prevented, Parsons, some way
or other; for any harm they can do the machinery, is not the worst of
it.—'Tis the rousing up people's attention again, Parsons, there's the
danger.—Just see what they've done about the blackamoor slaves, by
going on boring for everlasting, ding-dong, ding-dong, till they actually
got the thing done at last. Now the Philadelphy people and the Boston
people are just playing the very same game t'other side the water; and
when they have got their way, where will their national wealth be, I
should like to know?—And where will our national wealth be when
these rascals have contrived to stop the mills instead of working them?"

"Lord ave mercy upon us! Sir Matthew;—if you don't make me creep all over to hear you!" exclaimed Parsons. "'Tis a pity, sir, and often's the time I have said it, that you arn't in parliament yourself—you'd pretty soon show 'em what their meddling with factories would do for the country."

"'Tis likely I might, Parsons; but a man can't be in two places at once—and depend upon it, there's good to be done here, if we knew how to set about it. I shall make you stare, perhaps, Mr Parsons, when I tell you what I am about now. It came into my head by accident at first; but if I don't greatly mistake, I'll make a capital thing of it before I have done."

"There's no doubt of that, Sir Matthew, if you sets your mind to it, let it be what it will," replied the confidential overlooker; "and if it isn't a secret, sir, I should like uncommon much to hear it."

"No, it's no secret, Parsons—any thing in the world but that," replied Sir Matthew, laughing. "What should you say now, Mr Superintendent, to my taking a dirty little dog of a piecer out of the factory into my own house, and dressing him, and feeding him, and lodging him, all for the love of pure benevolence, and little boys?"

"I don't quite understand you, sir," replied Mr Joseph Parsons, looking very grave.

"No, dare say you don't. But I think I do, Parsons, and that's more to the purpose. Trust me, man, it will do good if it's only by giving the people something to talk of just now, besides this confounded girl's death. And now, my good fellow, tell me all you know of a boy called Michael Armstrong, for he you must understand, is the hero of my tale."

"That the boy, is it?—Then that's why the chap didn't come to work this morning," replied Mr Parsons. "I knows him well enough, Sir Matthew, in course; for he's going on for eight or nine, and he comed to the factory just about five."

"And what sort of a boy is he, Parsons?"

"Nothing very particular, Sir Matthew, unless it is because of the unaccountable fuss he makes about his elder brother, who is but a poor rickety, shriveldy sort of a child. For some reason or other, his bones never seemed to come rightly straight, and this Mike makes as great a fuss about him, as if he was his grandmother."

"Are the parents living?" inquired Sir Matthew.

"The mother is. She is a bedridden woman, and ought to be in the workhouse; but she's upish, and can't abide it, and so she lies abed, doing plain work and that, and the two boys' wages maintains 'em. But I did hear t'other day, she had given in, and was a begging to go into the house, and take the eldest boy with her. These creturs never know what they would be at. I suspect, howsomever, that she has got hold of a notion, that because he's so cripply, he beant to work no more; but I shall take care to see Butchel, the parish-overseer, about it. It is altogether a trick that, what won't answer—his fingers is just as able to handle the reels, and piece the threads as ever they was; and in course, a little dwarf like him, with his legs like crooked drumsticks, can't look for any but the youngest wages; so after all, he's one of them as answers best."

"No! Parsons, no!" ejaculated Sir Matthew with sudden energy. "That woman must not go into the workhouse. The whole thing shall be got up, I tell you, in the best possible style. What d'ye say now to getting the woman arrested for debt?—or having all her things sold?—and we just stepping in at the very nick of time, to save her from destruction!"

There was something so truly comic in the expression of the knight's countenance, as he said this, that even the saturnine Mr Parsons could not help laughing.

"If the born devils don't sing your praises through the country, sir," said he, as soon as he had recovered his gravity, "why we must find some other way to go to work with them."

"Now then be off, Parsons, and contrive some clever scheme or other to throw the *unhappy family* into a quandary."

"I understand, sir," said Parsons, nodding his head, and so parted the master and the man.

IV

A little cottage gossip—A visit of charity—Practical benevolence

THE PROMPTITUDE OF THE MEASURES taken by Mr Joseph Parsons, to bring to effect the wishes of his master, showed him to be deserving the post of confidence he held, as principal superintendent of Sir Matthew Dowling's factory. He lost not a moment in obtaining a short interview with one of the parish-officers, who was his particular friend, and then made his way to Hoxley-lane, with the intention of questioning the widowed mother of the two Armstrongs, as to the situation of her affairs, and the particular species of misery from which she might, at that precise moment, be suffering the most.

The statement pronounced in Sir Matthew's kitchen respecting the general eligibility of Hoxley-lane as a place of residence, was perfectly correct. It was the most deplorable hole in the parish—a narrow, deep-rutted parish-road (too hopelessly bad to be indicted), led from the turnpike down a steep hill to the town of Ashleigh. Exactly at the bottom of the hill, just at the point where every summer storm and winter torrent deposited their gatherings, there to remain and be absorbed as they might, began a long, closely-packed double row of miserable dwellings, crowded to excess by the population drawn together by the neighbouring factories. There was a squalid, untrimmed look about them all, that spoke fully as much of want of care, as of want of cash in the unthrifty tribe who dwelt there. It was like the moral delinquencies of a corporate body, of which no man is ashamed, because no man can be pointed at as the guilty one. It was not the business of No 1 to look after the filth accumulated in front of No 2; and the inhabitants of No 3, saw no use in mending the gate that swung on one hinge, because No 4 had no gate at all; and the dogs and the pigs who made good their entry there, of course found their way easy enough through the make-believe hedge, which throughout the row divided one tenement from another. The very vilest rags were hanging before most of the doors, as demonstration that washing of garment was occasionally resorted to within. Crawling infants, half-starved cats, mangy curs, and fowls that looked as if each particular feather had been used as a scavenger's broom, shared the dust and the sunshine between them, while an odour, which seemed compounded of a multitude of villanous smells, all reeking together into one, floated over them, driving the pure untainted air of heaven aloft, far beyond the reach of any human lungs abiding in Hoxley-lane.

"Where does widow Armstrong live?" demanded Mr Parsons of a woman who was whipping a child for tumbling in the dunghill before No 5.

"In the back kitchen of No 12, please your honour," replied the woman, making a low reverence to the well-known superintendent.

"No 12!—why that's Sykes's tenement—and they're on the ground-floor themselves."

"Yes, please your honour; but since the rents have been raised by Sir Matthew, the Sykes's have been obliged to let off the back-kitchen, and live in the front one."

"Why there's a matter of a dozen of 'em, isn't there?"

"Yes, your honour, they lies terrible close."

"Obstinate dolt-heads!—That's just because they pretend to fancy that it is not good for the small children to work—I know, for certain, that they have got two above five years, that they won't send to the factory; and then they have the outdaciousness to complain that the rents are raised—as if because they are above choosing to earn money in an honest way, Sir Matthew was not to make what he could of his own. 'Tis disgusting to see such airs, where people ought to be thankful and happy to get work."

"That's quite true, no doubt, sir," answered the woman, continuing to shake, and occasionally to slap the grub of a child she had taken off the dunghill. "But Robert Sykes's children are very weakly; and them as your honour talks of, is almost too small—though 'tisn't to be doubted that it is the bounden duty of us all to send 'em, sooner than see 'em starve."

"I fancy so, indeed," replied Mr Parsons; adding, with a finger pointed at the squalling child, who still continued under the cleansing process above described, "And isn't it a comfort now, Mrs Miller, to get rid of the plague of 'em?"

The woman ceased to shake her little boy, and looking for a moment at the clear blue eyes that, notwithstanding her rough discipline, were very lovingly turned up to her face—something like a shudder passed over her.

"Get along in with you, Bill," said she, as if afraid that the blighting glance of the superintendent should rest upon him; and then added, "as long as they be so very small, your honour, they can't do no good if they be sent."

"Stuff and nonsense! there's ways to teach 'em. But don't fancy that I want you to send your brats—confound 'em! They're the greatest plagues in nature; and nothing on God's earth but good-heartedness and love of his country would ever make Sir Matthew, for one, trouble himself or his men with any of the creturs.—No 12, is it, where I shall find the widow Armstrong?"

"Yes, please your honour—you'll be sure to find her. She's a cripple, poor soul, and can't stir."

"She's made up her mind to go into the workhouse, hasn't she?" demanded the manager.

"Have she indeed, poor thing?" responded the woman, in an accent of compassion.

"I heard so, as I come along, and that's the reason I'm going to her. Our good Sir Matthew, who to be sure is the kindest-hearted man in the whole world, has taken a fancy to her boy, and he'll be a father to him, I'll be bound to say he will; and that's why I think he'd like to give her a call, just to tell her not to fret herself about the workhouse.

If she don't like going there, she needn't, I dare say, with such a good friend as she's got."

The woman stared at him with an air of such genuine astonishment, that the superintendent felt disconcerted, and turning abruptly away, continued his progress down the lane.

By the time he had reached No 12, however, he had begun to doubt whether his sudden appearance at the bedside of the widow Armstrong might not produce an effect unfavourable to the object he had in view.

"As sure as steam's steam," thought he, "she'll be more inclined to fancy that I am come scolding about the boys for something, than to take her part, or do her pleasure; so I'll just say a civil word to the Sykeses, and then stroll away on, till such time as the parish officers have been after her. I'll engage for it, that Sam Butchel won't let no grass grow under his feet after what I said to him; and if I turn in when he's there, as if to see what was going on, it would certainly be more natural-like, and believable."

In accordance with this improved *projet de charité*, Mr Joseph Parsons walked on; but he had not proceeded far ere, on turning his head round to reconnoitre, he perceived, not the tall and burly Sam Butchel, the overseer of the parish, but the lean and lathy person of little Michael, advancing with an eager and rapid step towards his mother's dwelling.

"Soh!" ejaculated the sagacious Parsons, "here comes the charity job! It would be worth a week's wages to hear him tell his own story".

Mr Joseph Parsons had a Napoleon-like promptitude of action, which the unlearned operatives described by calling him "a word-and-a-blow man," but which in reality often deserved the higher epithet above bestowed.

Scarcely had the thought of overhearing little Michael's tale suggested itself, ere a sidelong movement ensconced him for a moment behind a favouring pig-sty, from whence, unseen, he watched the boy enter the door of No 12.

Again Napoleon-like, he remembered all he had heard from her neighbour concerning the position of the widow's dwelling-place; and rightly judging that Sykes's back-kitchen must, in some way or other, be in a condition to favour the emission of sound, he troubled not the household by making his approaches through the principal entrance, but striding over the inefficient fence of the tiny cabbage-patch behind, obtained a station as favourable to his purpose, as he could possibly desire. This was a nook between a protuberance intended for an oven, and the window close beside the widow Armstrong's bed, from whence prophetic fate, favouring the yet latent purpose of the manager, had caused three panes to be extracted by a volley of pebbles, intended for mother Sykes's cat, at least two months before.

To this safe and commodious crouching-place, he made his way just in time to hear the widow say, "Understand one word of Edward's story, Mike; so sit down dear boy, and tell me all."

"Why mother, 'tis like a story-book—and it's very fine to be sure— but yet—" And the boy stopped short.

"But yet you don't like it, Mike?" rejoined his mother. "That's what you was going to say. Tell the truth, my child, and don't go to keep nothing from me."

"That was it," said Mike.

"Ungrateful viper!" muttered the confidential superintendent between his closed teeth.

"Poor fellow! poor dear Michael!" exclaimed the woman, soothingly. "It was hard to go to sleep without kissing mother, wasn't it?"

"Yes, I didn't like that—nor I didn't like being without Teddy neither— and I didn't like the grumpy old lady as comed into the kitchen, and abused me; nor the gentlemen servants either, except the gardener, and he took hold of my hand, and led me along kind enough—and I like Molly too, that's she as give me my supper and my bed, and my breakfast this morning, mother. Oh, mother! how I did long to bring away some of the milk and bread and butter home with me!"

"Never think of such a thing, for your life, boy!" exclaimed the mother eagerly. "It would be thieving, nothing else, Michael—nothing more nor less than thieving—never mention that again to me, dear, that's a darling."

"I won't, mother; but I know I shall think of it every time I see them big pounds of butter, and jugs of milk, and minds how careful you be over your little scrimped bit in the broken saucer, and how you drinks your drop of tea without ever having any milk at all."

"Never you mind that, darling. But what are they going to do with you, Mike? And what for do they want to have you up at the great house? 'Tis a mystery to me, and thankful as we ought to be for any help, I can't say but I should be easier in my mind, if I understood something about it."

"Impertinent hag!" growled the surly Parsons from his lair. "Does she think they are going to trap him like a rabbit, for the sake of his skin?"

"But, mother, I don't understand any thing about it myself," said Michael, rather dolefully.

To this avowal, no reply was made for some minutes; upon which the superintendent grew impatient, and stretching forward his neck a little, contrived athwart the sheltering branches of an elder-bush, to peep through the broken window.

To the agent of Sir Matthew Dowling's benevolence the sight that presented itself was really revolting; though there may be others who would have been affected differently by it. Michael had flung himself across the bed; his arms were thrown round his mother, who was sitting upright with some piece of needlework in her hands, and his dark curls set off in strong contrast the extreme paleness of the face that looked down upon him. The widow Armstrong was still rather a young woman, and would still have been a very lovely one, had not sickness and poor living sharpened the delicate features, and destroyed the oval outline that nature had made perfect. Yet she had quite enough of beauty left to detain the eye; and such a hint of patient suffering might be read in every line of her speaking countenance, that few ever looked upon her harshly. Spite of her extreme poverty too, she was clean—her cap was clean, the bedclothes were clean, and the pale hands too, looked so very white, that if Mr Parsons from his hiding-place had ventured to speak any opinion concerning her, he would certainly have given utterance to a strong expression of indignation, at the abominable air of delicacy which her appearance displayed.

She looked as if she were struggling with some painful feeling, but did no weep, though her boy did, heartily.

For a little while she suffered his tears to flow without interruption or reproof, and then she kissed him once, twice, thrice.

"There now, Michael," she said, looking at him fondly; "have you not played baby long enough? Stand up, darling, and listen to me. You don't seem over-glad, Mike, of this great change, and if you did, perhaps I might have been over-sorry; but sorrow would be sin for either of us, when God has sent us help. 'Tis you that be the heartiest Mike, and 'tis you that want food the most, growing at the rate you do, and heart-sore have I been at meal-times to see you so stinted. So never let us trouble ourselves any more about the reasons for your getting so into favour, but just thank God, and be contented."

"But mother! How will you get on without me?" replied Michael, shaking his head; "I am sure that Teddy can't make your bed as I do—he hasn't the strength in his arms. And who's to fetch water? 'Deed and 'deed mother, you'd better thank Sir Matthew, and say no, unless he'll just please to let Teddy go instead."

"That won't do my dear child, in any way. 'Tis I must watch poor Edward. Little as I can do for him, I don't think he'd like to part from me, as long as God is pleased to let me stay."

"That's true mother—that's very true! Teddy would break his heart. No, no, 'tisn't he shall be patted from you; I'll show him how to make the bed, if I can't come over myself; but perhaps they'll let me, mother?"

"What's the business that you'll have to do, Michael?" inquired the widow.

"I haven't been told of any business yet," replied the boy.

"But you don't expect that you're going to be kept for nothing, dear?" said the mother, smiling.

"'Tisn't for my work, mother; 'tis for the cow," replied Michael, gravely.

"The cow, child? What is it you and Teddy have got into your heads about a cow? A poor starved beast, he says it was, that wouldn't have frightened a mouse, and you made it turn round, Mike—that's all I can make out. But he must be mistaken surely. What was it you did about the cow, darling?"

At this question, the boy burst into a hearty fit of laughter, which to say truth, offended the listening ears of Mr Joseph Parsons, still more than his weeping had done.

"I'll do his business for him, he may depend upon it," thought he. "If master must have a charity job, he must; but it don't follow that the cretur shan't be made to know himself just as well as it he was in the factory. I'll be your overlooker yet, master Mike."

Just as this prophetic sketching of the future had made itself distinctly visible to his mind's eye, the bodily senses of the agent announced to him that the tranquil *tête-à-tête* within the widow's chamber was disturbed by the entrance of persons, whose voice and step announced that they were men. Mr Parsons was at no loss to guess their errand. "Here they come!" muttered he. "Now we'll see how Master Butchel manages his job.

"We be commed to see," said a gruff voice within the widow's chamber, "whether or no you be commed to your senses, Mrs Armstrong."

"Sir?" said the trembling woman in return.

"You knows well enuugh what I means, without my going into it again; you knows well enough as I comes to talk to ye about the house again. We've had Larkins the baker, coming to inquire if there's parish pay to look to, for your bill, Mrs Armstrong—and I have told him, is not a farthing, not the quarter of a farthing, unless you'll come into the house. The parish have gone on allowing you two shilling a week, week after week, God knows how long—'tis a perfect shame and imposition, and the board says they won't do it no longer. You and the boys too may come in if you will, that's one thing; but living here, cramming 'em with as much wheaten bread as they'll eat without paying for it, is another, and it's what no honest parish don't tolerate. I'll be bound to say now, as you have brought up the scamps without their ever knowing the taste of gruel? Tell the truth, did you ever take the trouble to make a drop of gruel for 'em?"

"As long as I had my legs to stand upon, sir, I never minded trouble; and, when my husband was living, we did a deal better, and I have done cooking for 'em then, such as a few potatoes and a cabbage, may be, with a scrap of bacon on a Sunday; but, from the hour he died, we have never had a pot upon the fire."

"That's what 'tis to be so obstinate. If you'd come into the house you'd see the pot upon the fire all day long, a'most."

"My, £3.2.7!"

"But the children would be in one room, after they came from the factory, and I should be in another," pleaded the widow, "and I've got a few of the decent things as I married with, when I came from service, and it would be a grief to me to see 'em all sold."

"If the parish don't sell 'em, Larkins the baker will, you may take my word for that, Mrs Armstrong," replied the overseer. "However, 'tis your business, not mine. Here's a decent, respectable man, as is ready to take all you've got at a valiation, fair and honourable, but that's just as you please. I only called, as in duty bound, to tell ye that the parish don't mean to continy no such extravagance as paying you two shilling a week, no longer."

"God help me!" answered the widow gently. "If 'tis his will that so it should be, it would be a sin for me to complain."

"That's vastly fine, beant it?" said the brutal Butchel, "and now let's hear what you'll be after saying to Master Larkins, for here he comes, as sure as eggs be eggs."

An abrupt, and most peremptory demand, for three pounds two shillings and seven pence, was here made, by a sour-looking little man, who entered the small room without ceremony, making a group of intruders round the widow's bed, equally unwonted and unwelcome. Her over-taxed courage seemed to fail, for it was with something like a sob that she replied to his demand by saying, "I shall have twelve shillings to take for needlework, when this is done, and you shall have it every farthing sir, if you'll be so merciful."

"And who's to pay your rent, Missis Armstrong? if I may be so bold," said Mr Butchel.

The widow had not a word to say for herself, and, covering her face with her hands, wept bitterly.

"Now's my time!" said Parsons to himself, as he stealthily crept from his hiding-place. "Now for Sir Matthew's benevolence." And, in a minute afterwards, his tall, gaunt figure, and hard countenance, were added to the company. The noise he made in entering, caused the widow to uncover her eyes, and it was with an emotion little short of terror that she recognised the tyrant, at whose name her children's cheeks grew pale. Instinctively she stretched out her hand, an took hold of that of Michael, who was still seated on the side of the bed. But the boy shook it off, as if his mother's love was a secret treasure that the overlooker must not see, and, suddenly standing up, he remained, with his eyes fixed on the ground, and his hands hanging by his sides, as if petrified.

"Hollo!—why what's the matter now? Is all the parish come to wish joy to this good woman here?" said the overlooker, with as jocund an air as he could persuade his iron features to assume.

"Wish her joy?" responded the well-tutored parish-officer, "and for what, Mr Parsons, if you please? For having an honest tradesman come upon her with the gripe of the law, in hopes to get what's his own? She's got into trouble, I promise you, and I don't very well see how she's to get out of it."

"You don t say so?" said the confidential agent. "What! Is that you, Mr Larkins, coming to take the law of a poor body this way? I didn t think you was so hard-hearted."

"I don't deserve that character, sir," replied the baker sharply; for though desired to call and enforce his claim by the parish overseer, Mr Larkins knew not a word about Sir Matthew's scheme of benevolence; "and the proof that my heart isn't harder than other people's" he continued, "is, that I gave the widow here credit for what has been, excepting a few ounces of tea, her whole and sole living for months past."

"And very kind of ye, too," observed the conciliating superintendent.

"I should like to know, then, what became of all the money the two boys got, besides her own needlework, and, of late, two shilling a week from the parish, beside?" observed Mr Butchel.

"Why, that is rather puzzling, I must say," replied Mr Parsons, "but no matter for that, no matter for that, just now. This family have got a kind friend, I promise you."

"Yes, but it does matter," returned Larkins. "It can't be right, no how, for me to be out of three pounds two shillings and seven pence, and she with such lots of money."

"Indeed, indeed, sir!" said the widow, once more looking up at him, "I have done my very best, paying a little and a little at a time, as you know I never stopped doing, only for two weeks that my biggest—that is my oldest boy, was making up time that was lost, when he was home sick, and so got no wages. But the seven shillings a week that they get between 'em, and my uncertain bit of needle-work, gentlemen, can't stand for food, and clothes, and rent—and a little soap to keep us decent, and a bit of firing to boil a drop of water—it can't do all that, gentlemen, without getting behindhand, when any making up time comes in the factory."

"Well then, that's just the reason why you must come into the house," replied Butchel; "and, at any rate, you may depend upon getting no more money out of it."

Upon hearing these words, "the decent, respectable man," who was willing to take the widow's goods, at a "valiation fair and honourable," began examining the condition of a chair that stood near him; an operation which the widow eyed with the most piteous look imaginable.

"Come into the house, I tell you, without more ado," resumed Butchel. "And what, in God's name, d'ye think we want you in for but yer own good? D'ye think the parish have a fancy for maintaining crippled women and children, by way of a pleasure? 'Tis ruination any way; but when you're in, we know the worst of it at once, and that's something. The boys' wages will go a bit to help, and at any rate there'll be no two shillings to pay, which is what the overseers hates above all things; and what they won't continy to do. So now I have said my say."

And here Mr Butchel began to move his heavy person towards the door.

"Stop a minute, Mr Butchel, if you please sir," ejaculated Sir Matthew's superintendent. "I should be sorry to let you go back to your employers under any delusion or mistake whatever, and the fact is, that this good woman, the widow Armstrong, is no more likely to go into the workhouse than you are yourself, Mr Butchel; begging your pardon for naming such a thing."

"Then I suppose as it's yourself as means to keep her out of it, Mr Parsons?' replied the parish officer jocosely.

"Not exactly me, myself," replied the other in the same tone, "but it's one as much more able as he is willing. It is Sir Matthew Dowling as intends to befriend her, and that not only on account of the general charitableness of his temper, which all who know him really well are quite aware is very great, but because that little boy as stands there and who is one of our factory children, saved a friend of Lady Dowling's, last night, from something she looked upon to be a considerable danger."

"And does Sir Matthew mean to see me paid?" demanded the baker.

"Upon my word, Mr Larkin, that's more than what I've got authority to say," replied Parsons; "but, howsomever, I don't think that you had best go on, just at this particular minute, to persecute about it, seeing that in course Sir Matthew won't take it civil, when he's being such a friend himself to the widow."

"I don't want to do nothing uncivil to nobody," replied the baker, "but I don't quite understand this business. It is something new, is it, Sir Matthew setting up for a soft-hearted gentleman, among the factory folks?"

"New to you, may be, Mr Larkin, but not to me," replied the trustworthy agent. "There isn't another to be found, look which way you will, that can be compared with Sir Matthew Dowling, for real, true, benevolent, charitableness, when he finds proper objects for it."

The baker stared; the man of old chairs and tables scratched his puzzled head; the intelligent Mr Butchel looked at the speaker with a knowing wink; the widow fixed her eyes upon her patchwork quilt; and little Michael in astonishment, which conquered terror, raised his eyes to the superintendent's face, while that worthy advocate of a master's virtues stood firmly, striking his stout cane upon the ground, with the air of a man ready to do battle with all the world in support of what he has asserted.

"Well then, at any rate my business is done and ended," said Mr Butchel moving off, "and I wish you joy Mussiss Armstrong of your unaccountable good fortune."

"Come along, Jim!" said the baker to the respectable dealer in seized goods, "there's nothing to be done to-day, that's clear. But I hope you'll remember the twelve shillings as you've promised me, Mrs Armstrong."

"I will indeed, sir!" answered the widow earnestly; and, on receiving this assurance, Mr Larkin took his departure with his professional friend, leaving Mr Joseph Parsons, the widow Armstrong, and her son Michael to carry on whatever conversation they might wish for, without interruption.

"Well now, if I ain't glad they're gone, them fellows," said the superintendent shutting the door after them. "You are a favoured woman, Mrs Armstrong, to get rid of 'em as you have done, and I don't and won't, question that you are thankful to those to whom thanks are due."

"I always wish to be so, sir," said the widow.

"Well, there's no hardship in that I suppose. But about this son of yours, this young Master Michael, you must see to his doing his duty to his benefactor. If he was to prove ungrateful, Mrs Armstrong, it is but fair to tell you that I wouldn't undertake to answer for the consequences."

"God forbid he ever should be ungrateful to any as was kind to him!" replied the poor woman; "but indeed, sir, I don't think it is in his heart to be so. Since the day he was born, God bless him, I have had little besides love to give him, and indeed, sir, I think the child would die for me."

Michael slily stole his little hand sideways under the bedclothes, where it was soon clasped in that of his mother, but his eyes were again firmly rivetted upon the ground.

"Ay, ay, that's all very well; but it has nothing to do in any way with his duty and obligations to Sir Matthew. What I want to know is, whether he is ready and willing to do that which Sir Matthew will require of him—that's the main questions you see, Mrs Armstrong."

"And what will that be, sir?" said the widow, while Michael's eyes were again raised for a moment to the face of his taskmaster.

"He is to be made a gentleman of—that's to be the first work put upon him." The poor woman smiled; but little Michael shook his head. The superintendent appeared to pay no attenton to either; but again striking his cane magisterially upon the ground, he added, "Let him make up his mind to do all that he's bid, and come back to Dowling Lodge with as little delay as possible."

With these words, and without deigning to bestow any species of parting salutation upon those to whom they were addressed, Mr Parsons left the room.

V

A separation of loving hearts—A specimen of finished composition—Condescension and generosity—Sir Matthew clothes little Michael with his own hands

WHILE THE SUPERINTENDENT, IN HIS serpentine course homeward, scattered the tidings of his master's munificence towards the factory-boy, Michael Armstrong and his mother indulged themselves in a few parting words and very tender caresses; the mother continuing to repeat at intervals, "Be sure, darling, to be a good boy, and do what you're bid," while the son reiterated his entreaties that she and Teddy would take care one of t'other, and have him back again, spite of every thing, if they found that they could not do so well without him.

But even while this went on, Michael was improving his toilet by putting on the more carefully patched garments, which had hitherto been kept sacred for Sundays. When this operation was completed, and his hair, face, and hands made as clean as the joint efforts of himself and his mother could contrive to make them, the little boy turned to leave the miserable shed that had been his home, with a reluctant step and heavy heart, retracing the short distance between his mother's bed and the door, once and again to take another kiss, and to repeat, with im earnestness, the questions, "Isn't there nothing more I can do for you, mother, before I go away?—and will you be sure to tell Teddy to stop for me, morning and night, at the gate in the lane, where it all happened?—will you mother?"

But at length the lingering separation was completed, and Michael set off upon his return to Dowling Lodge. In the meantime, Sir Matthew himself had not been idle: but, retiring to his study, he composed a paragraph for the county newspaper, which, after considerable study and repeated corrections, was at length completed, and despatched by the post, in a feigned hand, the wax being stamped with the handle of the seal instead of his arms, and the postage paid.

The paragraph ran thus:

"ENGLISH BENEVOLENCE

"There is, perhaps, no class of men so cruelly misrepresented as the manufacturers of Great Britain; surrounded on all sides by a population of labourers, crowded together exactly in proportion to the quantity of work the neighbouring factories are able to furnish—they are continually reproached both with giving too many hours of employment to their poor neighbours on the one hand, and with the poverty which is the inevitable lot of operatives with large families on the other.

"That all manufacturers, however, are not the cruel mercenary tyrants they are so often, and so unjustly described to be, was shown within the last few days by an incident which occurred near the town of Ashleigh, not a hundred miles from D—l—g L—d—e. The owner of that splendid mansion, while escorting the amiable Lady — — round his grounds, had occasion to remark some symptoms of a very noble disposition in one of the children belonging to a neighbouring factory on his estate. On making inquiries, he discovered him to be the son of a poor widow, whose failing health made her, and her orphan children peculiarly eligible as objects of charity. This fact having been satisfactorily ascertained, Sir M—th—w D—l—g gave way to the warm impulses of his generous heart, and adopting the little orphan among his own children, at once gratified the gentle feelings of his amiable nature, and set them an example which it is impossible they should ever forget. It is more easy for the recorder of this charming anecdote to relate thus the principal circumstances of it, than to enter into any detail of the numberless delicate traits of character exhibited by Sir M. D—l—g in the course of the transaction. Those who know him thoroughly, will, however, be at no loss how to supply these; and those who do not, would scarcely understand the description, were it given with all the detail possible."

The value and the accuracy of the statements contained in this announcement, belonged wholly to the author of it; the phraseology to a private MS digest of newspaper eloquence, the result of many years of steady research, during which no morsel of fine writing that might assist in such occasional addresses to the public as the present, had been ever suffered to flow down the stream of time, and perish, without having been first carefully noted in the knight's repertory of fine periods.

Having concluded this business, Sir Matthew Dowling rang his bell. As it was only the study bell, it was answered, as usual, by one of the housemaids.

"Where is the little boy, my dear, that I sent into the servants' hall last night?" inquired Sir Matthew.

"Upon my word, Sir Matthew, I can't tell," she replied; adding, in that tone of familiar confidence which her master's condescension encouraged, "but if you sent him into the hall, Sir Matthew, he never got there, nor never will, you may take my word for that, as long as Madam Thompson reigns."

The housemaid was not a beauty—none such, as was before stated, ever made part of Lady Dowling's household; but she was a wit, and Sir Matthew was too clever himself not to feel the value of cleverness in others; he, therefore, raised his eyebrows in a comic grimace, very good-humouredly chucked the maid under her ugly chin, and instead of putting himself in a rage, as might have happened under other circumstances, he only said, "And how was that my dear? Come, tell me all about it—I like your stories, Peggy, they are always so funny."

"Whose stories wouldn't he funny, Sir Matthew, if they told of the airs and graces of Mother Thompson?" replied the lively damsel; "she's for all the world like an old owl, as sits winking his eyes and trying to look wise."

"But she's a prime favourite with my lady, Peggy, and into the bargain, knows a thing or two about soups and hashes; so we must be very respectful, my dear, in talking of her—but as to her daring to say, that the boy I ordered into the hall was to be turned out of it, that's rather more than possible, I think."

"That's because you don't know Mrs Thompson, Sir Matthew. I only wish you had heard and seen 'em last night, she, and the butler, and

Mrs Fine Airs, my lady's-maid, and Mr Fine Airs, my lady's footman! If it was not enough to make one sick, I wish I may never see you again, Sir Matthew."

"They are a confounded impertinent set of rubbish," replied Sir Matthew; but still without losing his good humour. "However, all people of fashion, that is, rich people, Peggy, always do have a confounded impertinent set of servants about 'em. That's one of the great differences between high people and low."

"To be sure you must know best, Sir Matthew," replied the saucy grisette, but with a look and accent somewhat ironical. "I don't mean to doubt that in the least, I'm sure; but in the places I've lived at—Lord Wilmot's, Lord Crampton's, and such like, I never *did* hear of my lord's commands being treated in that fashion. They might have their jokes in the hall, and the housekeeper's room too, no doubt of it, and impudent enough if you like it; but for downright flat disobedience, I never did hear of such a thing."

Sir Matthew on hearing this, became rather white about the lips, and red about the forehead; but Peggy knew the rising storm was not at all likely to fall on her, so nothing daunted, she went on.

"I don't think I should have taken much notice about it, Sir Matthew, if it hadn't been for not liking to see you treated with disrespect; for I'm not over and above partial to beggar children myself; but that sort of natural dislike was nothing in comparison to my feelings about you, sir: and if I had been placed in power, instead of having none, your will would have been obeyed, if every servant in the house had flowed at me for it."

"You're an excellent girl, Peggy," replied the knight, approaching her very condescendingly. "You know well enough that you are a favourite, and I know well enough, my dear, that you deserve to be so; and I tell you what, Peggy, I'll take care to let those animals, my servants, know that I am master here, as well as in the factory—and that my word's law!"

"And so it ought to be, Sir Matthew," replied the obedient domestic. "I hope I know my duty too well to dispute my master's will in any thing;" and as she spoke she very meekly yielded herself to receive the condescending salute, with which Sir Matthew was pleased to reward her excellent sentiments.

"You are an excellent good girl, Peggy!" he resumed after this little interruption; "and don't fear but I shall find means to reward you. But you must give me your help, my dear, to confound the impertinence of these fellow-servants of yours; if I don't make 'em wait upon that beggar's brat as if he was their lord and master, never trust me with a kiss more. Where is the little factory vermin, Peggy?"

"I ain't able to answer you, Sir Matthew; all I know is, that Mrs Thompson marched us all out of the kitchen where she sat in judgment on him, last night, and there he was left with the kitchen-maid and the fat cook; but what's come of him since, I am no ways able to say."

On hearing this, Sir Matthew raised his hand towards the bell, but suddenly recollecting himself, he smiled and said, "No, no, that won't do, Peggy, will it? Go, my dear, and ask where the boy is, and then come back and tell me."

The damsel, in return, furtively smiled too in acquiescence and approval of his discretion; and upon leaving his study for the purpose of prosecuting her inquiries among the servants, she encountered the object of them, as he entered the back-door, on his return from visiting his mother's cottage.

"Soh! here you are then? Well, you must come along this minute to Sir Matthew," said she, addressing him somewhat gruffly, and not too well pleased, perhaps, at this interruption to the confidential conversation with her master, which it had been her purpose to renew. But to the ears of Michael, the name of Sir Matthew was sufficient to render all other words indifferent; and conscious only, that into his dreaded presence he must go if commanded to do so, he followed the girl with a beating heart, and in a few minutes stood pale, and almost breathless, before the awful countenance of the great man.

Sir Matthew gazed at him for a moment with a sort of sneer, which, if interpreted skilfully, would have been found to address itself inwardly. Sir Matthew could not choose but sneer at the whimsical arrangements of accidents, which had converted him into a Mr Allworthy. The sneer, however, as far as it concerned himself, had no mixture of contempt in it. "Had another done this thing," thought he, "should I not have called him fool? and is it not ninety-nine chances to a hundred, that thereby

I should have described him truly? May the same be said of me? No! By the living God, it may not! How now, little boy? you have made yourself smart, I see—vastly fine, indeed! An inch of clean dowlas, a piece of span-new green baize for a patch, a pair of bony legs without stockings, and magnificent shoes—I did not say a pair, Peggy—but very magnificent shoes; one I suppose won in battle from a giant, and the other from a dwarf. Fine as a prince! isn't he, Peggy?"

As he thus jeered the little fellow, his eye wandered with malignant jocularity over his person, which was, in truth, the very model of make-shift poverty; while the child, as if he felt his eye palpably crawl like a reptile over him, shuddered he knew not why.

Then, changing his tone so suddenly, as to make even the confiding Peggy start, he continued, "You horrid lump of rags stand back—stand back! back! back! behind that high chair—d'ye hear? Stand close and stand still—if he does not make me as sick as a dog, Peggy, let me never smell musk more!"

"He does smell horrid bad to be sure, Sir Matthew!" replied the girl. "Hadn't I better take him back to Molly the kitchen-maid, and make her scour him?"

"No, hang him—that won't take it out of him—I know 'em all. No, Peggy, let the scouring alone, and just go upstairs to the nursery-maids, and tell them to send me down a good handsome suit of clothes, complete, of Master Duodecimus's—he is the nearest in size to this scaramouch; and I will dress him, Peggy, as if he were the son of a duke. It will be fun, capital fun, and will it not be generous, Peggy?"

"Generous, Sir Matthew? It will be past all belief! What? Him to be dressed up in the clothes of Master Duodecimus? oh, my! Sir Matthew, you must surely be joking."

"I'm as serious as an undertaker, girl. Get along with you, and do what I bid you—the longer you're about it, mind, the longer I shall have to sit in the same room with the ragamuffin in his own full dress—so make haste, if you please."

This was said in a manner to remove all doubts as to the munificent knight's being in earnest; and the active Peggy went and returned with a little delay as was consistent with the necessity she felt herself under, of entering into some short explanation with the nursery ladies; one and all of whom seemed much inclined, on the first opening of her mission, to treat the whole business as a hoax. When at length, however, she had succeeded in making it apparent that Sir Matthew was waiting for the suit of clothes in a most monstrous outrageous passion of a hurry, the messenger's arms were speedily loaded in exact conformity to the orders she had brought, and she returned to the knight's study with all that was needful to convert the rude exterior of little Michael into the nearest resemblance that nature would permit, to the elegant and accomplished Master Duodecimus.

Considering the loathing and disgust manifested by Sir Matthew towards the person and the poverty of his *protegé*, it was extraordinary to see the amusement he seemed to derive from dressing him up. Though the alert and obedient Peggy stood close by to do his pleasure, it was his own large hands that thrust the little limbs of Michael into the clothing he chose they should wear, and it was amidst shouts of laughter from both, that the ludicrous metamorphosis was completed.

But somehow or other when they had finished their masquerading work, the result was not altogether what Sir Matthew anticipated. The clothes were very handsome, well-made clothes, and as poor Michael, notwithstanding his leanness, was a very handsome, well-made boy, the incongruity between them seemed to vanish in the most unaccountable manner, as the operation drew towards a conclusion.

Peggy, however, was not such a fool as not to understand what was expected of her, so when the knight, catching up his son's tasselled cap, pressed it down upon the little curly head as a lusty packer of worthless goods thrusts down the cover that is to enclose them, and then pushed the child towards her with an impulse that nearly brought him upon his nose, she very judiciously renewed her noisy laughter, exclaiming, "Did any one ever see such a little quiz!"

"Quiz, girl?" replied Sir Matthew, eyeing him with no very fond expression. "It would be well for the scamp if that was the worst you could say of him—I know a thing or two Peggy, and that boy will be lucky if he gets drowned. I'll bet a hundred guineas that with a few lessons, he would forge any writing you could show him; but before

he is twenty, he will have taken as many shapes as Turpin. That boy was
born with a halter round his neck, I want no gipsy to tell me that."

During the whole of the undressing and redressing operations, the
boy's cheeks had been dyed with blushes, and his eyes so fixedly nailed
to the floor, that neither Sir Matthew nor his maid had been able to
enjoy their embarrassed expression; but as this dark prophecy fell on
him, he looked up, and it was well for him that his munificent patron
at the same instant turned his mocking glances towards the servant, as
he said, "There—gather up his rags, girl, and be sure yon wash well
after it;" for, had he met that speaking young eye, he could hardly
have misunderstood the scorn that shot from it. As it was, however,
he saw nothing but the patched garmeats that were scattered round,
and once more sneering as he looked at them, he added, "Lead the
little blackguard through the servants'-hall, and into Mrs Thompson's
parlour—d'ye hear, Peggy, up to her very nose, and tell her that I
have sent him to pay her a visit, and when she has had enough of the
compliment, lead him round to Mademoiselle's room, and we'll have a
little fun among the children."

By no means displeased with an errand which permitted her to affront
with impunity the autocrat of all the offices, Peggy gathered together
Michael's discarded wardrobe and then clutching hold of his hand, led
him, *bon gré mal gré* to the presence of the imperious housekeeper.

Mrs Willis, my Lady Dowling's own maid, and Mr Jennings, my Lady
Dowling's own man, were enjoying with that important functionary
a slight morning repast of fruit, cakes, and wine, and at the moment
Peggy and her charge entered, they were enjoying some very excellent
jokes together. But, Mr Jennings no sooner cast his eyes on the little
factory-boy, than he arose, looking rather abashed at being caught by a
drawing-room guest of even nine years old, with a glass of claret in one
hand, and a slice of pineapple in the other.

Peggy, to whom the conciliatory smiles of this gay gentleman did
not descend, enjoyed his mystification exceedingly; and relaxing her
rough hold of Michael's wrist, she led him respectfully towards the table
saying, "My master has sent this young gentleman to pay you a visit, Mrs
Thompson; perhaps he would like a little fruit. There, my dear, that's the

housekeeper Sir Matthew told you of, and if you will please to go and sit down by her, I dare say she will give you something nice."

Mr Jennings immediately placed a chair beside the gracious Mrs Thompson, who, after filling and setting before the young gentleman a plate with whatever she supposed would be most agreeable, said in a half whisper to his conductor, "Who is it, Peggy? I didn't hear never a carriage."

Before she could, or at least before she would answer, Michael, who had not accepted the chair offered to him, took his cap from his head, and with considerably more courage than he had yet shown said, "I am Michael Armstrong, the factory-boy."

"Who! What?" screamed the housekeeper; "what bold joke is this, Mrs Peggy Perkins? Do you think you have got a patent for your place, that you dare play such tricks as this?"

"If I keeps my place, I don't think I shall have to thank you for it, ma'am," replied the favoured housemaid, with very little civility. "My master ordered me to bring the boy *to pay you a visit*; those was his very words, Mrs Thompson, and as I was bid, so I have done."

"There's some people as will do every thing and any thing they are bid," observed Mrs Willis, again drawing out her favourite smelling-bottle, while with the other hand she extended a wine-glass to Mr Jennings, for a little Madeira, which she felt was absolutely necessary to support her in this very disagreeable emergency.

"Master, or no master, Sir Matthew Dowling doesn't know how to behave himself—it's I says it, and I don't care who repeats it to him."

Mr Jennings stared at the factory-boy for a full minute very attentively, and then gave a long low whistle, at the same time turning his eye with a look of much intelligence full in the face of the housekeeper.

"He isn't at all like any of 'em, Mrs Thompson," said he.

Mrs Thompson shook her head. "There is nothing at all in that, Mr Jennings, I'm sorry to say. But remember I do desire, and insist, that the subject is never alluded to in my presence again. When I lived with his grace, I always made it a rule that none of the household should ever discourse in my presence of any thing that it was not decent to hear."

"Well, ma'am," said Peggy; "when you have done looking at him, he is to go into Momsell's room for the children to see him."

The housekeeper, the lady's-maid, and the footman, all simultaneously lifted up their hands and eyes to heaven.

"Please to let me put on my old clothes and go home," said Michael.

"You little ingrateful wretch!" exclaimed Pesgy; "when Sir Matthew dressed you up himself with his own hands. What d'ye mean by that, you bad boy?"

"They'll laugh at me," said Michael, resolutely; "and I don't like it."

"You don't? Isn't that a good one?" said Mr Jennings, clapping his hands in ecstasy. "Oh, Lord! pray let us have him back again, Mrs Peggy, that is to say if Sir Matthew can bear to part with him. He's the finest fun I've got sight of this many a day."

"You must find fun for yourself Mr Jennings, for I shan't be at the trouble of bringing you none," replied the self-satisfied Peggy, again seizing the hand of Michael, and leading him off.

"Well, for a broom-maid, I hope she's saucy enough," said Mr Jennings; but the subject of his remark was already beyond hearing, threading her way through the long stone passages which conducted to the opposite wing of the mansion, the whole of which was appropriated to the younger branches of the Dowling family.

VI

Michael's introduction to all the Miss Dowlings—Sir Matthew feeds him with his own hand, and presents him to all his most valued friends

HAVING GIVEN A SHARP RAP on the door, Peggy was told to "com een," by the voice of Mademoiselle Beaujoie; whereupon she threw the door wide open before her, and stood with Michael Armstrong in her hand, in the presence of three grown-up Miss Dowlings, three middle-sized Miss Dowlings, two little Miss Dowlings, and their French governess.

The five youngest, all rushed as by one accord towards Michael. "What a pretty little boy!" was exclaimed by two or three of them. "Are you come to play with us? Mayn't we have a holiday, Ma'mselle?"

"What an elegant-looking creature!" exclaimed the eldest Miss Dowling, who with her two grown-up sisters, had come into the room for the advantage of practising duets on a venerable pianoforte totally out of tune, and whose loudest note could by no means compete with the shrill accents of the animated group who inhabited the apartment. "Did you ever see a prettier boy, Harriet?"

"Who is he, I wonder?" replied the young lady she addressed.

"How he blushes!" said the governess, tittering.

"What's your name, dear?" demanded Miss Martha, the third daughter of the Dowling race.

"Michael Armstrong, ma'am," replied the boy, looking up with an air of surprise, for Miss Martha, queer-looking as she was, spoke kindly. And queer-looking as she was, Michael met her eye with pleasure, for that too spoke kindly, though it was neither large nor bright.

Martha Dowling was in truth, about as ugly as it was possible for a girl of seventeen to be, who was neither deformed nor marked by the smallpox,—short, fat, snub-nosed, red-faced, with a quantity of sandy hair, that, if not red, looked very much as if it intended to be so; eyes of a light, very light gray, and without any thing whatever in external appearance to recommend her, except a smooth, plump neck and shoulders, with hands and arms to match, which, in truth, were very fair and nice-looking, and a set of well-formed, stout white teeth.

What made the unlucky appearance of this young lady the more remarkable, was the contrast it presented to the rest of her family. All the other young people were, like both their parents, "more than common tall," for their respective ages, and, like most other tall young people, rather thin, so that Lady Dowling was apt to indulge herself by declaring that, "though certainly some of her children might be considered prettier than the rest, there was not one of the whole set (except that poor vulgar Martha), who was not most particular genteel-looking."

"*Genteel looking*" she certainly was not, nor graceful, nor beautiful in any way; and the consequence was, that father, mother, brothers, and sisters, were all most heartily ashamed of her. This was a misfortune, and she felt it to be so pretty sharply, for poor vulgar Martha was far from being a stupid girl. But, in her case, as in a million of others, it might be seen that adversity, though

"Like the toad ugly and venomous,
Weareth a precious jewel in its head."

for of all her race she was the only one whose heart was not seared and hardened by the ceaseless operation of opulent self-indulgence. She felt that she was rather an object of pity than of admiration, of contempt than of envy, of dislike than of love. This is severe schooling for a young girl's heart, but if it produce not reckless indifference, or callous insensibility, it often purifies, softens, and even elevates the character. Such were its effects on Martha Dowling: that coarse-seeming exterior contained the only spark of refinement of which the Dowling family could boast. Never did high-born Hidalgo, in Spain's proudest days,

"What a pretty little boy"

inculcate among his race the immeasurable importance of pure descent, with more ceaseless or more sedulous earnestness, than did Sir Matthew, the omnipotence of wealth among his. Every child was taught, as soon as its mind became capable of receiving the important truth, that not only was it agreeable to enjoy and cherish all the good things which wealth can procure, but that it was their bounden and special duty to make it visible before the eyes of all men that they could, and that they did, have more money spent upon them, than any other family in the whole country; but Martha felt that all this could not apply to her.

Strange to say, the only tie resembling affection which prevented the total isolation of this poor girl among her family, was that which existed

between her hard-natured father and herself; but it was a sentiment not
easy to analyze. In Sir Matthew it probably arose at first from his having
been told that the little girl was very like I him; and, on hers, from his
being the only person in the house who had ever bestowed a caress
upon her. In both cases, cause and effect went on increasing. Martha's
face (saving its expression), as incontrovertibly like her father's; and, for
that reason, or from the habit it had at first created, her father, though
rather ashamed to confess it, was certainly very fond of her.

That, as a child, she should love him in return, was almost inevitable;
but that, as she advanced in years, she should feel for the being, the most
completely formed by nature to be hateful to her, an affection the most
unchanging and devoted, had something of mystery in it less easy to
be explained. Yet, so it was. Martha Dowling adored her hard-hearted,
vicious, unprincipled, illiterate, vulgar father, as heartily as if he had been
the model of every thing she most admired and approved. Nay, it may
be, that she loved him better, or, at any rate, more strongly still; for it was
rather with fanaticism than devotion, or like the pitying fondness with,
which a mother dotes on a deformed child, who sees only that because
it is less loveable it has more need of love than the rest.

It was not, however, on the same principle, that Sir Matthew's affection
for his ugly daughter increased as years rolled on; for he saw, that though
as a child she had been like him, she was now grown very plain and, in
company, he felt almost as much ashamed of her, as Lady Dowling herself.
But he could not mistake her love and true affection, nor resist the charm
of feeling that at least there was one being in existence, who would have
cherished him, even if he had not been the great man he was.

In private he scrupled not to yield to this feeling, and certainly
derived considerable pleasure from it; but before witnesses, he always
joined in the family tone respecting "*poor Martha*," and scrupled not
to push her on one side, upon all occasions on which any display of
Dowling elegance was contemplated.

It was this ugly Martha Dowling who now startled little Michael
with her voice of kindness, and, notwithstanding all her lady mother
said about the "horrid vulgarity of her manners," poor Martha had
a sweet and gentle voice. The child looked up at her, and with the

weakness that appeared constitutionally peculiar to him, his eyes were immediately filled with tears. Yet Michael was not a whimpering boy either; many had seen him harshly treated, for he had worked almost from babyhood in the cotton-factory, but nobody had ever seen him cry under it. But if his mother, or his poor sickly brother, touched his little heart, either with joy or tenderness, he would weep and laugh both, with very infantine susceptibility. So it was with him now, for when Martha added with a good-humoured smile, "And what brings you here, Master Armstrong?" he laughed outright as he replied, "Indeed, ma'am, I ain't Master Armstrong, and I don't know a bit what I be here for."

This speech, though addressed to Martha, being heard by all, the contrast between his appearance and his language considerably excited the curiosity of the two eldest Miss Dowlings.

"La! how he talks! I thought he was a gentleman by his jacket, didn't you, Arabella?" said Miss Harriet.

"Yes to be sure I did," replied the eldest sister. "But I am sure he is *not*, with that horrid way of speaking, what did you bring him here for Peggy?" continued the young lady with an air of authority.

"Because master bid me, miss," was the satisfactory reply.

"Well to be sure, that is queer! I suppose he's the son of somebody or other, or papa would never have sent him in to us. It is not at all his way to patronise vulgarity. Where do you live, young gentleman?"

Michael looked very much as if he were in danger of laughing again, but he did not, and replied very demurely, "in Mr Sykes's back kitchen, ma'am, in Hoxley-lane"

Though the answer was addressed to the inquirer, his eye turned to Martha as he uttered it, as if anxious to see how she bore it, but he encountered a look that altogether puzzled him; for though it was at least as kind as before, there was uneasiness in it, and she looked round her, as if uncomfortably doubtful of what would happen next.

She did not, however, wait long for the result; for Miss Sophia, Miss Louisa and Miss Charlotte, the three middling-sized Miss Dowlings, who had approached very near to the little boy, and were even growing so familiar that Miss Charlotte had taken hold of one of his dark curls, were severally and suddenly drawn off by the respective hands of their two eldest sisters, and the governess.

"Then he is not a young gentleman after all?" said Miss Sophia.

"La; how funny!" exclaimed Miss Louisa, "where did he get his clothes from?" interrogated Miss Harriet.

"Most like he stole them," responded Miss Arabella.

"Why 'tis Duodecimus's jacket!" ejaculated the observing Miss Charlotte.

"Oh! quelle horreur!" cried the governess driving her pupils all before her to the other end of the room.

At this moment and before any more active measures could be resorted to for the safety of the young ladies, the door of the school-room was again thrown open, and the portly person of Sir Matthew appeared at it, accompanied by the globe-like figure of Doctor Crockley.

"Good morning young ladies!" said the proud father, looking round him, and immediately entering into the jest that he saw was afloat. "How do you like the young beau I have sent you?"

"Good gracious papa!" exclaimed the elegant and much admired Miss Arabella, "he is a beggar-boy and a thief!"

Sir Matthew and his friend Doctor Crockley, both burst into such a shout of laughter at this sally, that it was a minute before either of them could speak; but at length the knight, turning to the doctor, said,

"Leave my girls alone, Crockley, for finding out what's what; don't believe there's one of them but what would have found that fellow out, if I had wrapped him up in the king's own mantle."

"They are sharp enough, there is no doubt of that," replied his friend, "but I must say you don't perform your charitable acts by halves, Sir Matthew. You have dressed up the little scamp so superbly, that nothing but the vulgar dark complexion could make one know that he was not one of your own."

"Why yes, there is some difference in the skins I must say," replied Sir Matthew, looking with most parental complacency on the fair skins, flaxen hair, and light eyelashes of his race.

"Difference, indeed! 'Tis Africa and Europe. And is it not remarkable Sir Matthew to see the look of him? Hasn't he got a sort of slavish, terrified air with it? I tell you what, Sir Matthew, I should not be at all surprised to find, when the march of philosophy has got a little farther, that the blackamnoor look comes along with the condition, and, that the influence of wealth and consequence is as quickly shown upon the external appearance of men, women, and children, as a field of clover upon the inferior animals. And why not? It is quite natural—perfectly conformable to the analogy, that, by accurately tracing cause and effect, may be followed through all creation. You have a head, Sir Matthew, for that sort of thing; you can understand me, if nobody else can."

The little doctor knew that this was *one* of the soft points at which his wealthy neighbour was assailable. Sir Matthew loved to be assured that his head was of a superior fabric.

"But why, papa, should you send a nasty beggar-boy to us, with Duo's clothes on?"" inquired the intelligent Louisa. Before he replied to this, the knight exchanged a glance with his friend, which seemed to say, "that's the right sort—she's in the clover-field."

"I have taken him in for charity, my dear," replied the knight, with a sort of pomposity that seemed of a new pattern. The young ladies had never seen papa look so before. Martha, from having found herself rather more frequently the object of Dr Crockley's jokes than she desired, had, on his entering the room, retired to the window, but now she came up to her father, and quietly, and as often happened, almost unnoticed, kissed his hand.

"For charity!" exclaimed the fair-haired Arabella, moving a step or two farther away from the object of this extraordinary caprice. "La Papa! why don't you send him to the hospital?"

Doctor Crockley laughed outrageously. "That girl, Sir Matthew," he said, when he had recovered his voice, "that girl is beyond all comparison the most thoroughly-born lady that ever I happened to hit upon—and that is saying something, I promise you. She hasn't a commonplace vulgar notion in her from top to toe. It is what I call the physiology of wealth—it is upon my soul—it is a study, a science. I have not got to the end of it, but I am certain I shall make a system out of it—and you'll be able to follow me, there's some comfort in that. I declare to God, that if I had not found you in the neighbourhood, I should have bolted. I cannot exist without occasionally bringing my mind in contact with superior intellect; you find that, too, Sir Matthew, I'm sure you do."

Sir Matthew assured him that he did, very much; and then pulling a Belinda lock that adorned the olive-coloured throat of Mademoiselle Beaujoie, he asked her if she had ever seen a brat, taken in for charity, so nicely dressed as that little blackguard.

"Brawt? ça veut dire petit vaut-rien. No, my honor Sire Matue, nayver! you are viddout no reval de most—"

Whilst the French governess struggled to find a word sufficiently expressive of admiration, and if possible, with some little meaning besides, Sir Matthew took the liberty of pinching her ear, while he whispered into it, "What, you little rogue? what?"

She gave him a Parisian *œillade*, by no means an unkind one, and turned away, while the two smallest Miss Dowlings ran up to her, and, in the jargon in which their mamma and papa delighted, demanded "si papa voulait let them jouer avec the little beggar-boy?"

This question, repeated nearly in the same words by Mademoiselle Beaujoie to the knight, appeared to cause him some perplexity, and, after reflecting upon it for a minute, he turned to consult his philosophical friend.

"I say Crockley, what do you think of that?" Then lowering his voice, he added, "you comprehend the job, doctor,—which will do best to help it? Parlour or kitchen, school-room or factory, drawing-room or scullery?"

"All and every of them," replied his friend, in the same low tone, but very decisively.   "No doubt in nature about that, Sir Matthew; he be here, there, and every where, and the thing will fly like mad."

"You are always right Crockley, there is nobody like you," replied the grateful knight, cordially slapping the round shoulders of his friend, "I twig, I twig, and so it shall be, by the Lord Harry."

"You are as rapid as lightning, Sir Matthew! I remember no instance of a cerebral formation so absolutely perfect as yours. Now then, let us visit my lady, shall we? I am as dry as brickdust, and it is about lunch-time I take it. Bring the boy with you, and introduce him before the servants in style."

"So I will—that's it—I twig, Crockley. Go, Martha, and see if the luncheon's laid."

The report being favourable to the wishes of the gentleman, the party, consisting of the three eldest Miss Dowlings, their papa and the doctor, left the young ladies and their governess to dine, while, with little Michael, who was ordered to follow, they all repaired to the dining-room, where a well-covered table awaited them.

Her ladyship and Mr Augustus were already there, and both expressed expressed the degree of curiosity which the knight desired, as to who the little gentleman might be whom they brought with them.

Miss Dowling, and Miss Harriet Dowling, burst into a loud laugh; Sir Matthew looked towards the sideboard, and seeing two servants in attendance there, spoke as follows:

"My dear Lady Dowling, I must bespeak your munificent charity, and universal benevolence in favour of this little unhappy boy. His mother is a widow, and—and something, I forget exactly what, is very unhappy about her—and this little boy behaved remarkably well—" Here Sir Matthew broke off in some degree of embarrassment, not wishing particularly to impress upon his lady's mind that it was his tender care for the Lady Clarissa Shrimpton, which had first introduced the fortunate factory-boy to his notice. But he passed all that over very skilfully, and ended his harangue by saying, "I know perfectly well, my dear lady Dowling, that there is not in the whole world so amiable a person as yourself, and therefore I entertain not the slightest doubt, that the benevolence which warms my heart on this occasion, will communicate itself to yours."

Lady Dowling raised her light eyebrows, and her still lighter eyelashes, into a look of the most unmitigated astonishment, and remained thus for a while, contemplating the extraordinary spectacle, of one of the handsomest boys she had ever seen, dressed in a style of unquestionable fashion, and presented to her as a being so deplorably miserable, as to have excited the pity of her husband. The first clear and distinct idea that suggested itself was the necessity of inquiring respecting this beautiful child's mother, and of finding out whether she might not happen to be beautiful too; the next arose from the sudden recognition of her own son's own clothes, and the complexion of the lady became extremely florid.

"I should like to know where he got those clothes from," she said in accents that by no means spoke composure of spirit.

"My dearest love," replied the most amiable and the most polite of husbands, "that is entirely my doing. You have known me long enough, my sweetest, to be aware that I never do any thing by halves—I saw that little fellow ragged and wretched, and I clothed him!"

"Well, I must say, I do think—" began her ladyship, when Sir Matthew, seating himself at the table, thrust a knife and fork into the very centre of a pigeon-pie, and accompanied the act by a sound, something between a slight cough and a grunt, which, in language matrimonial, was known to mean, "You had better hold your tongue and mind your business." Whereupon, Lady Dowling sat down too, but her fair complexion was rather more rosy than was becoming, and it was in no very sweet voice that she said to Martha, who ventured to take a chair next her, "Do get a little farther, child, can't you?—You know I hate to be crushed and crammed up so."

Here Dr Crockley, who had already fallen with vehemence upon a cold ham, stopped for a moment, and laughed vehemently. "My dear madam, you are of the slight and elegant order yourself, and you don't make allowance for poor people who are as fat and roundabout as Miss Martha and I—we can't squeeze ourselves into an eggshell, Miss Martha, can we?"

Her slim sisters tittered, and the witty Augustus observed, that "To be sure, Martha did look more like a collar of Oxford brawn, than any thing else in creation."

Meanwhile, the meal proceeded, and little Michael continued to stand half-way between the door and the table, as fixedly as if he had taken root there.

Martha was, in general, very philosophically inclined to let all things round her take their course; but she sat exactly opposite to the object of her father's benevolence, and there was something in the expression of his eye, as it rested upon the dainties before him, that was more than she could bear. "May I give the little boy something to eat, papa?" said she addressing her father in a timid voice.

"How shall we manage about that, Crockley?" whispered Sir Matthew into the ear of the doctor who sat close to him.

"Cram him, cram him, Sir Matthew.—You'll find it like oil on the surface of water, spreading far and wide," replied his counsellor, whispering, in return, "Let the boy have to boast of his high feeding, and it will do more good than if you were to endow him with lands and houses, and keep him lean."

"Say you so, my wise man! Faith, then, the matter is easy enough, for I believe Dowling Lodge is rather celebrated for its superfluity of good cheer. We'll have him gasping with indigestion within a week, see if we don't." Then raising his voice, he answered the petition of Martha, by repeating her words, "May you give the litle boy something to eat?" and then added with a laugh, "By all manner of means, Miss Martha and," taking some half-demolished fragments off his own plate, "he may boast of feeding as well as his master. Here, Master Factory, catch!" And so saying, the benevolent owner of Dowling Lodge skilfully cut the air with half a pigeon, which, taking exactly the direction he intended, struck Michael in the middle of his forehead. Whatever might be the effect of this liberality of heart and hand out of doors, Sir Matthew had every reason to be satisfied with the result within.

The whole Dowling family, with the exception of stupid Martha, burst into a simultaneous shout of delight, while Dr Crockley clapped his hands, and vociferated, "Bravo!" as loud as he could scream.

Just at this moment, the great bell at the front door, and it was a very great bell, resounded along passage and halls with prodigious clamour. This is a sound which produces, in those who hear it, emotions varying according to their varying temperaments. Genuinely fine, *poco curante* people, if they hear it, heed it not. Fussy folks, of whatever rank or station, prepare their looks and their books, themselves and their belongings, to receive the threatened visitation advantageously; but in a mansion of such professional display as Dowling Lodge, a ring at the door-bell is an event of serious importance. In such an establishment, the luxuries, or even the comforts of the family, are confessedly of no importance at all, when placed in competition with the display of their grandeur; and upon the present occasion, the whole family hastened to leave their unfinished repast, in order to receive the welcome spectator of their fine clothes and fine furniture in the drawing-room.

My Lady Dowling, and her two light-coloured elder daughters, Sir Matthew, his eldest son, and his learned friend, succeeded in reaching their respective sofas and bergères half a minute before the door was thrown open, and Lady Clarissa Shrimpton, Miss Brotherton, Miss Nogg, and Mr Osmond Norval were announced.

Great, of course, and very zealous was the joy expressed by the Dowling famiy at the sight of their illustrious friend and her cortège. Miss Brotherton was, indeed of herself, or rather of her purse, a personage pretty sure of being well received every where; but even Miss Mogg was (in yankee phrase) well shaken, and Mr Osmond Norval gazed at by the young ladies, as an emanation from the rays that encircle the brow of Apollo; while even the exquisite Augustus ventured, in compliment to his titled patroness, to shake him too, though he had never been introduced to him at Oxford.

But the feelings of Sir Matthew, at this prompt reappearance of his fair and noble friend, were something vastly different from any thing his family could participate in, nor did Lady Clarissa mistake them. There was a look that spoke infinitely more than any tongue could utter, and a meaning in the silent pressure of the hand, confirming the idea, which had often recurred to her during the night, that it would soon be necessary to make Sir Matthew understand the exact nature and extent of the flattering, but perfectly innocent preference she was conscious of feeling for him.

This first delightful, but somewhat cogitating moment over, Lady Clarissa hastened to explain the purpose of her visit.

"You guess why I am come, do you not, Sir Matthew?" she said, pointing to Mr Osmond Norval. "Permit me to present to you, and your highly-educated family, this young votary of the muses, who, if my judgment errs not, may fairly claim competition with the first poets of the age. Nor should we, of this remote neighbourhood, be insensible to the honour of being the first to assist in pluming the yet unfledged wing, which shall one day bear him aloft into the empyrean regions of eternal fame."

Nothing could be more touching than the manner in which Mr Osmond Norval pressed his hat between his two hands, and bowed low,

low, low, to the noble lady who thus announced him. Sir Matthew, with a stride which, for the vigorous distance it carried him, might have been compared to that of the knave of hearts, approached the young man, and strenuously pressing one of his slender hands in both his own capacious fists, attested the value he attached to her ladyship's introduction by saying, "Mr Osmond Norval—I will not deny, that I do occasionally myself offer tribute at the muse's shrine; and that being in some sort a brother of the craft, I most unfeignedly rejoice in making the acquaintance of a gentleman so distinguished in it as yourself. But that is not the feeling, sir, which principally leads me to tell you, that from this time forth, I shall hold you as one of my most esteemed friends—you understand me. That lady, sir," pointing to Lady Clarissa, "is a person whose lightest word ought to be law in this neighbourhood,—and to me, is so. If you publish any works, put Sir Matthew Dowling's name down, sir, for fifty copies; should you find yourself at any time in want of a library, pray remember that there is one of no very small limits at Dowling Lodge; and your reception, sir, in my drawing-room, and at my dinner-table, will ever be such as befits me to bestow on one honoured by the patronage of Lady Clarissa Shrimpton."

Before this speech was quite finished, Lady Dowling becoming rather fidgetty, ventured to mutter something about its being far better to sit down to talk; but Miss Brotherton was greatly too much amused by what was passing to hear her; and for Miss Mogg to sit while her patroness stood, was quite out of the question; so that Lady Dowling, and the two eldest Miss Dowlings, continued to stand like three finely-dressed flaxen-headed statues, to the end of it.

Sir Matthew than led the high-born lady to a chair, while Miss Brotherton perceiving that her conversation with the knight was now reduced to a whisper, and that consequently there would be no more fun in listening to it, condescended at last to answer a few of the amiable inquiries after her health, which were addressed to her by Mr Augustus and his two sisters. Meanwhile, the young Norval, with pensive eye intent on nature's beauties, stole his way to the open window, and there having twice or thrice passed his fingers through his long locks, which descended in disordered curls almost to his shoulders, and once and again buttoned and unbuttoned the broad shirt-collar which fell back, unrestrained by that most unintellectual ligature, a cravat, remained partly, it might be, to let the young ladies look at him, and partly to receive the fragrant breeze of summer upon his brow.

It was now that Dr Crockley felt he was called upon to do something that might bring him into notice, and waddling up to the young poet he addressed him with an air of incipient friendship, which seemed to say, "And I too am somebody."

"You will find this neighbourhood not very prolific, young gentleman, in such gifts of intellect as a poet requires in order to be duly appreciated. Nevertheless, I will not deny that there is amongst us a knot, a little knot, Mr Norval, whom, upon further acquaintance, you may find not altogether uncongenial. For myself, I may venture to say, that I am as warmly devoted to every subject, directly or indirectly, connected with the divine, ethereal, immaterial, intellectual part of our composite formation, as it is possible for a man to be, and it will give me pleasure, sir, to make your acquaintance. As this was spoken with energy, the sultry season made itself felt under the exertion, and Dr Crockley found it necessary so far to remember the viler portion of his composite formation, as to his face and bald head assiduously.

The poet bowed, but not as he had bowed to Lady Clarissa.

Meanwhile, Lady Dowling, her light-coloured daughters, and Miss Mogg, sat profoundly silent upon two chairs and one sofa of the splendid apartment; Miss Brotherton and Mr Augustus continued to talk about nothing, and Sir Matthew and Lady Clarissa ceased not to mutter, what none but themselves could hear, upon an ottoman, which stood in front of a distant window. If eye-beams could have interrupted a *tête-à-tête*, theirs would not have long continued to proceed undisturbed; for the mistress of Dowling Lodge did certainly cast not a few anxious glances towards the master of it; but it was not for that reason that he at length got up and rather hastily left the room.

While all this was passing in the drawing-room, Martha Dowling and Michael Armstrong remained alone together in the dining-room.

The flying pigeon, impelled by the beneficent SiR Matthew, having hit the forehead of his highly-favoured *protegé* at the very moment that the larum, announcing Lady Clarissa's arrival made itself heard, the greatly amused company left the room before it was possible to ascertain what would become of it.

The child "caught it ere it came to the ground;" but having done so, held it by one leg with an air of very comical indecision, till Dr Crockley, who respectfully walked the last out of the room, shut the door behind him.

The eyes of the factory-boy and the ugly girl then met. "Come to the table, my dear," said Martha; "and if you like that bird, eat it—here is a plate and knife and fork for you; but if you like any thing else better, leave it, and tell me what you will have."

Michael opened his magnificent black eyes, and looked earnestly at her. He approached the table, laid down the half-dissected pigeon, but said not a word.

"You would like something else better, would you not?" said Martha, smiling at him.

"I don't know," answered Michael, returning the smile.

"You don't know?—cannot you tell what you should like?"

"No ma'am, if you please; I don't know what any of it is."

"My dear child, it is all very good, I believe, only you know some people like one thing, and some another. Little boys generally like something very sweet. Here is some cake, what do you say to that?"

"I know what I should like best," said Michael.

"Do you?—then you shall have it, if you will tell me what it is."

"Something good for mother," said the child, blushing violently; "but you must send me, and order me to take it to her, or else it will be stealing it."

"Very well, I will send something to her; but you must eat something yourself first. What shall it be, Michael?" This arrangement seemed to put the boy into a state of perfect ecstasy; he clapped his hands, raised one foot, and then the other, with childish glee, and exclaimed in an accent from which all timidity had fled, "Oh! dear, oh! dear, how nice!"

"What, the cake?—or the grapes?—or what?"

"Taking it to mother! Taking it to mother!" cried Michael.

"Then you love mother very much, Michael?" said Martha, drawing the child towards her, and kissing his smooth dark forehead. Michael nodded his head, and nestled closer to her.

"Well, then, never mind about the cake at present; but I must find a little basket, must I not?—I will give you a basket if you will take care of it and bring it back to me, because perhaps we may want it again.—There, you may eat that if you are hungry, while I am gone away—I shall be back again in a minute." so saying, she placed some bread and meat before him, and left the room.

Michael had by no means lost his appetite by his morning walk to Hoxley-lane, and being in excellent spirits to boot, he sat down and began to devour what had been set before him with very zealous eagerness.

He had not, however, done one half of what he was capable of performing, when another door, opposite to the one by which Martha had made her *exit*, opened, and Sir Matthew Dowling walked in.

Michael's knife and active fingers remained suspended midway between his mouth and the plate; the colour forsook his cheek, and his eye sunk as if unable to meet that of his munificent patron.

"What stuffing still, you greedy little rascal? What have you touched with your nasty factory fingers? Not the grapes, I hope?"

Michael tried to say "no," but did not succeed in producing the sound; so contented himself by letting the forefinger of his left hand drop into his plate to show how he had been engaged.

"Don't look so like a fool, you oaf," said Sir Matthew, taking him by the shoulder, and shaking him with some vivacity. "You are to come along with me, do you hear that? and see a lot of fine folks, and to look up at them too, do you hear that; and by G—d if you blubber, or look grumpish, I'll have you strapped ten times over, worse than you ever saw done at the factory. Come along!—and mind what I have promised, for I'll keep it, and worse, that you may rely."

Michael behaved like a little hero. He remembered the promised basket, and the voice that had told him he should have it; he remembered Hoxley-lane too, and his mother, and Teddy, and their morsel of dried bread; so he walked manfully along beside Sir Matthew, and when they reached the drawing-room door, and his benefactor stretched forth a hand to take his, he yielded it to him, with scarcely a perceptible shudder.

Sir Matthew walked some steps forward, with the boy in his hand, into the drawing-roon and then standing quite still, pointed to the child, and said, "Lady Clarissa! behold the factory boy!"

Nothing could be more skilful than this form of presentation, for it told Lady Clarissa every thing, and Lady Dowling nothing. Lady Clarissa sprung from her seat and ran towards the child. "Is it possible!" she exclaimed with every appearance of violent emotion. "Oh! Sir Matthew!" these last words were audible only to the knight and the little boy; but as the latter could make nothing of them and the former almost any thing he pleased, it was evident that the lady was as well skilled in saying more than met the ear, as the gentleman.

"Indeed, indeed," said Lady Clarissa, drawing forth another of the coronetted handkerchiefs "indeed, indeed, this is a noble act, Sir Matthew!"

Here her ladyship pressed her handkerchief to her eyes, and remained in the eloquent silence of that position for a moment, then raising herself from the softness that, as she hinted to Sir Matthew, in a whisper, she felt stealing upon her, she called to Mr Osmond Norval, and said in a tone audible to all present, "Osmond Norval! favoured of Heaven, and the muse! Let not this beautiful subject escape you! Look at this pretty boy—look at the delicate air of aristocratic refinement which pervades his person. Osmond, the earth has not made her daily circuit round the sun since I beheld this child the very type of sordid wretchedness; would you know the hand that wrought this wondrous change? Would you learn what heart suggested it? Behold them here!" and Lady Clarissa laid her noble fingers on the coat-sleeve of Sir Matthew Dowling.

"Her ladyship does Sir Matthew Dowling no more than justice, Mr Norval," said Doctor Crockley approaching the group. "This is an act that ought to be given to fame, and, if Sir Matthew himself does not object to it, I would suggest its being recorded by your pen, in such a form as may give it general circulation."

The poet pressed his hand upon his heart, and bowed profoundly,

and then, raising the other hand to his forehead, he stood for some
time silently meditating on the theme thus offered to him. During
this interval, the different groups which surrounded him formed
a most charming picture. The young man himself stood apart, and
unconsciously, perhaps, became the centre to which every eye-beam
converged. Lady Clarissa and Sir Matthew, side by side, and, at no great
distance from him, awaited his reply; her ladyship with an affectionate
smile on her lip, that spoke at once her confidence in his power and
will to do what she required of him. Sir Matthew's expression of
countenance could not be read so plainly; it was grave, but it might be
doubtful whether its gravity proceeded from displeasure that the answer
should be delayed, or solely from the deep interest the subject possessed
for him. Lady Dowling, with her hands crossed before her, was seated on
a sofa exactly in front of them, with her light eyes rather more widely
open than usual, looking straight forward, and her small features seeming
to indicate that she was not in the sweetest humour in the world. Dr
Crocklay, his hands in his waistcoat-pockets, and his short legs rather
widely extended, in what dancing-masters term the second position,
swayed himself with nice balance to and fro, as if measuring the interval
of suspense by seconds vibrated by his person. Miss Arabella Dowling,
and Miss Harriet Dowling sat close together upon an ottoman, "like to
a double cherry," of the Bigarreau kind, with their four eyes so fixed
upon the poet that it seemed as if they had but one heart and one soul
between them; and on this subject at least, their hearts and souls, if not
one, were the same; for they had both, and at the very same instant,
fallen violently in love with Mr Osmond Norval.

In a deep arm-chair, in which she had almost buried herself, sat, or
rather lay, little Miss Brotherton, almost convulsed with laughter, and
with her pocket-handkerchief by no means elegantly applied to her
mouth (being nearly half of it within it), in the hope of stifling, at least,
the sound of her mirth, while Mr Augustus leant in an attitude of very
distinguished elegance on the back of her chair.

A little behind her appeared Miss Mogg, who was in truth neither sitting
nor standing, but perched very insecurely on the extreme edge of a couch
which uncomfortable attitude, she had chosen from not feeling quite certain

whether she ought to stand like Lady Clarissa, or sit like Miss Brotherton. The first she feared was too dignified and distinguished for her; the last too comfortable and she deserved credit for hitting upon a position so far removed from either; and lastly, very near the door by which he had entered, and to which he had slunk back he knew not how, stood Michael.

This picturesque state of things having lasted quite long enough, Osmond Norval raised his eyes from the ground to the face of Lady Clarissa, and made a sudden step forwards, dropped on one knee and seized her hand. He attempted to speak, but for some time his voice appeared perfectly choked by emotion. At last, however, he recovered the power of articulation and said, "Such a subject!—Oh, heaven!—at your bidding too! Best and dearest Lady Clarissa! Can you doubt that all my power and strength will be put in requisition for it? But I ask—Is it to be published by subscription?"

Without immediately replying to this interesting, and to Mr Osmond Norvall most important inquiry, Lady Clarissa suddenly clapped her hands together with a sort of vehement enthusiasn that looked very like delirium. Even Sir Matthew, though his intimacy with her had more than once made him the witness to some extraordinary freaks, looked at her with astonishment; Lady Dowling's eyes were more widely opened than ever; Miss Mogg instinctively thrust her hand into her bag in search of a smelling bottle, and Miss Brotherton took her handkerchief out of her mouth, and looked grave.

"I have got it! Oh, I have got it!" she exclaimed. "What a delicious idea!—Let us sit down! Mogg, push forward that couch, child.—Poor girl! She really is almost too fat to move. Gracious heaven, Sir Matthew! what would become of my etherealized spirit if it were so encumbered? But sit down,—sit down all of you.—Norval! Place yourself on that tabouret.—Mary Brotherton! Draw near and listen.—And all the rest of you give ear to what l am going to say, and answer the questions I shall ask with freedom and sincerity."

Thus conjured, every one in the room, except Lady Dowling, who stirred not an inch, drew round the place where Lady Clarissa had seated herself, and prepared with considerable curiosity to hear what she was going to say.

"Is not amusement the very soul of life?" she began.

"No doubt of it, my lady," from the lips of Dr Crockley, was the most articulate of the many acquiescent answers which followed.

"Is not a country neighbourhood fearfully, lamentably deficient in this?" pursued the animated inquirer.

"There cannot be two opinions on that point," replied Sir Matthew, with authority.

"And is it not the duty of neighbours, residing within reach of each other as we do, to exert every facility with which nature has endowed them, in order as much as possible to soften to each other the privations to which their distance from the metropolis obliges them to submit?"

In reply to this demand, there was a perfect clamour of approbation. "Well then," continued Lady Clarissa, "if such be your feelings, I am certain of success in the project that has come, like a spirit of light borne upon silver wings to visit my dull spirit. This noble act of Sir Matthew's must not pass away like an ordinary deed that is hardly performed, ere it be forgotten. No! it shall live in story—it shall live in song—it shall live again in action! Norval, dear gifted friend, did you ever write a drama?"

"Occasionally a scene or two, Lady Clarissa."

"That is enough, dear Osmond. I ask not a hackneyed worn-out pen. I will relate to him, Sir Matthew, this interesting anecdote exactly as it occurred—he shall dramatize it—perhaps introduce an episode, or underplot, to increase the business of the scene—we will all act it," and here Lady Clarissa gracefully bowed to the whole party, "and all the neighbourhood shall be assembled to enjoy the fête. What say you to this, Sir Matthew?"

"Upon my word, my lady, I think it is one of the cleverest and most agreeable ideas that ever entered a lady's head. If you and Mr Norval will arrange the drama, Lady Clarissa, I will take care to have one of the rooms fitted up as a theatre, and depend upon it we shall be in no want of actors. Upon my word I never liked any idea so much in my life."

"Will it not be pleasant, Mary Brotherton?" said Lady Clarissa, in her most caressing tone, to the heiress.

"Very pleasant, indeed," replied the young lady. "I should ask no better fun."

"And what does my Lady Dowling say?" resumed Lady Clarissa, with that stiffness of manner with which her ladyship now and then refreshed the memory of her plebeian friends, as to the difference of rank between them."

"Oh! dear me, I am sure I don't know," replied Lady Dowling, looking frightened.

"Well! we must not torment Lady Dowling by forcing her to act, Sir Matthew. There cannot be a doubt that we shall have volunteers in abundance. You will act, Mary Brotherton, will you not?"

"Act?—Most assuredly I will act, Lady Clarissa," replied the heiress. "People as much at liberty to please themselves as I am, seldom refuse to aid and abet a scheme so exceedingly full of amusement as it us seems to be."

"We will set such an example," cried Dr Crockley, rubbing his hands joyously, "that every county in England shall hear of us with envy—I know what Sir Matthew can make of a thing if he takes to it. Leave him alone for giving the go-by to all the world. Write away, young gentleman, write away; depend upon it you'll have a theatre, and actors too, that will do you justice."

At this interesting moment, just as the fair-haired Miss Dowlings began to whisper to each other something about characters and dresses, and Mr Augustus to whisper to Miss Brotherton his hope that he should have to act a great deal with her, the great bell sent forth another peal, upon which Lady Clarissa held up her finger in token of silence and before the next visitor entered, all the bright sallies of the party were as effectually extinguished as if they had been supplied by gas, which was suddenly turned off.

VII

A popular character—More benevolence—Interesting intelligence received with becoming animation—A select committee—A farewell full of meaning

THE PERSON WHO PRODUCED THIS very powerful effect was a lady not particularly distinguished either by wealth or station; but she seemed to possess the faculty of finding her way into every house within her reach whether the owner of it desired her presence or not.

Mrs Gabberly was the widow of a clergyman, who had formerly been vicar of the parish of St Mary's, Ashleigh, and having made herself the very largest acquaintance that ever was enjoyed by any country lady without a carriage, she determined upon continuing amongst them after her husband died, as it might have taken her, she said, more years than she was likely to live, before she could expect to make so many all over again. She therefore, on leaving the vicarage, contented herself with a very small house, as near the town as possible and went on very much as she had done before, only having one maid-servant instead of two, and contenting herself with a donkey-chair and a very little boy to drive it, instead of a one-horse chaise, and a steady man-servant of all work.

Considering the wealth and splendour of the neighbourhood in which accident had first placed her, and to which choice now held her bound, it may be looked upon as a matter of wonder that she should have made any intimacies at all. But, though the vicarage of St Mary's, Ashleigh, was far enough from being richly endowed, and the private fortune of the late incumbent not such as to enable him to approach to any thing like an equality in his style of living to even the least wealthy among the manufacturers in the district, there is still a species of respect for the profession of a clergyman, which opens to him and his family the houses of many, greatly their superiors in point of wealth; and it therefore pretty generally depends on the clergy themselves, whether they are on intimate terms with their neighbours, or not.

Now Mr Gabberly, or more properly speaking, Mrs Gabberly, who in strength of will had ever been his far better half, did greatly desire to be on intimate terms with her neighbours. Rich or poor, gentle or simple, old or young, she was determined to be intimate with them all. And she was intimate with them all, very intimate. One word more, and Mrs Gabberly shall be left to speak for herself, which she was certainly able to do, with as little impediment of any kind, as most people. Mrs Gabberly was the daughter of a physician; and from her earliest years had acquired so decided a taste for the theory and practice of medicine, that she could never wean herself entirely from it, but was thought by many to let it still occupy rather too large a share of her conversation and thoughts. Nevertheless, Mrs Gabberly was exceedingly popular, for though her discourse ran much upon bruises and bowels, rickets and rheums, spasms and spines, it ran also upon matters more attractive. If she could not tell what every body for three miles round had for dinner on the very day on which she was speaking, it was a hundred to one but she could tell, within a cutlet or a hash, what they had been all eating for a week before. She knew, with an approach to correctness that was perfectly astonishing, the amount of every body's expenditure, and every body's debts; could tell to the fraction of a new ribbon, how many bonnets each lady consumed per annum and was perfectly *au fait* of the quantity of corn and hay got through in every body's stables. No flirtation ever escaped either her eyes or her tongue, and the *Morning Post* was a less faithful record of fine parties, than the tablets of her comprehensive memory.

The Dowling family was aware of all this; and each in their way had a peculiar value for her society, for Mrs Gabberly knew how to be all things to all men, women, and children; but, at the present moment, it was Sir Matthew who felt the most decided movement of satisfaction at beholding her sharp black eyes, brisk step, and eager manner of reconnoitring every individual present, as she entered the room.

"Here is my general advertiser," thought the knight, as he extended his huge hand to welcome her. "We will have a theatrical representation that shall immortalize my charity, and here's the one that shall act the part of Fame, and trumpet it round the country."

"My goodness! what a charming party of you is got all together this morning," exclaimed Mrs Gabberly, smiling and bowing, and nodding, and courtesying, to every body in succession, all the time that Sir Matthew continued his cordial hand-shaking. "Now you must just tell me what you are all about, for if you don't I shall die, and there's the truth."

"No, no, Mrs Gabberly, you shan't die, if we can save your life," replied Sir Matthew, in his most jovial tone. "We are a gay and happy party, at this moment, I do believe, one and all," and here the knight thought proper to send a glance after little Michael, who, notwithstang his fine clothes, was looking pale and sad enough, in the more distant corner from the principal group to which he had been able to creep.

The experienced eye of Sir Matthew read past suffering and present terror in his speaking features, and he cursed the trembling child in his heart of hearts. But Sir Matthew Dowling might have removed as many coatings as the grave-digger in Hamlet, ere the looker-on could have penetrated so far; and it must have been a quick observer that could have detected the sort of lurid glare that for half an instant gleamed in the savage look he cast upon the boy. It was for no longer space that his joyous gaiety was obscured, and he then turned again his admiring glances upon the Lady Clarissa, and resumed his speech.

"This is the person, Mrs Gabberly, who must let you into the mystery. You must entreat her ladyship to be pleased to inform you what it is she is going to make us all do."

"Well then, I hope her ladyship won't refuse. You won't be so cruel, will you, my lady?"

"No, certainly!" replied Lady Clarissa smiling complacently on the knight. "If Sir Matthew complies with my proposal, I shall have no objection to its being proclaimed to all the world."

And here glances were exchanged between the knight and the lady, perfectly intelligible to each other, and which said very distinctly, "Ah! Lady Clarissa!" on the one part; and, "Oh! Sir Matthew! on the other".

"Speak then, my lady!" said the gallant manufacturer with a low bow; "and whatever you shall say, shall be law."

"Now then, ladies and gentlemen! all of you give ear; for not Mrs Gabberly alone, but every one present, should pay attention to what I am about to say." And here Lady Clarissa turned her eyes round about her in search of the hero of the scene. "Where is the little boy?" said she, in a tone of great theatrical feeling.

"Come here, my dear little fellow!" said Sir Matthew, again turning his glance towards Michael, and now looking amiable and benignant with all his might. But the child seemed to wither beneath this sunshine, even more conspicuously than when he had been left in the shade; and it was not till the knight made some gigantic strides forwards to meet him, that poor Michael formed the desperate courage necessary to bring him from his corner to the spot where his noble benefactress stood. Nay, the last steps were not made without the helping hand of Sir Matthew, which heavily laid upon his shoulder performed a twofold office; ostensibly caressing, while, in truth, it forcibly impelled the little trembler forward.

"Now then, Mrs Gabberly," said Lady Clarissa, "look at this interesting little fellow! It is he who is the hero of our *fête*."

"Indeed! And pray what may the young gentleman's name be?" said Mrs Gabberly.

"Is not that delicious?" cried Lady Clarissa. "Oh, Sir Matthew! how I envy you your feelings! Note that, dear Norval. The touch is exquisitely dramatic, and must on no account be omitted. This *young gentleman*, Mrs Gabberly," continued Lady Clarissa, with increasing animation, "this young gentleman as you most naturally call him, was a few short hours ago, a wretched, ragged beggar-boy! Sir Matthew Dowling, from motives, that I dare not wound his generous heart by thus publicly dwelling upon, has rescued him from poverty and destruction. This deed, so beautiful in itself, and so beneficial in its influence as an example, is about to be immortalized as it ought to be, by the pen, the rapid, brilliant, touching pen of my young friend, Mr Osmond Norval. He has undertaken to dramatize this charming trait of benevolence, and our excellent Sir Matthew, has consented to fit up a little theatre for the representation of it, at which all the neighbourhood are to be present as invited guests."

"Well now! If ever I heard any thing so delightful as that!" exclaimed Mrs Gabberly, clapping her hands in ecstasy. "Are the cards sent out, Sir Matthew?"

"Not yet, Mrs Gabberly," replied the knight, with his most friendly smile; "but depend upon it that when they are, you will not be forgotten."

"Well now, my dear Lady Dowling! I am sure you are always so kind to me!" cried the delighted Mrs Gabberly, making her way towards the sofa, where sat the lady of the mansion in frowning state; "I should not wonder if you were to contrive a bed for me on this great occasion, it would be just like you. And oh! my! I have got such a quantity of things I want to tell you, but I can't stop one instant longer now, if you'd give me the whole world. So, good by to you, all, my dears! I've heard something about you, Miss Arabella, but it must keep, my dear; and I've a secret for Miss Harriet's ear, too, when we have got leisure. But, good by, good by! Good morning, my Lady Clarissa," and away bustled Sir Matthew's *public advertiser* to spread the glorious news of private theatricals at Dowling Lodge, throughout the country. She paused for one moment, however, as she passed by Michael; and putting her hand upon his head, so as to make him turn his face up towards her, she said, after looking at him very earnestly,

"Well now, for a beggar-child, he is to be sure the genteelest looking little fellow, I ever did see; but, perhaps that may be owing to his being so pale and thin, which is certainly a great deal more elegant than fatness and red cheeks, though it don't quite seem so healthy."

"Oh! he is in perfect health, I do assure you, Mrs Gabberly, as you would have said, if you had seen the dear little fellow eating his luncheon with us just now," said the amiable Sir Matthew chucking him under the chin. "But, by the way," continued the merry knight, "I rather suspect that I called him away before he had quite finished and that's what it is makes him look so doleful, isn't it, dear? Well! never be ashamed about it—go back again, there's a darling! and don't forget to take a nice bit home to mother and brother—d'ye hear, Michael? Pretty fellow! how he blushes!"

And here the benevolent Sir Matthew himself opened the door leading to the dining-room, and playfully pushed the "darling" through it.

"Well now!" again exclaimed the astonished Mrs Gabberly "did ever any body see such a beautiful spectacle of charity as that?"

And without waiting for any reply, the brisk little lady made her exit without further pause or delay of any kind, and so completely charged "to the top of her bent" with wonderful intelligence, that she actually suffered from the repletion till half a dozen gossippings had relieved it.

Meanwhile, the party she left resolved themselves into a committee of managment upon the business in hand. Mr Osmond Norval was entreated to urge his eloquent pen with the greatest possible rapidity; while on his part, Sir Matthew promised that the necessary workmen should immediately be employed in preparing one of the largest rooms in the house as a theatre.

When the consultation reached this point, Lady Dowling suddenly rose and left the room; but this circumstance did not appear to produce much emotion in any of the party, and they remained together in a most delightful state of hubbub and excitement till the heiress grew tired, and ventured to hint that she thought it would be best for her to drive home first, and then send her carriage back for the accommodation of her noble friend.

This proposal brought the meeting to a conclusion; but not till Lady Clarissa had confessed in a whisper to Sir Matthew, that she never in her whole life remembered to have taken any thing that did her so much good, as the delicious grapes he had sent home with her the evening before.

VIII

*A very innocent tête-à-tête, but in which Miss Martha Dowling comes
to a wrong conclusion—An unfortunate embassy—An agreeable
excursion—A philosophical disquisition—A visit to the factory*

WHILE THESE THINGS WERE GOING on in my Lady Dowling's
morning drawing-room, the forgotten Martha—forgotten at
least by all but little Michael—employed herself in seeking such a basket,
as might answer the purpose of a viaticum between the object of her
father's charity, and the mother and brother of whom he had so fondly
spoken. Having at length succeeded in her quest, she returned to the
dining-room, and was almost as much disappointed at finding the object
of her good natured exertions flown, as the poor child himself had been,
when obliged to quit the room to which this kind friend had promised
to return. But Martha, though not a person very highly favoured by
circumstances, was nevertheless better off than Michael, inasmuch as
by keeping out of sight she could pretty generally contrive to remain
where she chose, and do what she liked. These enviable privileges
enabled her now to sit down at one of the large open windows of the
dining-room, and to draw from her unseemly-sized pocket, a volume
of Shakspeare, with which she determined to beguile the time till the
boy should return, or till by some means or other, she might be able to
discover what had become of him.

When therefore, impelled by the playful, but very effectual impulse
of Sir Matthew's shove, Michael once more entered the dining-parlour,
he had the satisfaction of being again greeted by the friendly eye and
friendly voice, which had already so greatly cheered him

"So, here you are again, my little man," said Martha, repocketing her book, and rising; "I thought you would hardly forget the basket: see, here it is, and now you shall help me pack it."

The help thus asked for, was afforded by the happy child's holding the basket in his hand, as he followed her round the table, while with a smile that spoke as much pleasure as his own, she selected all sorts of good things to put into it.

"There! now I don't think we can put in any more, Michael; so set off and carry it to your mother."

With eyes beaming rapture, and little hands that trembled with delight, Michael closed the lid of the basket, and proceeded towards the door; but ere he had fully reached it, he stopped short, and addressing Martha, in a tone as fearless and confidential as if she had been his sister, he said,

"But what d'ye think about Teddy? Mightn't I change into my old clothes again, and just step into the factory for one minute? Teddy can't almost never eat the dinner as we takes to the factory, and a bit of this would do him so much good!—May I?"

"Upon my word, Michael, I am rather puzzled what to say," replied his friend; "as papa has ordered you to have these clothes, he might not be pleased at your taking them off again, and it would be a great pity to make him angry with you when he is so very good and kind, wouldn't it?"

Michael hung his head, and said nothing.

"But why need you change your clothes, my dear boy?—I dare say Teddy would be very proud to see you look so nice."

Still Michael answered not, but began assiduously picking to pieces the handle of Martha's delicate basket.

"Don't do that, dear," said Martha, approaching, and taking the offending hand in hers; "but tell me what you are thinking about?"

"I am thinking," said Michael, "that if I walked into the midst of 'em this way, and up to poor Teddy, in his dirty ragged clothes, it would look"—and here he stopped without finishing the sentence.

"It would look, how?—as if you were proud, perhaps?" said Martha. The child shook his head.

"No, not that. Teddy would not think that," he replied.

"What would he think, then?—Tell me all that is passing in your little head and then I shall be able to advise you."

"Why, he'd think," said Michael, and tears started as he spoke—"he'd think that he and I could never be right down brothers any more."

Martha involuntarily kissed the little face that was turned up to hers, but replied, laughingly,

"Oh! that's foolish, Michael; do you think that a fine jacket could separate two little brothers that love each other?—I think I could love you quite as well in a shabby coat, as in a fine one."

Michael looked at her very earnestly for a minute or two, and then said, almost in a whisper, "Is Sir Matthew Dowling, as owns our factory, your father?"

"Yes, Michael," replied Martha, colouring from some painful feeling which expression of the boy's speaking features had given rise to. The child coloured too, but said, with good courage,

"Please, ma'am, I should love Teddy just as well, and Teddy would love me, only the others maybe would mock at him and me too—and I know Teddy could not bear it."

"Then they would not be as good children as I think you are. But tell me, Michael, something about the mill: papa has never let us see it yet, but I believe it is only because mamma thinks it is a dirty place. Is it very dirty, Michael?"

"Yes, please ma'am."

"And what makes it so, my dear? The cotton that goes into it looks as white as snow. I never can get any body to tell me any thing about a mill, but I think it must be very curious—and I want to know, Michael, what good such very little creatures as you can do there; yet I have heard papa say, that he pays a vast quantity of money to quite little children, and that's the reason, he says, that the factories are such a blessing to the country. You get wages, don't you, my little fellow?"

"Yes, ma'am; I gets two shilling a week, and Teddy eighteen-pence, 'cause he's weaker."

"That is not much, to be sure; but it's better than nothing, isn't it?"

"Yes, ma'am."

"Do the children in general like it?"

"Like what, ma'am?"

"Working in the factory, my dear, and getting money for their poor parents."

"The children likes to have the wages," replied Michael.

"But perhaps they do not like to do any work for them, Michael?" said Martha, laughing. "That's what papa says. But it is not right, my dear, for little boys and girls to be always at play, you know. Don't you think, Michael that it is proper for poor people's children to do something to help themselves if they can?"

"Yes, ma'am," said Michael, but in so low a tone, that it was as much as Martha could do to hear it; and so melancholy a look accompanied the words, that she could not help thinking there was a great deal of truth in what she had constantly heard repeated by most of her father's friends and neighbours, as well as himself—namely, that the factory children were a race of very idle, ungrateful little creatures; spoilt by the high wages and indulgence they received, and quite unconscious of the inestimable advantages they possessed over all the other children in the British dominions.

But, nevertheless, though this disagreeable conviction pressed very painfully upon her, Martha could not help feeling very kindly disposed towards little Michael; and upon his presently saying, "Shall I go to mother and Teddy, if you please, ma'am?" she almost forgot all the naughtiness she attributed to him and his fraternity, and only remembering the disadvantage that any disobedience to her father's wishes might bring upon him, said, "Wait one moment, Michael, and I will find papa, and ask if you may change your dress, in order to visit your brother in the factory."

So saying, she left the room, and having ascertained that the visiters were gone, ventured to seek her father in the drawing-room; where she found him deep in consultation with Dr Crockley, his two eldest daughters, and his son, as to the possibility of converting the school-room into a theatre all being of opinion that the great drawing-room must be reserved for the ball, and the dining-room for the supper, which it was agreed on all sides must follow the representation.

"May I speak to you, papa?" said Martha, timidly, on perceiving that the whole party were exceedingly earnest upon some theme or other.

"Oh! goodness, Martha, don't come to plague us now!" exclaimed Arabella.

"It is very odd, but Martha always does come in the way of every thing," said Harriet.

"I wish you were married or buried, child!" cried the lively Augustus; "for you make a monstrous bad hand at playing the young lady of fashion. Upon my life you grow fatter every day. Doesn't she, doctor? I wish you would dose her a little."

"That Miss Martha is a little opaque, I will not deny," replied Dr Crockley, familiarly coming behind her, and measuring the expanse of her waist with his two hands.

"May I speak to you, papa?" repeated the patient Martha, quietly retreating from the jocose hands of Dr Crockley, but apparently quite insensible to all the other attacks.

"What do you want to say, Martha?" demanded Sir Matthew.

Thus much encouraged, she drew near and whispered to him, "The litle boy that you have taken in, papa, wants to know if he may put on his old clothes again, and go to speak to his brother in the factory?"

"Do you hear this, doctor?" exclaimed Sir Matthew; "the boy wants to go back to the factory again. Isn't that an answer to all the trash that people have been trying to get up about their being over-worked? It is just like 'em—that's the very model of a factory child—do what you will, you can never content 'em."

"The chap want's to get back to the factory?" said Dr Crockley, addressing himself to Martha, with an accent that indicated surprise. "That's curious enough, any how."

"No, Sir, I do not believe he wants to do any more than speak to his brother, who is at work there—he wanted to take him something that was left at luncheon, papa."

"And to show off his own good living to the factory? That's it, I suspect, doctor; one can understand that—and what do you say to it? I should have no objection, I think; what's your opinion? only I don't see the fun of his going in his old rags, if he went as you saw just now, it would make some fun, wouldn't it?"

"Capital, by Jove!" replied the doctor. "How quick you are, Sir Mattlew you seize every thing in a moment. What do you say to our going along with him? Mightn't we catch a hint or two, as to how things were going on?"

"If I'm quick, Crockley, upon my soul you are not slow," replied the knight. "You've got your horse here, of course?" The doctor nodded assent. "Then I will order mine, and we'll ride down to the mill together. So get along, Martha, and tell the boy that I will take him to the factory with me, but that he is not to change his clothes."

Martha felt quite aware that she had not executed her commission successfully. But there was no help for it, and therefore with the best grace she could, she told her little client the result of it.

The whole aspect of the boy changed as he heard it, and, as if instinctively, he placed the precious basket, that till now he had continued to hold firmly in his hand, upon a table near him.

"But take your basket, Michael," said the kind-hearted Martha, in a voice that was intended to cheer him; "I am sure papa won't be angry at your doing that, for I told him about it."

"No, please ma'am, I'd rather not," said Michael.

"Well, then, go into the hall, by that door, and wait till Sir Matthew comes through. Perhaps he will speak to you about it, and at any rate you had better carry it as far as that."

The child obeyed her, and taking up again the treasure he no longer valued, passed out into the hall; but before Sir Matthew and his friend entered it, Michael had put the worthless basket out of sight.

Hardly had he done so, when he heard the coarse laugh of Sir Matthew and the respondent titter of the doctor approaching. The little fellow started, and jumped aside, in order to place himself out of their way; but the knight, striding to the place where he stood seized him by the shoulder with his hand, while with a vigorous action of his enormous foot, he sent him forward towards the house door. This feat, which was performed with considerable dexterity, met its reward, in the shout of laughter with which Dr Crockley welcomed it. "By Jove, Sir Matthew!" he exclaimed, as soon as he had recovered his breath; "there is nothing like you on the face of the earth.—It is a confounded monopoly though, let me tell you. No man has a right to be the deepest reasoner, the best jester, and the most finished man of taste of his age. It's monstrous, Sir knight, and a conspiracy against you would be a very honest plot."

And as he spoke he held his sides, as if still suffering from the effects of his excessive merriment.

A servant who followed the facetious pair now opened the door, and on the broad esplanade of gravel before it a couple of grooms were holding the gentlemen's horses. As soon as they were seated in their saddles, with a mounted attendant behind them, the great manufacturer turned round his head to seek the object of his charity. Michael stood doubting and trembling on the lowest step of the portico, while a faint hope fluttered at his heart, that the grand gentlemen would ride away and forget, him; but it was quickly chased by the voice of Sir Matthew, who, bringing his horse's head so close upon the child, as to touch him, while he seemed almost to shrink into the pillar by which he stood, to escape it, said in a voice, the jeering tone of which again almost convulsed Dr Crockley with laughter,

"Pray, young gentleman, may you happen to know the way to Brookford factory?"

The boy looked out upon the wide-spreading park; and though, despite the carefully-chosen position of the mansion, many towering grim-looking chimney cones were seen to rise amidst their own lurid smoke in the distance (for in that direction lay the town of Ashleigh), he could catch no glimpse of the hated walls that for years past had formed his daily prison-house. He, therefore, answered, but not very audibly, "No, sir, if you please."

"Speak up, my hero!" vociferated Sir Matthew, advancing upon him,—"Yes, or no?"

"No;" replied the boy, distinctly.

"Then be pleased to have the kindness to do me the favour of following my horse, and I will have the honour of showing you the way."

So saying, Sir Matthew gave a merry look of intelligence to his friend, and they set off together at a brisk trot.

"Don't you think I should make a
good dancing Master?"

Michael, for a piecer,★ was a tall child of his age; and, though his limbs were
wretchedly thin and attenuated, they had sufficient elasticity to enable him for
some time to keep at no great distance, though it was a constantly increasing
one, from the two gentlemen but, by degrees, his breath and strength failed,
and perforce his speed, relaxed into a panting, shuffling, walk.

Sir Matthew, who from time to time turned round a laughing face to
look at him, now reined up his horse and awaited his approach; upon
which Michael redoubled his efforts, and in a few minutes stood beside
his benefactor.

"Step on, young gentleman; step a little quicker, if you please; or,
perhaps, I may find a way to mend your pace: I am not very fond of such

★ The children whose duty it is to walk backwards and forwards before the reels, on
which the cotton, silk, or worsted is wound, for the purpose of joining the threads
when they break, are called piecers, or pieceners.

lazy company." And, suiting his action to his words, he gave the quivering child several sharp cuts across the shoulders with his riding-whip.

"He trots out in style now, doesn't he, doctor?" said Sir Matthew gaily, making his well-bitted horse cross and recross the road in such manner, that, at each manœuvre, the goaded child fancied himself already trampled beneath his feet. "Don't you think I should make a good dancing-master, Crockley?"

"Capital, by Jove!—Egad, the youngster has learned some vastly pretty steps already. By the way, Sir Matthew," continued the philosophical physician, "when one watches that pale-faced young scamp making such active caprioles for no reason on the earth, but because he hears your pretty gentle jennet snuffing at his shoulder,—when one watches that, it is impossible not to see that nothing in the world but sheer wilful laziness makes those obstinate little brutes, at the factory, pretend to totter, and stumble, and faint, and the devil knows what; when all their work is to walk backwards and forwards as leisurely as if they were parading for pleasure. Nothing shall ever make me believe but that all the grunting and grumbling we hear about overworked children, proceeds from a regular conspiracy among the worst of the parents. And, upon my soul, if you yield to it, you'll soon have to look after the wheels yourself."

"Get on with ye, to the lodge there, you lazy cur," said the knight, addressing his panting *protégé*, "and wait till we come up." Then reining up his horse, Sir Matthew drew close to his highly-valued intellectual companion, and falling into a gentle foot-pace, continued the scientific discussion with deep interest, and a wonderful clearness of perception.

"It's quite curious to me, Crockley," he said, "to observe how common sense and observation will often make a man of tolerable ability hit upon the very same facts, and come exactly to the very same conclusions as the man of science, who has passed his whole life in study. What you have mentioned now, is precisely what has occurred to me over and over again, a thousand times, I am sure, at the very least, since I have been working Brookford factory. For just watch, my dear Crockley, any little village vagabond that you may chance to see as you ride about the country—just watch him at play; and tell me where you'll find a grown man that can keep moving as he does?"

"Nowhere, Sir Matthew, nowhere upon the face of the earth; and it stands to reason, in spite of all that the confounded canters can say to the contrary, that nature made them so on purpose. Why, what's steam?—Let them answer me that. Is steam man's making? Isn't it sent by Providence? And what for, I should like to know? Isn't it for the good of mankind? And how is that good to be had, if the nimbleness of children is not brought to bear upon it? It is neither more nor less than a most shocking impiety, Sir Matthew; and, upon my soul, if I were you I would build a meeting-house of my own, and hire a preacher too, at a pretty good salary, to preach against it. But no Church of England parson remember, because, if they don't preach the doctrine you like, you would have no power to turn 'em out."

"You're right, Crockley. That's a devilish good idea; I'll turn it over in my head, and I shall like to hear some more of your notions about it. By the way, Crockley, you must not think of going home to dinner to-day. We'll have a cool bottle of claret, and talk the matter comfortably over. And there's another thing, too, I want to speak to you about. There's a devilish deal of talk about the health of the factory brats; and I have a notion of appointing a regular medical practitioner upon my establishment, who might always be ready, if called upon, to answer any questions that might be asked. Now, I hear you are a man, Crockley, capable of obliging a friend that deserves it; and, if it's agreeable to you, instead of looking in now and then to give us an opinion as you do now, you shall have a regular appointment, with a couple of hundred a year, just to look after the health of the children."

"I should like such an arrangement exceedingly well, Sir Matthew. You know my love of science; and this would give me a capital opportunity for speculating upon different constitutions. Egad, Sir Matthew, I should like to write a book upon the subject. I think a monstrous deal of good might be done that way."

"No doubt about it, Crockley: a clever fellow, like you, may throw an amazing deal of light upon a subject that is really becoming exceedingly important; especially when one recollects that the national wealth and prosperity depends upon it altogether. You must come and dine with me often, Crockley, without any ceremony; and we may be able to hit out many a good thing over the bottle."

The two gentlemen now reached the lodge-gates, where little Michael stood waiting for them; and as the high-road soon turned in such a direction as to make Brookford factory visible, he was ordered to run on, and wait at the gates without minding them. They accordingly proceeded in their conversation without interruption and in the course of it, some very excellent hints were thrown out relative to the manufacturing interests in general, and to that of Brookford factory in particular.

Having reached the gates of what was generally termed his "magnificent establishment," and waited till the stylish groom in attendance upon him came up, Sir Matthew, and his estimable friend, left their horses with him, and entered the court, which, protected by a very lofty wall, surrounded the buildings on all sides.

Those persons who have, once in their lives, seen a large cotton-factory, need no description of it; for it has features which, once looked upon, can never be forgotten; but, for the information of those who have not, a slight sketch of Sir Matthew Dowling's establishment shall be given.

It consisted of very extensive buildings constructed in the centre of the enclosed court, and forming three sides of a vast square; the fourth being open on the side fronting the principal gates of entrance. When it is stated that the edifice consisted of six stories, and that each side of it presented six lines of windows, containing forty windows in each line, some idea of its magnitude may be conceived.

Michael was already at the gates, and, on the approach of Sir Matthew, rang the bell, a ceremony necessary to obtain admittance both for masters and labourers; no means of entrance or exit being ever left unsecured for a single instant.

The summons was answered by a lame boy, stationed within to perform the office of porter. He bent low before the great man, and low too before his jeering friend; though the jocose visits of the latter to the factory were dreaded as much as the lash itself.

Neither the one nor the other seemed to see him, but passed on. Then followed poor little Michael, hating most cordially the bravery of the attire, which made him expect to meet the ridicule, rather than the sympathy, of his late companions.

On seeing a young stranger, the lame porter looked up; but from him, at least, Michael had nothing to fear; for the boy's languid eye surveyed his altered person, without the slightest suspicion of ever having seen it before. Sir Matthew, like most others of his craft, was not in the habit of indulging his family by exhibiting to them the secret arcana of that hideous mystery by which the delicate forms of young children are made to mix and mingle with the machinery, from whence flows the manufacturer's wealth. This divine portion of the vast engine being considered, however, as a very inferior, though necessary, part of it. But, although they had never honoured the premises with a visit, it was, of course, well known to all that Sir Matthew Dowling was the father of a numerous progeny; and Michael passed on amidst such blessings as human nature, under such circumstances, was likely to bestow on one of them.

The party entered the building, whence—as all know who have done the like—every sight, every sound, every scent that kind nature has fitted to the organs of her children, so as to render the mere unfettered use of them a delight, are banished for ever and for ever. The ceaseless whirring of a million hissing wheels, seizes on the tortured ear; and while threatening to destroy the delicate sense, seems bent on proving first, with a sort of mocking mercy, of how much suffering it can be the cause. The scents that reek around, from oil, tainted water, and human filth, with that last worst nausea, arising from the hot refuse of atmospheric air, left by some hundred pairs of labouring lungs, render the act of breathing a process of difficulty, disgust, and pain. All this is terrible. But what the eye brings home to the heart of those, who look round upon the horrid earthly hell, is enough to make it all forgotten; for who can think of villanous smells, or heed the suffering of the ear-racking sounds, while they look upon hundreds of helpless children, divested of every trace of health, of joyousness, and even of youth. Assuredly there is no exaggeration in this; for except only in their diminutive size, these suffering infants have no trace of it. Lean and distorted limbs—sallow and sunken cheeks—dim hollow eyes, that speak unrest and most unnatural carefulness, give to each tiny, trembling, unelastic form, a look of hideous premature old age.

But in the room they entered, the dirty, ragged, miserable crew, were all in active performance of their various tasks; the overlookers, strap in hand, on the alert; the whirling spindles urging the little slaves who waited on them, to movements as unceasing as their own; and the whole monstrous chamber, redolent of all the various impurities that "by the perfection of our manufacturing system," are converted into "gales of Araby" for the rich, after passing in the shape of certain poison, through the lungs of the poor. So Sir Matthew proudly looked about him, and approved; and though it was athwart that species of haughty frown, in which such dignity as his is apt to clothe itself, Dr Crockley failed not to perceive, that his friend and patron was in good humour, and likely to be pleased by any light and lively jestings in which he might indulge. Perceiving, therefore, that little Michael passed on with downcast eyes, unrecognised by any, he wrote upon a slip of paper, for he knew his voice could not be heard "Make the boy take that bare-legged scavenger wench round the neck, and give her a kiss while she is next lying down, and let us see them sprawling together."

Sir Matthew read the scroll, and grinned applause.

The miserable creature to whom the facetious doctor pointed, was a little girl about seven years old, whose office as "*scavenger,*" was to collect incessantly from the machinery and from the floor, the flying fragments of cotton that might impede the work. In the performance of this duty, the child was obliged, from time to time, to stretch itself with sudden quickness on the ground, while the hissing machinery passed over her; and when this is skilfully done, and the head, body, and outstretched limbs carefully glued to the floor, the steady-moving, but threatening mass, may pass and repass over the dizzy head and trembling body without touching it. But accidents frequently occur; and many are the flaxen locks, rudely torn from infant heads, in the process.

It was a sort of vague hope that something comical of this kind might occur, which induced Dr Crockley to propose this frolic to his friend, and probably the same idea suggested itself to Sir Matthew likewise

"I say, Master Michael!" vociferated the knight in a scream, which succesfully struggled with the din, "show your old acquaintance that pride has not got the upper hand of you in your fine clothes. Take scavenger, No 3, there, round the neck; now—now—now, as she lies sprawling, and let us see you give her a hearty kiss."

The stern and steady machinery moved onward, passing over the body of the little girl, who owed her safety to the miserable leanness of her shrunken frame; but Michael moved not.

"Are you deaf, you little vermin?" roared Sir Matthew. "Now she's down again.—Do what I bid you, or by Heavens you shall smart for it!"

Still Michael did not stir, neither did he speak; or if he did, his young voice was wholly inaudible, and the anger of Sir Matthew was demonstrated by a clenched fist and threatening brow. "Where the devil is Parsons?" he demanded in accents that poor Michael both heard and understood. "Fine as he is, the strap will do him good."

In saying this, the great man turned to reconnoitre the space he had traversed and by which his confidential servant must approach, and found that he was already within a good yard of him.

"Love conquered Fear"

"That's good—I want you Parsons. Do you see this little rebel here, that I have dressed and treated like one of my own children? What d'ye think of his refusing to kiss Miss No 3, scavenger when I bid him?"

"The devil he does?" said the manager grinning; "we must see if we can't mend that. Mind your hits, Master Piecer, and salute the young lad when the mules go back, like a gentleman."

Sir Matthew perceived that his favourite agent feared to enforce his first brutal command and was forced, therefore, to content himself with seeing the oiled and grimy face of the filthy little girl in contact with that of the now clean and delicate-looking Michael. But he felt he had been foiled, and cast a glance upon his *protegé*, which seemed to promise that he would not forget it.

Having made known to the superintendent, that it was his pleasure to enter the room where the brother of Michael was at work, Mr Parsons led the way to the fifth floor of the building; Sir Matthew, however, ordering the door of each chamber, as he passed up, to be opened for him, that he might look in upon his stifling slaves and satisfy himself that neither wheels nor sinews were loitering in unthrifty repose.

The air that issued from each, was nauseous; and on entering the room, at the farther end of which Edward Armstrong was employed, Dr Crockley secretly resolved, that when making the final arrangements for his promised appointment, it should be specified that he should never enter the working portion of the establishment. For though by no means a particularly scientific practitioner, the little doctor knew quite enough of the business he followed, to be aware that, in his own case at least, the air which filled it, could not be breathed with impunity.

"Now then, sir," said Sir Matthew, addressing himself to Michael, while Parsons opened the door on the fifth floor, and announced that this was the room that contained Edward. "Now, sir, walk on, and find your brother; and, if your pride does not stand in your way, let him be made to understand all the extraordinary kindness I have shown you. Take care that you let him and all his companions know that I have adopted you as one of my own family; and that henceforward, they will always see you dressed as well as you are at present."

All that Michael clearly understood from this harangue was, that he had permission to go forward and speak to his brother; and though not venturing quite to run, he moved onward at a pace that speedily brought him within sight of Edward. The little fellow who, despite his gay disguise, immediately recognised him, uttered a cry of joy.

"Love conquered fear;"

and dropping the reel he had just taken between his fingers, he rushed from the place he occupied before the mules, and the next moment was fondly clasped in his brother's arms.

Every labourer in the factory, within sight of the spot where this meeting took place, forgot all standing orders in their astonishment, and stood with gaping mouths and eyes fixed upon the astounding spectacle. Sir Matthew, too, forgot for an instant, that every movement made within that crowded chamber, not having for its object the transmutation of human life into gold, was a positive loss to him; for the display of his extraordinary benevolence was, he conceived, of high importance, and he looked round with great contentment on the multitude of wondering faces which he saw peering over the machinery in all directions, to gaze on the sight he had prepared for them.

"This will be talked of, or the devil is in it," thought he. "I should like to know who would dare to mention night work and hard usage now. A capital scheme this, as ever was hit upon."

And from the gazers, he now turned his eyes upon the object that fixed their attention, when, to his inconceivable astonishment and rage, he perceived that the two boys, who still stood locked in each other's arms, were both weeping bitterly.

"Not loud, but deep," were the curses that he breathed against the unfortunate object of his affected bounty; and faithfully did he pledge a promise to his own heart, that he should pay for the vexation he thus occasioned him. But for the present, he condescended to veil the feeling by a smile more bland than any one ever before witnessed from him within those walls; and striding forwards to the sobbing children, he laid a hand on the shoulder of each, while he said in voice that seemed

endowed by nature with an especial power of competing with the
thunder of a cotton-mill—

"Come, come, my dears! I know you are crying for joy; but you must
not go on so, or it will look as if little Michael was ungrateful for all
I have done for him! Have you told your brother, dear, how I ordered
you to take some nice things home to your mother? That will make him
look up, I'll answer for it! There, now I'll leave you here that you may
tell all your friends that you have been made a gentleman of, on account
of your good behaviour, and because you was faithful to your master.
Let them have ten minutes, Parsons, with the mules standing still, that
they may all hear the story."

Sir Matthew then turned about, and hastened out of the factory,
followed by Dr Crockley; and as they slowly rode homewards by some
rout lanes that were shaded from the sun, they discussed high thoughts,

———"Such as Lyrergus loved,
   When he bade flog the little Spartans."

And ere they reached the luxurious abode of the knight, had between
them sketched such a scheme of political, moral, and religious defence
for the factory system in all its branches, and in all its bearings, that the
doctor as he descended from his horse, snapped his fingers triumphantly,
exclaiming, "A fig for them all, Sir Matthew! If they mine, egad we'll
countermine, and we start with a pretty tolerable advantage. You are
a man of science, Sir Matthew Dowling; and I need not tell you, that
a powerful movement once in action, is devilish hard to stop. The *vis
inertiæ* will work for us, my friend—not to mention that when the
animals find out their only alternative is labour or starvation—labour,
such and so much as you in your bounty will be pleased to bestow—
they will all grow as patient as so many sucking doves."

These words were spoken as they slowly mounted together the steps
of the stately portico; Sir Matthew, as a reply, shook his friend cordially
by the hand, and leading the way to the cool and lofty library, ordered
iced water and claret, to wash away the effect of their half-hour's visit
to the factory.

IX

*Some particulars respecting Miss Brotherton—A demonstration
of neighbourly friendship and anxiety—The wilfulness of
an heiress—A gleam of light caught in the darkness*

THE MANSION OF MISS BROTHERTON, at the distance of three miles
from the town of Ashleigh, though less splendid in external
appearance than that of Sir Matthew Dowling, was quite as elaborately
elegant in its interior, and moreover, incomparably superior to it in
every point in which taste was concerned. To this superb home we must
now follow the young heiress, as circumstances will hereafter frequently
blend her name with that of Michael Armstrong.

The position of Mary Brotherton was a very singular one, and in
many respects far from being fortunate. At the age of twenty-one years
and eight months, she found herself, by the death of mother, in the
uncontrolled possession of two hundred thousand pounds. Her father,
dead some six or seven years before, had been a manufacturer of the old
apprentice-system school, and his fortune made long before the humane
bill of Sir Robert Peel, the elder, had, in some degree, weakened the
chains which bound thousands of friendless orphans to unmeasured and
unmitigated drudgery.★

But of all these circumstances, his daughter was totally and altogether
ignorant. Educated, from a very early age, at a fashionable London

---

★ It was not till after the first number of this work was printed, that the author learnt
that the name of Brotherton existed along the capitalists of Lancashire. But when in
that county, she heard it mentioned with great esteem.

boarding-school, she knew nothing concerning the neighbourhood of her home, but that its hills and valleys were deformed by tall chimneys and dirty smoke; and that none of the young ladies who paid her visits during the holidays were at all like her school-fellows in London.

Of course, the little lady soon learned to know that she was a person of great consequence; and at the age of fourteen, had most completely acquired all the airs and graces of a spoiled child. But the death of her father was a great advantage to her; as his only child, and the only heir of his immense wealth, he rather worshipped than loved her, and the attentions he paid her, seemed more like acts of homage than of affection. Had she not given herself airs, he would have been miserable; and had it been possible that any act of hers could bring upon her a reprimand, it would have been something indicating her belief, that she was formed of the same sort of materials as the wretches who toiled for him.

Fortunately, however, she was fond of her mother, who, being a great invalid, lived quietly in the midst of her splendour; and the holidays of her daughter were thus passed quietly too, which saved her from much early adulation. She had remained at school till nearly eighteen; and from that time, to the period of her mother's death, which happened about fifteen months before the opening of this narrative, she had led a life of great retirement, dividing her time between attendance in her sick mother's chamber, galloping about the country on horseback, and reading every book she could get hold of, good, bad, and indifferent.

On first finding herself alone in her own great house, the poor girl wept bitterly. Her mother's increasing sufferings had long made her release from them an event to be ardently desired by the only being who loved her; but when at last it came, and she had herself to think of, and nobody else, there was something almost terrible is her utter loneliness. She was personally acquainted with very few in the neighbourhood, and felt no affection for any of them. Of relations, to the best of her knowledge and belief she possessed not one in the world; and with all her advantages; for she had many, being young, pretty, talented, and rich, she would gladly have changed places during the first weeks of her dismal mourning with any girl of her own age who had father, mother, brother, and sisters to love, and be loved by.

Mrs Gabberly was the nearest neighbour she had on one side, and Lady Clarissa Shrimpton on the other, and both these ladies had occasionally been admitted to see her mother till within a few days of her death. When, therefore, this long-expected event at length took place, they both thought themselves privileged to assume the freedom of intimate friends, and penetrate to the lone boudoir of the mournful heiress. Fortunate for her it was, that they did so; for though neither of them possessed any single quality of sufficient value to win and wear the esteem, or even the liking, of an acute, clearsighted observer, such as the half-spoiled heiress certainly was, it was better to hear the sound of almost any human voice uttering words of kindness, than to sit lonely and apart, and hear none; so that neither the twaddling larum of Mrs Gabberly, nor the absurd affectation of Lady Clarissa were without their use.

It might, however, have been somewhat dangerous to the moral development of the young lady's character, had she long continued to find her only relief from sorrow and solitude in the society of persons who could only amuse her by their absurdities. Almost the first time she exerted herself for the purpose of pursuing some of her ordinary occupations, she drew forth her drawing-box, and produced a caricature of Lady Clarissa reciting verses from the pen of Mr Norval; and the first observations she committed to paper, were the result of a tolerably accurate counting of the number of times Mrs Gabberly had uttered "Well now!" during her last visit.

At length, the first dismal fortnight betng over, Miss Brotherton appeared at church; and then the whole neighbourhood rushed in to express their sympathy, till her very soul sickened under the cuckoo-note of sorrowless lamentation. Nevertheless, there was so touch of real sadness in the spectacle of a young girl thus left utterly alone in the world, that despite the golden light her wealth threw around her, many among her herd of visitors might have felt more for her, perhaps, than she gave them credit for. But, unfortunately such persons are not those who make their "griefs and clamour roar" most audibly, so she knew nothing about it, if it were so, and thereby lost any advantage which her temper might have gained from emotions that soothe and soften.

Instead of this, she had to undergo what she felt to be a very severe persecution, from the prodigiously active interest which Mrs Gabberly took in her, and her concerns. As some of the singularities of Miss Brotherton's character, will eventually produce results of considerable importance to our hero, it may not be amiss to recount the particulars of a scene which took place in her *boudoir* exactly three weeks after the death of her mother.

On the morning in question, Mrs Gabberly had as usual made her way unannounced to the young lady's presence, by dint of that assumption of extreme intimacy in her manner of inquiring for her, which in this case, as in a multitude of others, succeeded in putting to the rout the protecting discretion of her servants.

"Well now, dear child!" she exclaimed on entering; "how are you to-day? Upon my word, Mary, you are too pale. You know my dear, the *palor*, as we call it, is not natural to your complexion, and therefore the symptom must be attended to. Have you any camphor in the house, dear?"

"Thank you, Mrs Gabberly; but I want nothing of the kind."

"Well now! then I must think of something else."

"Not for me, ma'am, I shall not take any medicine whatever."

"Dear child! How very odd that does seem to me! We people of science, Mary, are so used to turning to it upon all occasions, that it a looks like losing one's wits altogether, to go on so, and take nothing."

"People of no science, ma'am, do not require it."

"Well now! so much the worse for them; but that was not the point I came to talk about. Do you know, my dear, I am perfectly miserable in my mind about you. I can't sleep at nights for thinking about the impossibility of your living on, all by your own self, in this great palace of a house."

Miss Brotherton turned away her head, and resting her elbow on the mass of cushions that were piled beside her on the sofa, concealed her eyes with her hand, while her neighbour proceeded to discuss her condition.

"Did you ever hear of such a thing in your whole life, my dear? No, never! that's quite certain. It is quite out of the question, and impossible; and to speak out the whole truth at once, it is not in any way decent."

Something a little approaching to a start, produced a slight movement in Miss Brotherton. Mrs Gabberly proceeded.

"Well now, my dear! I have been thinking that what you must do, is to find out among your friends and acquaintance, some respectable person in the situation of a gentlewoman to live with you. Sumebody already known in the neighbourhood, would be the most desirable, because then you would not have the trouble of introducing her; for of course it will be in no wise proper for so young a person as you are to visit about, even in the country, without a proper chaperone."

Again the cushions were slightly moved, but this time it was not a start, but a shudder which caused it.

"Well now, my dear Mary!" resumed the friendly Mrs Gabberly; "what do you think about it?"

"It requires longer time than I have yet had, before I can answer your question, Mrs Gabberly," replied the young lady.

"Well now, that's very true, and very discreet, and sensible; and God forbid, my dear, that I should make you do any thing in a hurry. Only you must not forget that every body will be on the look out to observe what you do. Depend upon it, that they won't wait to make their remarks—that's all."

The heiress retained her meditative position, but said nothing.

"Don't you think what I have said is true, my dear?"

Mary bowed her head, but without changing the position of the hand which concealed her face.

"I wish she would look up at me," thought Mrs Gabberly; "I might guess then, perhaps, if there was any chance for me."

"It would be a comfort, as well as a protection, wouldn't it, my dear, to have a kind, affectionate friend, always near you!"

Mary bowed again.

"Well now! I wish you would open your dear heart, and speak out. Tell me, don't you feel very lonesome, when you sit down to dinner?"

"I have been long used to that, Mrs Gabberly."

"Yes; but then you had not got to think all the time, as I am sure you must do now, that there was *nobody* near you; that there was *nobody* in the whole great house but your own self, besides the servants; that there

was *nobody* to drink your health; *nobody* to say won't you take a little bit
more, my dear? *Nobody* to say isn't this very nice? *Nobody* to give you a
nod and a smile when you look up. *Nobody* to ask, 'Shall I peel an orange
for you, my dear?' or, 'Shall I mix your strawberries and cream, my love?'
Now isn't this all dismal?"

"Very dismal, ma'am!" replied the young lady in a voice that showed
plainly enough, that the picture was not an indifferent one.

"Well now! that's saying something; and I can't help thinking, dear
Mary! I can't help saying, that it has come into my head, that if—"

"Mrs Gabberly!" cried Miss Brotherton, starting suddenly up. "I must
now beg you to leave me. You have described my situation so forcibly
that I feel more than ever the necessity of making some arrangement
that may better it. But I will not do this without reflection. Leave me,
now. I thank you for your kind concern, and when next you call upon
me, you shall find that what you have said has not been disregarded."

"Well now, that's all right, and I'll go directly. Shall it be to morrow,
dear, that I call again?"

"No, ma'am, if you please, not till next Saturday."

"Saturday? Why, my dear, this is only Monday—it is a great while for
me to live in such suspense about you, dearest."

"No, ma'am, not very long. Saturday it must be if you please; and I
shall be happy if you will stay and dine here on that day."

"Thank you, my dear. I shall like that very, very much indeed. And
then we can talk every thing over, my dear Mary. God bless you, my
love. Take care of yourself, dearest, till Saturday; and just let me say one
word in your ear at parting. Remember, that there is nobody in the
whole wide world that loves you as much as I do."

Miss Brotherton submitted herself passively to the embrace which
followed; and when the door closed after her affectionate neighbour, she
stood, as it seemed, patiently, while her sharp, short, retreating footsteps
were heard along the spacious corridor, and when they were heard no
more she applied her hand to the bell. But something made her pause
ere she rang it, and stepping to a window, that opened upon a balcony
filled with skilfully-shaded exotics, she peeped forth from among them,
till the active-moving little figure of Mrs Gabberly trudging along the

drive below, became visible, and then the heiress turned again to the bell-rope, and pulled it vigorously.

"Tell nurse Tremlett—tell Mrs Tremlett to be so kind as to come to me immediately," was the order given to the servant who answered it.

After the interval of a few minutes, during which Miss Brotherton stood with her arm resting on the mantelpiece, with a countenance and attitude of deep meditation, the door opened again, and a pale, thin, little old woman entered, who, had not her wrinkles and gray locks betrayed her, might have passed for five-and-twenty, so active and nicely moulded was her little person. But despite her still clear and bright black eye, her face showed that she could not honestly count less than twice that sum of years.

"Come in, dear nurse!" said Miss Brotherton kindly, "come in, and sit down by me."

The old woman obeyed this command without further ceremony; and, by her manner of doing it, showed plainly that it was not an uncommon one.

"What have you been about, my child?" said she, "you don't look well."

"I dare say not," replied Mary abruptly, "I have been bored and plagued, nurse Tremlett; and now I am going to bore and plague you, in order to comfort myself."

For all answer, the chartered nurse put her arm round the young lady's neck, and gave her a very loving kiss.

"Nay, it is very true, Mrs Tremlett; and no joke in it, I do assure you. I am going to make a terrible change in your manner of life, my dear old woman. I am going to make a state-prisoner of you."

"You may plague and puzzle your old nurse as much as you like, my darling, so you will but smile and look a little less dismal than you have done of late. And what is it you are going to do to me, Miss Mary? I dare say it is nothing that I shall think very hard."

"I don't know that, Mrs Tremlett," replied Miss Brotherton very gravely.

"Mrs Tremlett, and Mrs Tremlett," said the old woman, looking earnestly at her, "what does that mean, Miss Mary?—I don't like it."

"I know you won't like it. But you must bear that, and a great deal more, my dear old friend. You must make up your mind to lead a new life altogether; and I am very much afraid that you will not like the change."

"Oh! goodness, Miss Mary, what is it you mean? You are not going to send me away from you, are you?"

"Is that the worst thing I could do to vex you?" said the young lady, very cordially returning the caress she had received; "you need not be afraid of that, at any rate. The misfortune I threaten is of quite a different kind."

"Well, then I shan't mind it; let it be what it will. But I don't think it is any thing very bad, my dear; for you look as if you were ready to laugh, though you try to look grave, and talk of a misfortune."

"It will be no misfortune to me, I assure you, but quite the contrary. I shall like it very much, and that is the reason you see me ready smile; and if you will be a dear good woman, and make no difficulties about it, all will go well. Mrs Gabberly has been here, nurse Tremlett; and she tells me that I must immediately take some elderly lady into the house, to sit with me and take care of me; because, as she says, I am too young to live alone, and that all the neighbourhood will be making remarks upon me."

"Well my dear, and I dare say she says no more than the truth. Your great fortune, and your prettiness, and all that, will certainly bring many and many an eye upon you, my dear child; and, of course, it won't do for you to go on without having some steady lady of a companion like, to be living with you."

"But I hate all ladies that would come to live as a *companion like*," replied the young lady. "What should I do with a Miss Mogg, trotting about after me, to ask if I wanted my smelling-bottle, or my pug-dog? And that is not the worst that could happen to me either. As sure as you are there, nurse Tremlett, Mrs Gabberly has made up her mind to come and live here as my companion herself!"

"And you would not like that, by your manner, my dear? I do think she is rather too bustling and busy for you. You are such a reader that you would not like any one that was over talkative and fidgety about you. But don't fret yourself for that, dear; you must make some civil sort of excuse to Mrs Gabberly. You are clever enough to find one, I dare say."

"Yes, nurse Tremlett, I think I am—I have found one already."

"That's very right, Miss Mary; and what shall you say to her, my dear?"

"I shall tell her that you are going to live with me as my companion."

"Nonsense, dear! That is the joke, is it, that you were looking so merry about?"

"Mrs Tremlett, I am not jesting in any way," replied Miss Brotherton, very gravely; "and I entreat you to listen to my proposal as seriously as I make it. I am friendless, very friendless, dear nurse; and trust me, with all my money, I am greatly to be pitied. Why, in addition to the misfortune of not having a relation in the world, should I be doomed to the misery of hiring a stranger to pester me with her presence from morning to night? It is a penance that I cannot, and will not endure. Yet I know that all people will say, that I ought not to sit up here alone to receive company, and I do not wish to be spoken of as a person who either knows not or values not propriety. But if you will do what I desire, Mrs Tremlett, you may save me from this, and from what I perhaps should unhappily consider as a greater misfortune still, namely, the being forced to pass my life with a person whose presence was a pain to me."

Tears flowed down the cheeks of the heiress as she spoke; and the devoted servant who sat beside her, though absolutely confounded by the strange proposal, could find no words to utter in opposition to it.

"Dear nurse!—you will not forsake me, then?" said Mary, smiling through her tears. "There's a dear soul—you will let me have my own way in everything—about your dress, you know, and all that? It will be worth any thing in the world to see Mrs Gabberly, when she first beholds you sitting up in state in the drawing-room!"

From the moment the old woman had perceived that her beloved, but wilful darling, was not only serious, but sorrowful, and that, too, concerning no imaginary grief, but from the contemplation of the truly melancholy isolation of her condition, all disposition to resist her vanished; and yet nurse Tremlett was perfectly capable of perceiving all the inconveniences likely to arise on both sides from so strange a scheme. But even while such thoughts silently took of her, leaving perhaps some legible traces on her countenance, her young mistress looked so kindly and so coaxingly in her face, as if at once reading and deprecating all she had to say, that she felt nothing was left for her but obedience.

"Do what you will with me, my dear," said she, with a fond smile and a shake of the head, that seemed to say, "I know you must have your own way, Mary."

And thus was conceived and established a mode of life for the pretty heiress which left her as completely uncontrolled as to all she did, and all she said, as if nurse Tremlett still occupied her quarters in what was once called the nursery, but had since become the favoured nurse's sitting-room.

Mary's delight in dressing and drilling the old woman for her new duties was childish and excessive; and most triumphant was the satisfaction with which she perceived that rich black silks, and delicate white crape, performed their office upon her nice little person so effectually, as to give her quite as much the air of a gentlewoman, as the majority of those who were likely to meet her.

So, on the following Saturday, Mrs Gabberly found Miss Brotherton no longer the solitary occupant of her elegant boudoir, but with a remarkably well-dressed elderly lady, seated in the most luxurious of all the newly-invented chairs which decorated the apartment, with a small work-table before her; while on the footstool at her feet, sat the heiress, looking a vast deal more happy than she had ever before seen her.

The mystification did not last long. The eyes of Mrs Gabberly were of that happy fabric, which enables the owner to retain for ever the memory of every face they have ever looked upon; and it was with heightened colour, and no very sweet expression of countenance, that she exclaimed, "Soh! you have taken your old nurse, Tremlett, to sit with you?"

"My nurse no longer, but my most kind friend, Mrs Gabberly, who has affectionately consented to forsake many of her former comforts, in order to be useful to me. You will perceive, ma'am, that your advice has not been lost upon me."

"Well now! that is a strange whim, Miss Brotherton. But of course, you are not serious in trying to make me believe that it is your intention to let nurse Tremlett assist you in receiving your company. If it be so, I think it but fair to tell you at once, as my experience is rather greater than yours, that not one single soul among all our rich folks, will care to visit you at all. I don't wish to affront you, nurse Tremlett; but you won't contradict what I say, I am quite sure of that."

Mrs Tremlett showed herself an apt scholar, for she bowed her head, went on with her knitting, and said nothing.

If she was silent, however, Miss Brotherton was not. "Listen to me, ma'am, if you please, for a few minutes, while I explain to you my ideas on the subject; and having done so, I desire that it may never be alluded to again. I am left, Mrs Gabberly, as I dare say you know—exceedingly well, in the possession of an ample fortune, with unlimited power to spend it as I please. Now I do not please to spend any part of it in putting myself under circumstances that I should feel annoying to me. For this reason I will not hire a gentlewoman—in all human probability of much higher birth than myself—to watch my caprices, and endure my whims. If any one now in existence really loves me, it is Mrs Tremlett; and I, too, most sincerely love her; therefore I flatter myself, that drawing tighter the tie that has long united us, will occasion pain to neither. If the obscure tradition I have heard respecting my grandfather be correct, he received much kindness when travelling the country as an itinerant tinker from Mrs Tremlett's father, then a flourishing farmer in Yorkshire. So you perceive, Mrs Gabberly, that I am really honoured by the association. But if any one should fancy the contrary—if any one should feel that the luxuries of my house and table—the only attractions I know of, by which I may hope to draw my neighbours round me—if any should feel that the value of these are lessened by the presence of Mrs Tremlett, they must give them up. For the price I shall put upon my good dinners and fine balls, will be the most courteous and kind politeness to that dear and valued friend. And now that we have finally and for ever dismissed this subject, will you tell me if I may hope for the pleasure of your company at dinner to-day, Mrs Gabberly?"

From this period, Mrs Tremlett never quitted Mary Brotherton, excepting when the heiress accommodated Lady Clarissa Shrimpton by the use of her carriage, when they were both going to visit at the same mansion; an arrangement which had often taken place during the late Mrs Brotherton's lifetime, and which was of such very obvious mutual convenience, that one was rarely invited without the other.

Miss Brotherton by degrees recovered her natural high spirits, and though she not unfrequently felt the weight of great loneliness, she was rapidly learning to enjoy her independence. She read a great deal, though nobody knew any thing about it. She dearly loved flowers, and often assisted in their culture with her own hands, despite her half-dozen gardeners. She laid out whole miles of gravel walks in her own grounds with almost as much skill as went to form the Cretan labyrinth, in order that she might walk, and walk, and walk, without passing her own lodge-gates, and so running the risk of being called "imprudent." She still indulged herself, and with no sparing licence, in caricaturing her neighbours; and, if all the truth must be told, derived no small portion of amusement from the variety of modes she adopted to assure the almost innumerable pretenders to her hand, that it was not in her power to reward their valuable and flattering attachments.

Such was Mary Brotherton's condition when she complied with Lady Clarissa Shrimpton's request, to drive over to Dowling Lodge the day after they had dined there. Upon this occasion, as upon many previous ones, the young lady, for lack of other amusement, occupied herself in selecting subjects for her merry pencil. The best excuse to be offered for her offences in this line is, that nobody but Mrs Tremlett ever saw her saucy productions; so that assuredly they gave pain to no one—and when the heart is empty, and the head full, much allowance must be made for such freaks and fancies.

While laying up stores of sketches from Sir Matthew, Lady Clarissa, and the poet, her eye suddenly became fixed upon the beautiful child who had been brought in for general examination. Like most other limners of the human face, Miss Brotherton had considerable skill in physiognomy, and ere she had long gazed on the pretty, nicely-dressed, little boy, she felt persuaded that in spite of his gay *habit de fête*, the child was ill at ease, and under great discomfort.

It is difficult for persons residing at a distance, and not "to the manner born"' to conceive the extraordinary degree of ignorance in which the ladies of the great manufacturing families are brought up, as to the real condition of the people employed in the concern from whence their wealth is derived.

There is, however, a homely proverb that may help to explain this: "You should never speak of a rope in the house of a man that was hanged," and it is probably on the same principle, that no one speaks of the factory in the house of the manufacturer. Be this as it may, the fact is certain, and Mary Brotherton, like perhaps a hundred other rich young ladies, of the same class, grew up in total ignorance of the moans and the misery that lurked beneath the unsightly edifices, which she just knew were called the factories, but which were much too ugly in her picturesque eyes for her ever to look at them, when she could help it.

Little did the kind-tempered, warm-hearted girl guess, that for hours before she raised her healthy and elastic frame from the couch where it had luxuriously reposed through the night, thousands of sickly, suffering, children were torn from their straw pallets, to commence a long unvaried day of painful toil, to fill the ever-craving purses, of which her own was one. She knew that Sir Matthew Dowling was considered as the richest man in the district—richer even than her father had been, and this was all she knew about him, except that her sharp observation had enabled her to perceive that he was ignorant, vulgar, and most ludicrously crammed with pretensions of all sorts.

After having looked into the face of little Michael, till she was perfectly convinced of his being exceedingly unhappy, she next directed her attention to his benefactor, as she heard him clamorously hailed on all sides; and his countenance, though smiling, spoke a language she liked not. It was evident to her that he was very keenly watching the boy, and more than once she detected a look from Sir Matthew, directed towards him, which was instantly followed by an attempt on the child's part to look less miserable.

Then followed all the nonsense about Mr Osmond Norval, and his promised drama which was to place upon the scene some prodigiously generous action of Sir Matthew Dowling's, towards this little boy. Mary

Brotherton did not believe a word of it, and sick of the false and fulsome flattery that was bandied about between the knight, the lady and the poet, she made, as we have seen, a somewhat hasty retreat.

On her road home she was more than usually silent, being occupied in a meditation on the features of Michael Armstrong. For some time she suffered her ridiculous ladyship to run on in a violent strain of panegyric upon Sir Matthew, his talents, and his generosity, without offering any interruption, but at length it struck her, that fool as she was, Lady Clarissa might be able to tell her what she wanted to know; and therefore, after answering "Indeed!" to some tirade about Sir Matthew's great qualities, Mary ventured to come across the torrent of her ladyship's eloquence by saying,

"Pray, Lady Clarissa, who is that little boy?"

"Who, my dear? Good gracious, what an odd question! Is it possible you do not know he is a poor little factory-boy, that Sir Matthew has most benevolently taken out of that sad way of life, because he behaved so remarkably well about that cow, you know, my dear, last night?"

"But why should you call it a sad way of life, Lady Clarissa? It is the way that all our poor people get their bread, you know."

"Yes, I suppose so. But yet, my dear, you cannot but allow that it must be a very different way of life from what the little children lead whose parents, from father to son, for a dozen generations, have worked on the domains of one family. There can't be the same sort of family feeling and attachment, you know. However, I have not the least doubt in the world, that good Sir Matthew does his very best to make them comfortable."

"Is this boy to live in Sir Matthew's family?"

"I am not quite sure about that. I believe it depends in a great degree upon the manner in which the little fellow behaves; and so it ought, you know, my dear Miss Brotherton. I rather think Sir. Augustus was making himself too agreeable this morning for you to hear much of the story. However, the exquisite muse of our friend, Norval, will set the transaction before all the world in a proper point of view; and then you, like every body else, will be able to form your own judgment respecting the conduct of Sir Matthew."

Again, Mary sunk into a reverie concerning the respective countenances of Sir Matthew and the little factory-boy; but feeling quite sure that she should obtain none of the information she was burning with impatience to acquire, from Lady Clarissa, the remaining part of the drive was passed entirely in silence on her part, excepting that when Lady Clarissa asked her if she did not intend to take a part in the theatrical performances about to be brought out at Dowling Lodge, she replied, "No, certainly Lady Clarissa Shrimpton, I do not."

X

*More wilfulness on the part of the heiress—Private theatricals—
Failure of a young performer, and its consequences—
Philosophical breakfast-table—A morning's excursion*

NO SOONER DID MISS BROTHERTON enter the room where she had
left her old friend, who was still tranquilly enjoying the perfumed
air which visited her through the open window as she sat knitting
before it, than throwing her bonnet on one side, she began to examine,
and cross-examine her as follows:

"Pray, Mrs Tremlett, do you know any thing about the factory people
that work in all these great ugly buildings round about Ashleigh?"

Mrs Tremlett looked up at her for a moment before she replied, and
then said, "I know very little about them, Miss Mary,—not much more
than you do, I believe."

"I have just been thinking, Mrs Tremlett, how exceedingly wrong it is
that I should be so profoundly ignorant on the subject."

"Wrong?—I don't see any thing wrong, my dear, in your not knowing
what you was never told."

"I have been wrong in never wishing to be told; but, in truth, I have
never thought upon the subject, and I have been very wrong in this. That
silly body, Lady Clarissa, said a few words to-day, which—quite unlike
the usual effect of what she utters, made a great impression upon me.
Speaking of the children who work in these factories, nurse Tremlett, she
said theirs was a very different way of life from that of the children whose
parents, from father to son, have worked for a dozen generations on the
lands of the same family. There could not be the same sort of family

feeling and attachment, she said. But why should there not, Mrs Tremlett? These people work on, I dare say, from generation to generation, and yet, Heaven help them, poor souls!—from the hour of my birth to the present day, I never heard any body talk of attachment to them. Can you explain this difference to me? I do not at all understand it; but I am quite certain it cannot be right. Why do not we know something about our poor people, as the people with landed estates do about theirs?"

"Upon my word, my dear, you have asked me a question not over and above easy to answer—that is to say, as to its being right. But it is easy enough too, in another way, for *I* may say plain and and straight, without any fear of blundering, that the thing is impossible."

"What thing is impossible, Mrs Tremlett?"

"Why that factory people should be noticed by the gentlefolks, and treated in the same way as labourers that work the land,"

"You are too wise a woman, Mrs Tremlett," replied Mary, "to assert so positively, what you did not know to be true; therefore I will take it for granted, that it is impossible for people working in a factory to be treated in the same way as people working on a farm. And now, seeing that I am most frightfully ignorant, I must beg you to tell me what it is that causes this extraordinary dissimilarity between the different classes of the labouring poor?"

"My dear child, it would hardly be decent to enter into all the reasons. Country folks, that is the field-labourers I mean, are just as likely to be good and virtuous, as their betters, and so they are for every thing that I have ever seen to the contrary. But it is altogether a different thing with the factory people. By what I can hear, for of course I never went among them, they are about the worst set of creatures that burden God's earth. The men are vicious, and the women dissolute, taking drams often, and often when they ought to buy food; and so horridly dirty and unthrifty that it is a common saying, you may know a factory-girl as far as you can see her. So I leave you to judge, Miss Mary, whether such ladies as visit the cottages of the poor peasantry, could have any thing to say to such as these."

Mary uttered no reply, but sat for many minutes with eyes steadfastly fixed upon the carpet. At length she raised them again to the face of her companion, and said, "It is then among such people as these, that children, almost babies—for such is the one I have just seen—are often employed?"

"Often, my dear? They are always employed with them. And there's no particular hardship in that you know, because these very men and women are the parents of the children, and so they could not be separated any how."

"What a dreadful class of human beings, then, must these factory people form! Is it not considered as a great misfortune, Mrs Tremlett, to the whole country?"

"Why as to that, my dear Miss Mary, there's many will tell you that it is the finest thing in the world for the places where the great factories are established, because they give employment to so many thousands of men, women, and even the very smallest children that can stand, almost. But you must not ask me, my dear, what I think about that, for of course I am no fair judge at all. I, that spent my childhood in playing among the hairbells, raking up little cocks of hay for the hardest work I was put to, and going to school to read, write, and sew, like the child of decent Christian parents in a civilized country—I can hardly pass fair judgment on goings on so very different. But I have heard, my dear, for I believe these things are talked of more in the servants' halls than among the great manufacturers themselves, especially when the ladies are by,—I have heard that a great many of the learned gentlemen in parliament say, that the whole system is a blessing to the country."

"Then your account of it must be a very false one, nurse Tremlett," said the young heiress severely.

"I only speak after much that I have heard, and a little that I have seen," replied the old woman meekly. "However, my dear, dear Miss Brotherton," she added, "if you will take an old servant's advice, who loves you very dearly, you will just make up your mind, neither to talk, nor to think any more upon the subject. I am quite sure that it will give you no pleasure, and it does not seem possible to me that you should do any good; for you know, my dear, that you have nothing at all to do with any of the factories now, any more than Lady Clarissa herself. Will you promise to take my advice, my dear child, and think no more about it?"

"On the contrary, Mrs Tremlett," replied the young lady "I am perfectly detemined that for some time to come I will think of nothing else."

*   *   *   *   *

Mary Brotherton kept her word. During the whole time that the Dowling Lodge theatricals were in preparation, while every other young heart in the neighbourhood, male or female, was eagerly anticipating the *fête*, hers was fixed steadfast and immoveable upon the mysterious subject that had seized upon it. That man was born to labour, that he was condemned to live by the sweat of his brow, she knew from high authority; and though under the social compacts which civilization has led to, some portion of every race have found the means of performing the allotted task vicariously, she felt not called upon to say that the arrangement was a bad one. It was by no means difficult to conceive why it was so, nor why of necessity it ever must be so. She felt, as all must do, who reflect on tbe subject, that if all distinctions were by some accident suddenly removed, and the entire organization of society to begin *de novo*, each man standing precisely on the same level as his neighbour, the earth would not complete one revolution round the sun, ere the equality would be violated.

"Strength will be lord of imbecility."

And when nature made one man more active, more intelligent, or more powerful of frame than another, she made the law in which originated inequality of condition. That, as time rolled on, and mankind became bound together, nation by nation, substituting the conventional distinctions of civilized society for those derived from individual strength,—that when this happened, occasional anomalies should appear in the arrangement, seemed inevitable, and of necessity to be endured. That it was inevitable, she conceived to be pretty nearly proved by the fact that no single authentic record makes mention of a nation in which hereditary distinction of some kind or other did not exist. Nor did it seem desirable that when the prowess, the wit, the wisdom, or the toil of an individual had endowed him with wealth beyond his fellows, he should be denied the dear privilege of endowing withal the children he loved, instead of leaving it at his death to be struggled for, and borne away by the most crafty or the most strong. At this, Mary Brotherton, in her little wisdom of twenty-two years and a half, could without difficulty reason upon and understand. But that among those whom fate or fortune had doomed to labour, some should be cherished, valued, honoured by the masters who received and paid their industry, while "other some" were doomed, under the same compact of labour and payment, to the scorn, avoidance, and contempt of the beings whose wealth and greatness proceeded from their toil, was an enigma she could in no wise comprehend.

"There must be something wrong," argued the young girl, as day by day she paced her gravel walks in solitary meditation; "there must be something deeply, radically wrong in a system that leads to such results. I may perhaps be silly enough to look with something approaching envy at the noble who traces his thirty descents unbroken from the venerable ancestor, whose valour won in a hard-fought field the distinction he still bears on his armorial coat, yet when I look round upon what the industry of my father—the only one of his race whose name I ever heard—when I contemplate what one man's industry can bequeath to his child, I feel that there is no very substantial cause for complaining of hereditary inferiority of condition. Nay, were I one of the peasants of whom the Lady Clarissa and nurse Tremlett speak, I can well enough believe that I might live and die contented with a life of healthful and respected toil. But to exist in the condition of these outcast labourers— to be thrust out, as it were, beyond the pale that surrounds and protects' society—to live like the wretch, smitten by the witches' curse, 'a man forbid,' must be hard to bear. Children, young creatures still wearing the stamp of heaven fresh, upon their brows, are, as it seems, amongst these wretched ones. I will find out why this is so, or be worried to death by Sir Matthew Dowling and his fellow great ones in the attempt."

Towards the end of the month which preceded the grand display expected at Dowling Lodge, Mr Osmond Norval requested permission to submit his composition to Miss Brotherton's perusal; a compliment she graciously consented to receive, being desirous, before she witnessed its performance, of learning all she could respecting Sir Matthew's rather mysterious adoption of the factory-boy, and also of the poor child's equally mysterious sufferings under the benevolent process that was performing on him.

The little drama, therefore, which for obvious classical reasons the poet denominated "A Masque," reached her hands enveloped in delicately-scented paper. But all she learned thereby was, that Mr Norval had thought proper to entitle it, "Gratitude and Goodness," or, "The Romance of Dowling Lodge," and to prelude it by a sonnet to be spoken by himself as prologue, in which a modest allusion was made to Milton's composition of Comus for the use of the Bridgewater family. She had, moreover, the gratification of discovering in what order Sir Matthew, Lady Clarissa, the poet, the governess, most of the young Dowlings, and little Michael himself were to appear upon the scene, and then she returned the young gentleman's MS with a very honest assurance that she doubted not the composition would most satisfactorily answer every purpose for which it was intended.

Absurd as the whole business appeared to her, she resolved to be present at the representation; and having perceived, in her study of the exits and entrances, that no part was allotted to the homely Martha, she determined to place herself near her during the performance, in the hope of eliciting the information she was so anxious to obtain.

On many occasions Miss Brotherton had remarked that this young lady either kept herself, or was kept very much apart from the rest of the family, which circumstance had been quite sufficient to propitiate her kindness, for most cordially did Mary Brotherton dislike the whole Dowling race. But so deep-seated was the feeling of poor Martha herself that nobody did, or could wish, to converse with her, that the hand shakings and smiles of the heiress had never suggested to her the idea that she mighy wish to be better acquainted. This shyness had hitherto effectually kept them apart; but no sooner did Mary perceive that the neglected girl was the only one of the family, above the age of a mere baby, to whom no part in Mr Norval's drama was allotted, than she resolved to profit by the circumstance, and, if possible, get from her such a commentary upon the piece, as might enable her to comprehend its plot and underplot.

Accordingly, when the great night of representation arrived, Miss Brotherton reached the Lodge somewhat before the hour named in the invitation, and finding, as she expected, the room where the company were to be received unoccupied, she desired one of the livened attendants to send Miss Martha Dowling's maid to her. A female servant soon appeared. "Are you Miss Martha's maid?" said the young lady.

"Oh! dear no, ma'am, I am Miss Dowling's and Miss Harriet's maid. Miss Martha never wants a lady's maid at all; but I can take any message from you, ma'am, that you may please to send."

Miss Brotherton took one of her own cards, and wrote upon it with a pencil—"Dear Miss Martha, if you are not going to act in the play, will you have the kindness to come to me."

This note the *soubrette*, as in duty bound, first showed to her own young ladies.

"Good gracious! How very odd! What can Miss Brotherton have to say to Martha? Martha! of all people in the world. She is not ill, Crompton, is she?" said Miss Arahella.

"Oh! dear no, ma'am—at least she don't look so. She seemed in a great hurry, however, for me to take the card."

"Well, take it then," cried Miss Harriet, impatiently, "and make haste, or I shall never get my ringlets done: they take such a time. Do give her the card, Arabella. What good is there in spelling it over a dozen times? I dare say she only wants to cross-question her about Augustus, and what he's going to act. So take the card, Crompton, and return with it to Martha as fast as you can."

Crompton and the card found Martha sitting still undressed in the obscure little room allotted to her in the children's wing. She was deep in the pages of a new romance, and being, if possible, more certain than usual that her presence would not be wanted, had made up her mind to enjoy herself till the time arrved for the commencement of the play, when it was her purpose to join the large party invited, in their progress from the drawing-room to the theatre.

On receiving Miss Brotherton's card, however, she hastily resumed the business of her toilet; for though the summons was as unintelligible to her as to her sisters, she felt, at least, an equal desire that it should be civilly complied with. It never took long to make poor Martha as smart as she ever thought it necessary to be and in a very few minutes she joined Miss Brotherton in the drawing-room.

"This is very kind of you, Miss Martha. I hope I have not hurried you?" said the heiress, taking her hand so kindly, that the shy girl could not but feel encouraged to speak to her with rather more confidence than usual.

"Why are you not going to take a part?" was the next question.

"I take a part! Oh! Miss Brotherton what should I make of acting?" said Martha, laughing and blushing, in reply.

"Nay I think you are very right, Martha. I assure you nothing could have persuaded me to have made the attempt. But I thought that if you did not play, you would perhaps have the kindness to take charge of me, and let me sit by you; for unless I have somebody to tell me what it all means I shall be horribly puzzled."

"I will tell you every thing I can," replied Martha, good humouredly. "But I don't think I understand much about it myself."

"What sort of a little boy is it that your papa has been so kind to? Every body is talking about it, and Lady Clarissa says there is something quite sublime in what he is going to do for him. But I suppose Sir Matthew must have remarked some qualities particularly amiable and good in the child, or he would not distinguish him so remarkably from all others of the same class."

"You have heard the story of his saving Lady Clarissa Shrimpton from the cow that was going to toss her, have you not, Miss Brotherton?"

"Yes, my dear, I heard all that, you know, the morning I was here;— though, by the by, you were not in the room, I remember. But there must be something more in it than that. Do tell me all you know."

"Indeed I don't know any thing more," said Martha.

"What sort of a child is it?"

"A very nice little fellow indeed, and I think if I had been papa I should have done the same thing myself."

"Really! Then you do think this child is something out of the common way, I suppose? Pray tell me, dear Martha, will you, if you hear much about the people that work in the factories? and the children in particular?"

"No, indeed, Miss Brotherton, I know nothing in the world about them; except that I sometimes hear papa say that they are all very idle and ungrateful," replied Martha.

"I have been told that they are a very wretched set of people. But, perhaps, they cannot help it, Martha?" returned Mary.

"I do not know how that can be, Miss Brotherton; every body can help being idle, and every body can help being ungrateful, I should think."

"But it seems that they all live together, and make one another worse; and, in that case, the children are very much to be pitied; for, poor little things, the cannot help themselves. What makes you think this little boy is a nice child? Have you ever talked to him much?"

"Yes, a good deal; but papa has been taking him about to a great many houses; and besides, he has been occupied very much in learning his part, for Duo, who was teaching him, said that he could hardly read at all. So I have been trying to help him, and he is very quick. But I like him, too, because he appears so fond of his mother and brother. He cares for nothing that can be given him, unless he can take some of it to them."

"And does your papa let him do so?"

"Oh! yes, every day."

"That is very kind. Then I suppose the little fellow is superlatively happy?"

"I don't know," replied Martha, with a slight shake of the head.

"It is very strange if he be not," observed Miss Brotherton. "If he were kept from his mother I could easily understand that he might be very miserable, notwithstanding the great good luck that has befallen him; but if he is permitted to see her constantly, I can't imagine what he can want more."

"I don't know," replied Martha.

The expected guests began now rapidly to assemble, and refreshments were handed round previous to their being conducted to the room prepared for the evening amusement.

"Don't forsake me, dear Martha!" whispered Miss Brotherton, "I am not very intimate with any of these ladies or gentlemen, and I shall not enjoy the evening's amusement, unless I am seated next you."

Martha felt a good deal surprised at the compliment, but readily agreed to the proposal; and in a few minutes, Lady Dowliog, who was any thing rather than pleased by the whole affair, gave the assembled party to understand that the time fixed for their entering the theatre had arrived.

On tiptoe with curiosity, and eager beyond measure, to see what Lady Clarissa Shrimpton, Mr Osmond Norval, and "all the Dowlings" would look like on the stage, the numerous company almost ran over one another in the vehement zeal with which they prepared to obey her.

Of course no expense had been spared in fitting up the apartment allotted to the purpose in form and style as like as might be to a theatre; and, thanks to the taste and ingenuity of the little French governess, the thing had been not only expensively, but well done. The space railed in for the orchestra very conveniently divided the company from the actors; and, when the curtain drew up, the well-lighted stage exhibited just such a carpeted, draperied, mirrored, and flower-adorned arena, as well-dressed amateur ladies and gentlemen delighted to appear in.

The very sight of the stage elicited a shout of applause; and when Mr Osmond Norval, habited at all points according to the most accredited draped portraits of Apollo, came forth from behind the sky blue silken hangings which formed the *coulisses*, all the ladies began clapping till their little palms and fingers tingled with the unwonted exercise.

The young poet certainly looked very handsome; and not the less so because he knew that besides Miss Brotherton's eyes, which he was certain must be fixed upon him (though he could not distinguish her in the obscure corner in which she had chosen to place herself beside Martha), those of Miss Arabella and Miss Harriet Dowling (both estimated at twenty thousand pounds), were fixed upon him too. Not to mention the speaking orbs of Lady Clarissa Shrimpton, whose nobility, he had little doubt, might he won to smile upon and endow him with all the little earthly goods she had, could he make up his mind to believe that he could do no better.

All this flattered, excited, and inspired him most becomingly; and as he stood with one silken leg slightly advanced, and so firmly planted as to require only the toe of its fellow to support him from behind, with a lyre suspended round his neck, and a wreath of bay-leaves mixing with the dark curls upon his brow, at least two dozen young ladies in the manufacturing interest declared to their secret souls that they never could hope to see another like him.

Having first recited the pretty sonnet before mentioned, in which he modestly hinted at more points of resemblance than one between himself and Milton, he suddenly changed his hand, and having, as he expressed it to Lady Clarissa, "gleaned with the hand of a master," he spoke the following lines, which in the copies printed for private circulation, were headed

"SHAKSPERIAN PROLOGUE

Open your ears!I For which of you will stop
The seat of hearing, when loud rumour speaks?
I, from the orient to the drooping west,
Making the wind my post-horse, will unfold
The act performed by virtuous Dowling here.
Oh! for a muse of fire that should ascend
This brightest heaven of description!
Then should the noble Dowling, like himself
Assume the form of mercy; and, at his heels,
Leashed in like hounds, should famine, pain, and labour,
Crouch, all subdued!" &c. &c.

The applause which followed this lasted so long, that the performers began to fear there would not be time enough left for the piece. But by degrees the tumult subsided, Apollo was permitted to retire, and the business of the scene began.

There was something more nearly approaching a balance of power at Dowling Lodge than is often to be found in the domestic arrangements of gentlemen and their wives—for, though it may be a very doubtful

An Accomplished
Family

point, whether man or wife most frequently get the mastery, it but rarely
happens that the matter long remains unsettled. At Dowling Lodge,
however, there was a beautiful alternation of power, which the measured
movement of the engine in their factories, first sending up one side,
and then the other, might, perhaps, have suggested. If matters came to a
downright quarrel, however, Sir Matthew was sure to be the conqueror;
for her ladyship got frightened, and gave in; but when any differences of
opinion arose on points of no great importance, the lady's murmurings
and mutterings were equally sure to be victorious, and Sir Matthew let
her have her way, merely because, like the organ-grinder, "he knew the
wally of peace and quiet."

On the subject of the private theatricals, there was, most decidedly, a difference of opinion between the heads of the Dowling family, and some rough skirmishing might have ensued, had not Mademoiselle Beaujoie hinted to her good friend, Sir Matthew, that if they could introduce a scene or two, where all the dear little children could be shown off, Lady Dowling's objections would probably give way. The experiment was made, and ansered completely; on condition, that "Gratitude and Goodness" should open and close with scenes in which the whole family should appear in fancy dresses, and be grouped by the dancing-master in the most graceful attitudes he could invent Lady Dowling withdrew her opposition. As soon, therefore, as Apollo had retired from the front of the stage, no less than sixteen male and female Dowlings rushed forth from the silken hangings, and formed themselves, after some little confusion, into a *tableau*, declared, on all sides, to be of unrivalled beauty. Again bravoes and clapping of hands announced the delight of the spectators; and, when this was calmed, some very pompous verses gave notice that this display of young grace and beauty, was on occasion of a rustic *fête*, in which the *dramatis personæ* were to amuse themselves *al fresco*. Then entered the Lady Clarissa; but, for some good reason or other, it had been decided, between the knight and herself, that she should enter alone; and from a most poetical scream of terror, soon uttered by her lady it became evident that a dragon, or a cow, or some other dread animal had been pursuing her. Again and again, with most picturesque effect, she looked behind her towards the blue silk *coulisses,* from whence she had issued, till, at length, the feelings of the audience were worked up to a wonderful pitch, by her ejaculating,—

"It comes! It comes!"

This was little Michael's cue; and, as soon as the words were spoken, he entered from the opposite side, holding a ragged cap on high, and dressed, in all respects, precisely as he had been on the memorable night of Lady Clarissa's vaccine adventure.

In dumb show, the lady indicated the direction from whence the dreaded monster would approach; and the most energetic and unsparing action of the limbs and person secured the audience, as well as her deliverer, from any possible mistake on the subject. Michael, too, performed his part with great spirit, exaggerating, as he had been commanded, by every possible means, the manœuvres necessary for turning the front of a cow.

To this scene, too, the audience gave loud applause, and in the midst of it entered Sir Matthew, who was, of course, greeted by bravoes, "long drawn out," till the ladies and gentlemen having nearly deafened one another, ceased at last, and listened to the beautiful explanation which followed.

First the company were made to comprehend that the danger was over; for the well-taught Michael turned about, and manfully facing the audience, pronounced distinctly

"The beast is gone!"

Then Sir Matthew, after bowing respectfully to the lady, said,

"Permit me, madam, to express my joy,
That you've been saved by this good little boy."

It was, however, uttered in an accent of such temperate and measured feeling, that not even Lady Dowling saw any thing very particular in it. A precaution by the way, which had been suggested by the gentlemen during the frequent rehearsals.

Lady Clarissa's acting then became animated indeed; for the poet, following her instructions, had composed for her in smooth, yet startling rhymes, about thirty lines of the most fervent thanksgiving, in which, now laying one hand on the head of the ragged child, now clasping both together in the eagerness of her address to Sir Matthew, and now gracefully extending both arms towards the audience, as if to make them sharers in her generous emotions, she produced an effect more easily imagined than described.

The speech which followed from Sir Matthew was very noble, and at once let the audience into all the secret purposes of his benevolent heart. The by-play of Michael during this scene had been prepared for by his benefactor with particular care, but somehow or other the boy was not apt in catching the knight's idea; for instead of the tender but joyous smile with which he had been instructed to look up into the face of his munificent patron, his countenance expressed nothing but terror.

"That little fellow does not look happy, Martha," whispered Miss Brotherton.

"Oh no! he looks very frightened," replied Martha, "but that is very natural, is it not, considering the novelty of his situation?"

"I don't know," said the heiress.

The piece went on to exhibit the beautiful manner in which this adoption of a ragged factory-boy into the bosom of the Dowling family had been hailed by all of them as an especial grace from heaven, on account of the opportunity it afforded for relieving the overflowing generosity of their hearts. Sir Matthew, while looking round upon his sixteen full-dressesd offspring, who were now again skilfully grouped upon the stage, was made to exclaim with clasped hands, and an almost sobbing excess of emotion,

"The widow and the orphan are more dear,
To their young hearts, than million pounds a year!"

Every body was touched, and again the applause was deafening.

Then came a very striking scene indeed. Michael appeared superbly dressed, and on each side of him was a middling-sized Miss Dowling, holding lightly and gracefully each a little basket, from under the covers of which peeped out grapes and peaches on the one side, and something that had the semblance of a flask of wine on the other.

Then spoke the fair-haired Louisa.

"Dear little boy, this basket's all your own,
'Tis to reward the courage you have shown.'

And then Miss Charlotte.

"So is this too, my pretty little boy,
We hope 'twill give your poor old mother joy."

And when Michael, having received a basket in each hand, appeared preparing to depart, the two young ladies exclaimed together,

"'Tis papa sends it, who's so very kind,
How to do good, is all he seeks to find!"

Upon this, Michael turned round again towards the audience, and stood stock still. It was quite evident that he had some speech to make which he had apparently forgotten, for it was impossible for any child to look more completely distressed and at a loss.

At length it became pretty evident that, *in lieu* of all other performance, the poor boy was going to cry; and some ingenious persons doubted whether it might not be in his part to do so; but this idea was speedily removed by the very matter-of-fact pokes and nudges which the two young ladies bestowed upon him. In addition to this it seemed as if the little fellow caught some stimulating sounds from the *coulisses,* for he cast more than one furtive glance in that direction, and at length, with what was evidently a great effort, he stammered out,

"My mother's a dear, and so's my brother too,
But dearer still are your papa and you.
His charity's so great, his heart so good,
He gives the naked clothes; the hungry food;
And I for—one—will—day—and night—in prayer,
Ask blessings—for—him—and—his—worth declare."

The two last lines were so completely choked by the tears, which all his efforts could not suffice to restrain, that they were perfectly unintelligible to the audience.

"Is all that vehemence of weeping a part of Mr Norval's composition?" inquired Miss Brotherton in a whisper to Martha.

"Upon my word I don't know: but I should think not," was the reply.

"Martha!" said the heiress, very earnestly, "that child is suffering from an agony of terror."

"I should hope not," said Martha, in a voice that somewhat faltered

"Do you know any thing about this boy?" pursued Miss Brotherton, continuing her whispering. "Do you know any thing about the mother he talks of?"

"Nothing whatever, Miss Brotherton."

"Do you feel quite satisfied, my dear, that this romantic adventure has been, or will be, advantageous to him?"

"I think," replied Martha, "that one can hardly doubt his being better off here than in the poverty of his mother's dwelling. You saw, Miss Brotherton, what a ragged condition the clothes were in which he had worn before."

"Decent clothes are a comfort, my dear Martha, there can be no doubt of it; but compared with the other circumstances which influence the happiness of life, they are of no great importance. Of course, I suppose that your father means to educate him. Do you know whether he can read his bible yet?"

"I know that he could not," replied Martha, "when he came here."

"Poor little wretch! That is very terrible neglect somewhere. What sort of person is the mother?"

"By Michael's account," replied Martha, smiling, "she is a very estimable person indeed; but it certainly seems that she has not taken much pains with his education, poor little fellow!"

"What a sad thing it is," continued Miss Brotherton, "that we all of us know so little of the poor people employed in the factories! I believe they are said to be exceedingly well paid, but still I don't think it is quite right for the rich people in a neighbourhood to take no notice whatever of the poor. I know it is not so in other places; for I have heard my schoolfellows continually talk of their fathers' tenants and work-people, and of their schools, and their clothing societies, and all sorts of things, and I have been trying to do a little good just at home with the families of some of the work-people about the place. But I have just now got my head strangely full of these factory folks. I wish you could give me some information about them, Martha."

"Indeed, my dear Miss Brotherton, I know as little as you do. I am told that they are very good-for-nothing, that they receive enormous

sums annually in wages, and yet that they are never contented, but for
ever complaining, just because they have work to do for what they get,
and yet papa says that it is the very prettiest lightest work in the world.
And indeed I am afraid it is but too true, for this little fellow, though he
is so interesting and intelligent that it is impossible to help liking him,
always speaks of the factory as if he hated it."

"And if he does hate it, Martha, why, if you question him should he
conceal it?"

"But I never have questioned him about that; I should not think it
right to do so. Only I remember his making me laugh, just after he came
here, by saying something exceedingly naive about their all liking wages
but not work. Now, though I am not very deep in political economy,
it is impossible not to see that poor people must work for what they
get—don't you think so?"

"Assuredly, and rich people too. I have no doubt that both your
father and my father had to work very hard for the fortunes which have
rewarded their industry. In our class of life this is necessary. But that
does not settle the question that is working in my head at present, and
which, to tell you the truth, will not let me sleep by night nor amuse
myself by day. How comes it that ALL the people—the only phrases I
have heard upon the subject were very comprehensive—how comes it,
Martha Dowling, that ALL the people, young and old who work in the
factories are classed as ignorant and depraved?"

"My dear Miss Brotherton, how is it possible that I should be able
to answer you?"

"Have you not heard the same statement, Martha?"

"Oh, yes! very often. I know mamma says that nothing in the world
should induce her to take a girl who had worked in the factories into
the house, even in the very lowest situation. Oh! I believe they are very
bad!"

"Very bad? But, good gracious! why are they very bad? What is the
cause of this strange degradation of one peculiar class of human beings?
It surely cannot arise from the nature of their employment; for if it did,
of course the clergy of the neighbourhood would interfere to stop it.
It is quite out of the question to suppose that in a Christian country

many hundreds—nay thousands—Mrs Tremlett tells me there are many thousands employed in the factories—it is impossible to suppose, is it not, that any labour or occupation could be permitted, which by its nature, and of necessity, tended to corrupt the morals of those employed in it? There must be some other cause for their wickedness, if wicked they are."

"Oh! they are *very* wicked, I am quite sure of that; for I have heard it again and again ever since I was born, and you know I have not been away like you, Miss Brotherton, always in London. I have never lived any where but here, and I never remember the time when I did not hear that the factory people were the very wickedest set of wretches in the world."

For a few minutes Miss Brotherton was silent, and even seemed to have restored her attention to the silly business of the gaudy stage, for her eyes were fixed in that direction; but she presently gave evidence that, wherever her eyes had been, her thoughts had not wandered from the subject to which she appeared so earnestly to have devoted them. For she said in the low, slow, even tone, which denotes concentrated feeling—

"If this be so, Miss Martha Dowling, if thousands of human beings in a Christian country are stigmatized as wicked, because their destiny has placed them in a peculiar employment, that employment ought to be swept for ever and for ever from the land, though the wealth that flowed from it outweighed the treasures of Mexico."

Martha Dowling started, but said not a word in reply; there was something in the manner of her neighbour which awed her. True, genuine, deep feeling, is always sublime, be it manifested by such a young girl as Mary Brotherton, or such an old king as Lear. But, though Martha was silent, her companion suffered not the conversation to drop; and presently resumed in a tone of less exaltation,—"Do you think, my dear, that I could get hold of your little Michael some day, so that I might have a little conversation with him?"

"Yes, certainly, Miss Brotherton," replied Martha, "I think papa would be quite pleased, for he seems to like nothing better than seeing every body take notice of him."

"Do you think your father loves the little boy, Martha?"

"I am sure he is very kind to him," replied the conscious daughter a little piqued. "For it can be nothing but kindness that makes him take the child into the house, and feed him and clothe him for nothing"

"And, of course, Martha, he will get some instruction here?"

"Oh! he has begun to read the bible already," replied the kind hearted girl, eagerly. "I have undertaken that business myself. The poor little fellow seemed to suffer so, when he was learning his part. I never saw a child appear so heartily ashamed of any thing."

"One almost wonders at that too; brought up, as he must have been, in the very lap of ignorance. I should have thought, after all I have heard, that he would have been ashamed of nothing. However, I should like to talk to him. At what hour do you give him his reading lesson, Martha?"

"When I can catch him," replied the young lady, laughing. "You have no idea, Miss Brotherton, how much the little gentleman is engaged. Papa has taken him about with him in the carriage, almost every where, and such quantities of people have been to see him!"

"And does he seem greatly delighted with it all?"

"No, I don't think he does. He seems to me to care for nothing in the world but his mother, and a little crippled brother that he talks of."

"That does not look as if he were thoroughly confirmed in wickedness as yet," observed the heiress.

"No, indeed! It is his affectionate temper that has made me take to him; for I do believe he is very idle, and hates his work, just as papa says they all do," answered Martha.

"Does he visit his mother every day?"

"He either goes or sends to her, I believe. Papa makes a great point of something very nice being taken down to Ashleigh every day for Michael's sick mother to eat; and the child always carries it himself, when papa do not send him elsewhere."

"And at what hour does he generally go?"

"Always after luncheon."

"Don't you think the play must be almost come to an end, Martha?" said Miss Brotherton, after looking again on the stage for a few minutes, and yawning rather more conspicuously than politeness could warrant.

"I should think it must," replied Martha, catching, and returning the yawn.

There was, however, a good deal to be done. There was a figure dance to be performed and a trio to be played on the pianoforte harp, and violoncello, by two eldest Miss Dowlings, and their music-master.

This last was a very long business: and the heiress, who, instead of having been instructed to endure annoyances patiently, had been rather taught never to endure them at all, got up in the middle of it, and telling Martha that her head ached too much to permit her remaining any longer, made her way out of the room, which she effected the more easily from having taken her station near a side door, which led from the theatre (in ordinary phrase the school-room) into the private apartments of Mademoiselle Beaujoie.

Martha Dowliog, of course, followed her, and expressed much concern for her malady, offering all the specifics usually suggested by one lady to another under such circumstances. "No, thank you," was the reply she received to all, "I only want to get away."

"But it will not be very easy to do so, this way," replied Martha, "unless you will condescend to go through the passage that leads from the offices."

"Never fear, dear Martha," returned the self-willed young lady, "I will condescend to go through any passage that will lead to fresh air, for indeed that place was too hot!"

The room they first entered on passing through the door, was one dedicated to the reception of globes, slates, guitars, dumb-bells, dictionaries, embroidery-frames, and sundry other miscellanies connected with an enlarged system of education. Beyond this was the bedchamber of Mademoiselle, which again led to an apartment opening upon that part of the school-room now occupied as the stage. This room, which was denominated Mademoiselle Beaujoie's parlour, was now converted into a general green-room and dressing-room, for into this, all exits from the stage were made.

While still in the bedroom, Miss Brotherton, and her more than half-frightened companion, heard voices speaking in no very pleasant accents from this this theatrical retreat, and the angry tones of Sir Matthew Dowling himself were soon unmistakably audible.

"Let us go back, pray let us go back!" said the greatly distressed Martha, in a whisper.

"I am too ill, my dear, to bear that room again," rewhispered Miss Brotherton. "Let me sit down here for a few minutes, and I shall recover myself; and then we can return, and go out the other way with the rest of the company."

It was impossible to argue the point; so poor Martha submitted, though cruelly distressed at the idea of her father's private violence of temper being listened to by one of those who had never seen Dowling Lodge, or its inhabitants, excepting in full dress. This distress was by no means lessened when some very audible words made it evident that Michael Armstrong was the object of the angry feelings to which he was now giving vent. As the best thing to be done under the circumstances; she pointed to a sofa at the greatest distance from the imperfectly-closed door from whence the sounds issued; but Miss Brotherton had already dropped into a chair so near this door of communication that she not only heard, but saw all that was passing in that part of the green-room which Sir Matthew Dowling occupied. That this was the last place in which a gentlewoman would have been likely to place herself at such a moment, is most certain; but the capricious heiress was wont to exclaim on many occasions, when observance and restraint were irksome to her, "I am not a gentlewoman—and why should I torment myself by affecting to be one."

It was probably by some such reasoning that she now justified to herself the strong measure she was adopting; in order to become acquainted with what was passing *behind the scenes* respecting Michael Armstrong.

Circumstances were favourable to the object; for Sir Matthew was in one of those towering fits of passion, to which his family and dependants knew him to be subject, though the majority of the world declared him to be an extremely good-natured man.

"Blackguard!—Vermin!—Devil's imp!"—were among the first intelligible words which reached the heiress, after she had seated herself; and these were accompanied by cuffs so heavy on the head and shoulders of Michael, that it required a very powerful effort over herself to prevent her darting forward to seize the arm that gave them. But this prudent effort was dictated and sustained by a stronger feeling than curiosity; and she remained perfectly still to await what should follow.

Dr Crockley, who, though not among the corps of performers, had been permitted to be useful behind the scenes in a variety of ways, and among the rest had acted as prompter, stood beside the trembling child, and it was to his friendly ear that the irritated Sir Matthew addressed himself.

"Will you believe he did not do it on purpose? Will you believe Crockley, that there was any thing to make him cry then? Had we not borne with all his beastly stupidity, expressly for the purpose of keeping the little ungrateful monster in good humour? Hadn't I fed him, and crammed him, as you bid me, with what was too good for him ever to have reached the smell of? Didn't I cosset his lazy beast of a mother with such niceties as the dirty beggar never heard of before? And his crook-shanked rat of a brother, too, haven't they been all fed at my cost for more than a month past? And then to see this black trait come upon the stage, and cry before all the company as if his heart was breaking?"

"It's too bad to bear," replied Dr Crockley, "and if he was to be flayed alive and salted, it would not be half what he deserved."

"Wouldn't the best thing I could do be to send him back into the factory to-morrow morning, Doctor?" demanded Sir Matthew, suddenly quitting his hold of the child, and setting his square arms akimbo. "By Heaven I am sick of the job."

"I will be very good, sir, if you will," said the boy, "and I won't go to sleep at the work at all, and no more won't Edward neither, if you will but please to let me go back again."

"You see how much he dreads the factory," said Sir Matthew, with a grim smile. "But," nodding his head, and winking his eye familiarly to the child, "we shall see, my pretty dear, if Mr Parsons can't contrive to do something more than just keep you awake. He *shall* go back, Crockley, upon my soul he shall. It is the only way to prevent his driving me mad. I loathe the very sight of him."

"You must do as you like, Sir Matthew," replied his confidential friend, "but it will be the most foolish thing you ever contrived in your life, if you do. I tell you the story is doing wonders every where; and now, because a stupid brat can't say his lesson perfect, you are just going to spoil it all."

"His lesson perfect! Confound the sly vagabond, that was not the point, Crockley. It was not the *lesson* that choked him. How much will you bet me that if I get fifty lines written down abusing me and nothing else in 'em he won't learn them off as glib and perfect as any actor on the stage? I know his black heart, and he shall find out that mine is not made of pap before I have done with him."

"That's all right and fair enough, and I have nothing to say against it," replied the friendly physician, "and let us talk it all over quietly to gether to-morrow morning; but for to-night—" And here Dr Crockley, taking his friend by the arm, led him to the door which opened upon the stage, from whence issued a *tintamarre* of instruments sufficient to cover whatever he might wish to say, not only from the ear of little Michael, but from all others. The moment selected by the angry knight for relieving himself of the wrath which burned within him would have been a most favourable one, but for the accidental vicinity of Miss Brotherton. While the whole corps of performers, excepting the manufacturer and the factory-boy, were grouped upon the stage, in a style the most favourable for the display of their persons and dresses, the trio above mentioned augmented, by way of finale, by tambourines and triangles, went steadily on in a *crescendo* movement that ended in a clamour rendered perfect by the last peal of applause from the well nigh worn-out audience, so that their secret conference was not otherwise likely to be overheard.

At the moment after Sir Matthew had declared his intention of teaching Michael to know what his heart was made of, and just as he was himself led off by his friend Crockley, Miss Brotherton, pressing her two hands strongly upon her breast, involuntarily pronounced the word "MONSTER!" and then placing her hands before her eyes remained lost in no very pleasing revery. But hardly had her meditations lasted a moment, ere they were chased by hearing the sound of some one falling near her, and looking round, she perceived poor Martha stretched insensible upon the floor.

lnexpressibly shocked at remembering, which she did by no slow action of the mind, the suffering to which her own unscrupulous curiosity had exposed the unfortunate girl, she ran to her with eager haste, and with much repentant tenderness raised her head and did all her small experience suggested towards restoring her. The comfortable insensibility did not last long; and Martha, who with restored animation immediately recovered her recollection, and in whose composition no affectation of any kind had part, raised herself without assistance from the ground, and silently placed herself upon a sofa.

"Dear excellent Martha!" exclaimed Miss Brotherton, with much true feeling, "fear not that I should ever repeat what I have so accidentally heard; and let not your good and dutiful nature suffer thus, because I have heard it. We have all our faults, Martha, and it is the duty of each to pray for the conversion of their own hearts first, and then for the repentance of others. And what prayers, dear girl, so likely to be heard, as those of a good and dutiful child? Let us slip back to our places, Martha. This clapping of hands announces, as I take it, the conclusion of the piece."

Martha, though wounded to the very sonl, uttered no word of deprecation or complaint; but there was an unsophisticated simplicity of character about her which made her decline, by a courtesy that had a little of the stiffness of ceremony in it, the offered arm of Mary, and stepping forward she opened the door by which they had left the theatre, till the heiress had passed through it, and resumed her place.

XI

Miss Brotherton pushes her inquiries further—A well-arranged scheme disagreeably defeated—A visit, and its consequences

MARY BROTHERTON CERTAINLY DID NOT return home that night with any doubts on her mind respecting the nature of Sir Matthew Dowling's benevolence; but the fever of spirits which had seized her was greatly increased by the information she had gained.

There was a vast deal of energy and strength of purpose in the mind of Mary Brotherton, but hitherto all this had lain latent and inert. The sentiment which in ninety-nine cases out of a hundred is the first to awaken the female heart to strong emotion seemed to be totally powerless to her. She had never yet felt the slightest approach to the passion of loves; nor was it very likely she should, for one among her many peculiarities of character was the persuasion that every man who paid her attention was in pursuit of her fortune, an idea, which to such a temper as hers was calculated to act as a sevenfold shield against all amatory attacks upon her heart.

Most truly therefore, up to this time, had she continued

"In maiden meditation, fancy free."

But this could be said no longer; neither fancy nor any other faculty could be termed free in one whose thoughts fixed themselves by night and day upon one single subject, while feeling that to it she was ready to sacrifice every thing else in life.

On re-entering her house on the memorable night of the Dowling
Lodge theatricals, Miss Brotherton retired to her apartment without
even the intention of sleeping. She laid her head upon her pillow
deliberately determined not to close her eyes in sleep till she had made
up her mind as to the best way of rescuing the pale trembling child,
whose voice and form haunted her, from the horrible bondage of Sir
Matthew Dowling's charity.

The question was not altogether an easy one. She could hardly doubt
that very strong indignation would follow any open effort on her part
to interfere with a child publicly held up as the favoured object of Sir
Matthew's loudly-vaunted benevolence, and moreover, privately marked
out by his vindictive nature as a victim to his hatred.

Whether as a rival for his munificence, or a champion against his hate,
it was pretty certain that her interference would render her obnoxious
to her pompous neighbour's displeasure, and this she had no inclination
to encounter if she could help it. For though at this moment she felt
within her a strength and firmness of purpose not easily shaken, the
poor girl knew that she stood alone in the world, with no friend to
support her more powerful than nurse Tremlett, and nothing but her
two thousand pounds' worth of this world's trumpery to enable he to
have her way, and her will, in many matters that she feared might turn
out rather difficult to manage.

So she determined to avoid quarrelling with Sir Matthew Dowling
as long as she could, and though the image of Michael struggling with
his tears, and the plaintive sound of his voice as he pleaded for leave
to labour again, absolutely haunted her memory, she determined upon
being cautious, wise, and very deliberative in any measures she might
eventually take to ensure his release.

Under the influence of these prudential resolutions, Miss Brotherton,
for the present, abandoned her purpose of seeking a conversation with
the child himself, and determined to find her way to the cottage of
his mother instead. Yet even this she felt must be done with caution.
Her carriage and her liveries were about as splendid and conspicuous
as carriage and liveries could be, and though she knew not precisely
in what direction the widow Armstrong might be found, it was easy

enough to guess that did she make use of her ordinary mode of conveyance in reaching her abode, let it be where it might, she would attract more attention than she desired.

It was to Mrs Tremlett that she determined to apply in this dilemma, and at their *tête-à-tête* breakfast on the following morning, she once more led the conversation to the factories.

"You must not scold me, dear friend," said she, "if you find that I have, as I told you I would, disobeyed your advice altogether, about thinking no more of the factory people, for I cannot get them out of my head, nurse Tremlett."

"I am sorry for it, my dear," replied the good woman, gravely; "because I am quite sure that you will only vex yourself, and do no good."

"You ought to know me better by this time, Mrs Tremlett, than to fancy that your manner of speaking on this dark subject is the way to check my curiosity. It was pretty effectually awakened perhaps before; but had it been otherwise, what you say would be quite enough to set me upon inquiring into it. Nurse Tremlett, I WILL know every thing that the most persevering inquiry can teach me respecting the people to whose labours all the rich people in this neighbourhood owe their wealth, and myself among the rest. And when I tell you that at the present moment this is the only subject upon which I feel any real interest, I think you are too wise to attempt turning me from it, by saying, 'My dear you will only vex yourself.'"

"I do indeed, my child, know you too well to fancy that if you have set your mind upon it, you will not give it up; so I have nothing more to say, Miss Mary."

"Well then, my dear woman," replied Mary, taking her hand, "if, through all the years we have passed together, I have shown such a determined spirit for no reason in the world but only to get my own wanton silly will, do me the justice to anticipate that I shall not be less obstinate in this one thing, that I believe to be right, than in all the many wherein it was most likely I suspected myself to be wrong. I do believe, nurse Tremlett, that it is my duty to understand this matter better than I do; and if this be so, I will trust to God to make up to me for all the *vexation* your prophecy threatens it will bring."

"If that is the way you think of it, my dear child, Heaven forbid that I should seek to hinder you. But rich as you are, dear Mary, if you was to give it all, and ten thousand times as much besides, what good could it do? The mills would go on just the same you know."

"I don't want to stop the mills, nurse Tremlett. Why should I? Industry, ingenuity, science, enterprise, must of course be all brought into action by this flourishing cotton-trade, and, beyond all doubt, it would be equally wicked and wild to wish its destruction. That is not the notion I have got hold of, good nurse, very, very far from it, I assure you. What I want to find out is whether, by the nature of things, it is impossible to manufacture worsted and cotton wool into articles useful to man, without rendering those employed upon it unfit to associate with the rest of their fellow-creatures? This seems to me so gross an absurdity that I cannot give faith to it, and therefore I suspect that the depravity and wickedness you and Miss Martha Dowling talk about, must arise from these people having too much money at their command. This, perhaps, may lead to intemperance and extravagance. Don't you think this may be the case, Mrs Tremlett?"

"Good gracious, no, Miss Mary! Why they are all the very poorest starving wretches upon earth."

"But they can be poor because they are extravagant, nurse. They must get a most monstrous quantity of money, for though none of the gentlemen ever talk much of their factories, I have repeatedly heard allusion made to the enormous sums paid every week to the work-people. And it is quite clear that all the families must get a great deal, because all the little children work, which can hardly be the case elsewhere. I cannot help thinking, nurse, that a great deal of good might be by teaching them a little economy, and inducing them to lay by their superfluous money in a savings-bank. That is one great reason why I want to get acquainted with the people themselves. Now, for instance, that poor sick widow Armstrong—the mother of the little boy that Sir Matthew Dowling has taken; I am quite sure that she can have no wickedness to hurt me—and I am determined, nurse, to go a call upon her."

"Well, my dear, that can't do no great harm, certainly; and, if you like it, I can go in the carriage with you."

"Most certainly I should like you to go with me, but not in the carriage, Mrs Tremlett. I don't want to have all the people in her neighbourhood staring at me, or at her either; and that they would be sure to do if we went in the carriage. I mean to walk, nurse."

"Do you know where the woman lives, my dear?"

"No; I must leave you to find that out."

"What is her name, Miss Mary?"

"Armstrong. She is a widow, and lives somewhere in Ashleigh. Let us walk into the garden, and while I am looking after my seedlings, you can inquire of one of the under-gardeners, or the boy. And if you manage the matter well, the next prime blossom that I get from my experience shall be called the Tremlett geranium."

★   ★   ★   ★   ★

While this conversation was going on at Milford Park, the residence of Miss Brotherton, Dr Crockley arrived to enjoy a *tête-à-tête* breakfast with Sir Matthew in "*the study*" at Dowling Lodge. This room, though not so splendid as some of its neighbours under the same roof, could, nevertheless, be made very snug and comfortable upon occasion, and an excellent breakfast was spread before them; while the two gentlemen sat in judgment upon little Michael's contumacy and consulted on the best method of bringing him into better order.

"Confound the imp!" exclaimed Sir Matthew, as he selected his favourite dainties, "is it not provoking, Crockley, that I should have taken such an aversion to him? Upon my soul, I never hated any thing so much in my life. In the first place it is disgusting to see him dressed up, walking about the house like a tame monkey, when I know that his long fingers might be piercing thousands of threads for two shillings a week; and it is neither more nor less than loathsome to see him eat, at luncheon, sometimes when we have had him in before company, exactly the very same things that my children eat themselves; and then upon the back of it all, to know that the ungrateful little viper hates the very sight of me. I don't believe, Crockley, that any good can come of all this, equal to what it makes me suffer in the doing. It is perfectly unnatural

to see him close within an inch of my own legs. I'd rather have a tame
toad crawling about by half. I must give it up, Crockley—I must, upon
my soul."

"You are the master, Sir Matthew. I can't stop you, if do it you will;
but I can tell you this, I have been calling at fifty different houses,
at the very least, since this job began, and I pledge you my sacred
honour that in every one of them the only thing talked of was your
benevolence and generosity. 'Such an example!' cried one; 'So heavenly-
minded!' said another; 'It is enough to bring a blessing upon the whole
country,' whined a third; and, 'It is to be hoped that such goodness will
be rewarded in this world and the next,' observed a fourth. Think, Sir
Matthew, how all this will tell against the grumblings about Miss Nance
Stephens and her sudden demise."

"That's true—devilish true; Crockley—and yet it's no cure for my
being sick at the stomach every time I see him."

"I don't know about that; I should think it was, or, at any rate, if you'll
only bear it a little longer I should not be at all surprised if you were
to be relieved by some other great capitalist setting up in the same way,
and as your name has been sung out, that would do just as well. Upon
my soul, I'm in earnest; I should not the least wonder if, before the
end of three months, every one of your first-rates were to have a tame
factory-child in their houses, to act like the hedgehogs we get to eat
black-beetles for us. And they'd do their work well too, Sir Matthew: all
the nasty, creeping, multiplying plagues, in the shape of evil tales against
the factory system, would be swallowed up by the clearing-off effects of
these nice little hedgehog gentry."

"You are as keen as your own lancet, Crockley; and I never turn a
deaf ear to any thing you say. But it's monstrous hard though, that I
can't walk about my own house without running the risk of seeing this
odious little grub. By the way, Crockley, why could not my lady take a
factory-girl in by way of charity? Some of the little wenches are sightly
enough before they have worked down their flesh too far; and, though
I can't say I am particularly tender over the lanky idiot-looking slatterns
that we mostly get at the mill, I'll bet what you please that I should
never hate the sight of a girl, as I do the sight of this boy."

"Very likely not, Sir Matthew," replied the doctor, laughing immoderately. "But what would my lady say? and what would all the other ladies say? No, no, leave that alone, and make up your mind to let the boy have the run of the house for a month or two; after which you may send him to the devil if you will; for the good will be done, and the boy himself forgotten."

"That's all vastly easy for you to lay down, chapter and verse, wise man that you are," replied the knight. "But if I tell all, I can let you into a secret, Crockley, that would make you change your mind, perhaps. The long and the short of it is, that I can't keep my hands off him, and if the young black-hearted scamp—I know he is black-hearted, I'm quite sure of it on account of a look he has got with his eyes, that makes one always feel so uncomfortable—if he were to take it into his vile ungrateful head to go about the country telling every thing that I may have happened to say and do to him, when his nasty ways have pushed me further than I could bear, I don't think the history of the charity job *would* do much good, doctor."

Doctor Crockley gave a long low whistle; and then, after a minute's meditation, said, "That's a bore."

"I know it is," sharply responded his patron, "a devilish bore. But you don't suppose that I am to stand bursting with rage, and not take the liberty of speaking my mind to a factory grub, do you?"

"Heaven forbid! A whole factory full of wenches may all drop down dead, I hope, before it comes to that," replied his friend. "But what you have stated is worth attention, Sir Matthew. I don't like the notion of the child's having tales to tell. It spoils all."

"I know it," returned the vexed knight. "Martha told me just now, not ten minutes before you came, that Miss Brotherton said she should like very much to talk to the boy: she is as sharp as a needle, you know, and I'll answer for it would find out all he has got to tell, and a devilish deal more, perhaps, in no time. Pretty work that would make! would it not? Augustus is sure of her, he tells me; and just fancy such a match as that spoiled by the forked tongue of this little viper! the very notion makes one mad."

"A cure may be found for that mischief, let it cost what it may," replied Crockley; "and for the future it might be better, perhaps, for your charity, Sir Matthew, to show itself some other way. You are too honest-hearted, that's the fact. A fine bold intellect, like yours, can't descend to the paltry patience belonging to inferior minds. Is there no getting rid of the boy? No possibility of sending him 'prentice some where or other?"

"'Prentice?" said Sir Matthew, looking with a very singular expression into the face of his friend. "'Prentice?" he repeated, and stretching out his hand, he seized upon that of Doctor Crockley, which he shook with extraordinary ardour. "Send him as a 'prentice! Upon my soul, Crockley, if you had laid down five hundred pounds upon the table, I should not have considered it as of one half as much worth as that one word 'PRENTICE. Yes, by Jove he shall be a 'prentice. Oaf that I was for not thinking of it before! You don't know half the good you have done me by that word. 'Tis but lately, my dear fellow, that you and I have come to understand one another thoroughly; and I have never yet talked to you about one or two points particularly interesting to all our capitalists. I never mentioned to you, did I, the Deep Valley Mills, not far from Appledown Cross, in Derbyshire?"

"Never, Sir Matthew, as far as I can recollect," was the reply.

"Well, then, I will tell you something about them now, that will make you perceive plainly enough what a capital good hit you have made in talking of apprenticeship for my young darling. Deep Valley Mill, Crockley, is the property of my excellent friend Elgood Sharpton. He is one of the men born to be the making of this country. A fine, manly, dauntless character, who would scorn to give up his notions before any act of parliament that ever was made. His idea is, Crockley,—and I should like to see the man who would venture to tell me that it was not a glorious one,—his idea is, that if we could get rid of our cursed corn-laws, the whole of the British dominions would soon be turned into one noble collection of workshops. I wish you could hear him talk; upon my soul, it's the finest thing I know. He says that if his system is carried out into full action, as I trust it will be one of these days, all the grass left in England will be the parks and paddocks of the capitalists. Sharpton will prove to you as clearly as that two and two make four, that the best thing for the country would be to scour it from end to end of those confounded idle drones, the landed gentry. They must go sooner or later, he says, if the corn-laws are done away with. Then down goes the price of bread, and down goes the operative's wages; and what will stop us then, doctor? Don't you see? isn't it plain as the nose on your face that when the agricultural interest is fairly drummed out of the field, the day's our own? Who shall we have then spying after us to find out how many hours a day we choose to make our hands work? D'ye see, Crockley? if we choose to work the vitals out of them, who shall say we shan't ?"

"I never heard a finer, clearer line of argument, in my life, Sir Matthew," replied the attentive listener. "That man, that Elgood Sharpton, seems born for a legislator. But I question not that when you two get together you act like flint and steel upon one another. Is not that the case?"

"Pretty much I believe," replied Sir Matthew: "and I promise you, Crockley, I give no bad proof of my confidence in your honour and friendship, by letting you into a few of our notions, for matters are by no means quite ripe for us to speak out, as yet. Our policy is, you must know, to give out that it is the operatives who are clamouring for the repeal of the corn-laws, whereas many among them, saucy rogues, are as deep as their betters, and know perfectly well, and be hanged to 'em, that our only reason for trying to make '*down with the corn-laws*,' the popular cry is, that we may whisper in their ears, 'down with the wages' afterwards. Ay, doctor, if we can but manage this England will become the paradise of manufacturers!—the great workshop of the world! When strangers climb our chalk cliffs to get a peep at us they shall see, land at what point they will, the glowing fires that keep our engines going, illuminating the land from one extremity of the island to the other! Then think how we shall suck in—that is we the capitalists, my man—think how we shall suck in gold, gold, gold, from all sides. The idea is perfectly magnificent! The fat Flemings must give up all hopes of ever getting their finical flax to vie with our cotton again!—Crockley," but here Sir Matthew paused for a moment, as if half doubtful whether he should go on. The confidential impulse within him, however, worked so strongly in favour of the friendly smiling physician, that all reserve gave way, and winking his eye at him with a truly comic expression, he proceeded—"Crockley, they don't understand spinning in Flanders: they don't know yet how many baby sinews must be dragged, and drawn out to mix as it were with the thread, before the work can be made to answer. No, no, we have fairly given Master Fleming the go by in his own trade, so for the future he must just be pleased to go on hand-digging, and sowing every inch of his dung-muxen, till it teems with corn for exportation. That's what he's fit for; whereas science has put us rather in advance of all that, my good doctor. Our friends in Poland, too, shall plough away to the same tune, and Russia, from end to end, will become one huge granary at our service. Where will your aristocratic landholders be then, Crockley? Perhaps you can't tell? but I suspect I can. They'll be in the factories, sir. Your manors and your preserves (we can get game enough from abroad), your manors and your preserves will be covered with factories, except just here and there, you know, where we capitalists may have taken a fancy to my Lord This-thing's grounds, or the Duke of T'other-thing's mansion, for our own residences. And this I maintain is just as it should be; and the reason why, is plain. We have got before all the world in machinery, and so all the world must be content to walk behind us. By Jove, if I had my way, Crockley, I'd turn France and the Rhine into a wine-cellar, Russia into a corn-bin, and America, glorious America, north, south, east, and west, into a cotton plantation. Then should we not flourish? Then should we not bring down the rascals to work at our own prices, and be thankful too? What's to stop us? Trust me there is not a finer humbug going, than just making the country believe that the operatives are rampant for the repeal of the corn-laws."

"It is a treat to hear you, Sir Matthew. I should be at a loss to name any man that I thought your equal in the gift of eloquence. But, nevertheless, we must not forget business. We must not forget Master Michael Armstrong, Sir Matthew.

"No, no, my good friend, we will not forget him. Be patient for a moment, and I will make you understand how my friend Elgood Sharpton, and my darling *protegé* have been mixed up in my mind together. Sharpton's factory at Deep Valley is one of the most perfect institutions, I take it, that the ingenuity of man ever produced. It is perfect, sir,—just perfect. In the first place, it is built in a wild desolate spot, where the chances are about ten thousand to one against any of the travelling torments who take upon themselves to meddle and make about what does not concern them—it is a hundred thousand to one against their ever catching sight of it. You never saw such a place in your life, Crockley. 'Tis such a hole that I don't believe the sunshine was ever known to get to the bottom of it. It was made on purpose, you may depend upon it. Well, sir, Sharpton, who whatever he undertakes is sure to get over the ground faster than any other man, for he never lets any thing stop him, Sharpton felt quite convinced, you see, that the only way to carry on the work to any good purpose was to UNDERSELL. And how was this to be done without loss instead of gain? That's a question I promise you that has puzzled many a man that was no fool—but, egad, it did not puzzle him. He knew well enough that it was not the material—that came cheap enough—nor yet the machinery, though Heaven knows that's dear enough; but 'tis the labour, sir, the wages going on, on, on, for evermore that drains the money away. And what then does he do, but hit at once upon the very perfectest scheme that ever entered a man's head to lessen that ruinous burden. He knew well enough, for he has a most unaccountable deal of general information, that there were lots of parishes in England that didn't know what on earth to do with their pauper brats. There's many, you know, that say this one thing, this nasty filthy excess of pauper population is the very mischief that is eating up the country, and destroying our prosperity. But who's the greatest political economist, Crockley, the man who talks of the evil, or he who sets about finding a remedy? The political economists of the nineteenth century ought to erect a statue to Elgood Sharpton; and so they will, I have no doubt, when the subject comes to be more perfectly understood. For just mark what he has done. First he finds out this capital spot for the job, and builds a factory there; next he either goes himself, or sends agents, good, capable, understanding men, to all the parishes that he finds are overburdened with poor. Then, sir, he enters philosophically into the subject with the parish authorities, but of course with proper discretion, and proves to them that in no way could they do their duty by the parish children, particularly the orphans, or those whose parents don't trouble them, so well as by apprenticing them to a GOOD TRADE."

Here Sir Matthew paused, and a merry glance was exchanged between him and his companion.

"Well, Crockley, it is a good trade, you know, a devilish good trade, isn't it? At any rate I promise you that so many parishes felt convinced of it, that Elgood Sharpton had soon got Deep Valley factory as full of young hands as it could cram. Now it is since that, you must know, that old Sir Robert took it into his head that little children must not be overworked. He it was, I believe, that first set up that nonsensical cry to any purpose; and to be sure, nothing ever was so absurd in a country where every body knows that if the young pauper spawn could but be made to die off, every thing would go on well. Is it not strange now, that old Peel could not be contented to grow rich, and hold his tongue? But no, he got bit by some poisonous humanity notion or other, and a devilish shake he gave to the system just at first, by his absurd bill for the protection of infant paupers; but such men as Sarpton are not to be knocked down like ninepins, either by law-makers, or law; and to say the truth, old Sir Robert Peel's bill was to all intents and purposes a dead letter within two years after it was passed. Bless your soul, it was the easiest thing in the world to keep the creatures so ignorant about the bill, after the first talk was over, that they might have been made to believe any thing and to submit to any thing. In fact the question for them always lies in an egg-shell. They must either do what the masters would have them, or STARVE. That fact is worth all the bills that ever were passed: and another thing is, that as long as there's nothing to prevent our own friends and relations from being among the magistrates, even if complaints are made, we can manage them."

"How true it is, Sir Matthew, that there is no inequality of accidental condition than can equal the inequality produced by a decided superiority in the intellectual powers," said Dr Crockley. "At this moment I give you my sacred honour that I look upon you, and your friend Mr Elgood Sharpton also, as standing in a much more commanding position than any duke in the country. What's a long descent compared to a long head, Sir Matthew? I'll tell you what the difference is. A long descent pretty generally helps a man to empty his purse, whereas a long head will never fail to help him fill it. It is as clear to me, as that the sun's in heaven, Sir Matthew, that the game is in your own hands. I know—for I have made some curious experiments that way—I know what a dog may be taught to do by hunger, and you may rely upon it that it is just as powerful in a man. Egad, Sir Matthew, it is a very fine subject for scientific experiments. It is difficult to say how far it might go. If a dog, for example, may be taught tricks by hunger, that approach in ingenuity to the powers of man, why may not man, skilfully acted upon by the same principle, be brought to rival the docility of a dog?"

"I see nothing in nature to stop it, doctor," replied Sir Matthew, with an air of great animation. "But remember, my dear Crockley, this is not a point to be touched upon in the book we were talking of. The public, you know, can have nothing on earth to do with the private regulation of our affairs. People have just as much right to inquire at what o'clock my lord duke expects his valet to get up, and moreover what the valet eats for breakfast when he is up, as they have to know what hours our hired labourers keep, and what they feed upon. It is a gross inquisitorial interference, Crockley, and ought not to be thought of in a free country."

"That's a first-rate idea though, Sir Matthew," said the doctor, taking out his pocket-book and pencil. "I must book that. It is turning the parliament into an office of the inquisition. The canters may call it a *holy office*, if they will, but the British people will never bear the notion of AN INQUISITION. That's a capital idea, I promise you. As to my parallel, you know, between a dog and a man, it is merely between ourselves, or such an out-and-out-friend as Mr Sharpton, and it may be worth thinking about, perhaps, practically and scientifically, I mean; but certainly I should never dream of printing it. A hundred years hence, human intelligence may have reached such a point of improvement that the plain good sense and practical utility of the idea may make it properly appreciated. But as yet we are not sufficiently advanced in the science emphatically denominated "*the positive*" in contradistinction to "*the ideal*." It will come though, if we do but go on in the path we are in. But we are generalizing too much, Sir Matthew; nevertheless I suspect

I have caught your idea. You have thoughts of sending your young favourite to Deep Valley mill, by way of putting the finishing stroke to your benevolent projects in his favour?"

"Exactly so, my dear friend. But we must have indentures, observe; and there is some little difficulty in that."

"I suppose you know best, Sir Matthew; else I should say that indentures cannot be necessary. From your description, the locality of this factory, with its romantic name, must be like the valley of Rasselas, at least in one particular—namely, that without wings the happy dwellers there would find it impossible to escape," replied the doctor.

"Difficult, exceedingly difficult, certainly; but not quite impossible; for without indentures a runaway could not be legally pursued. And to tell you the truth, friend Crockley, I should not much approve giving a subject for a second part of Mr Osmond Norval's drama, in which the hero should appear upon the scene after a few months' residence in Deep Valley mills."

"That's true. But I don't see under what pretence you are to get the brat apprenticed to your friend Sharpton," remarked the cautious counsellor.

"If he is apprenticed to me, it will do just as well," replied the knight, "for I could make over the indentures to Sharpton easy enough, but it strikes me I might have some difficulty in making the mother consent to it."

"Not if you will be upon your P's and Q's, Sir knight," said his friend: "you have nothing to do but go on sending tit-bits to the sick woman, and the rickety boy that you mentioned, and when they have got a little used to it she'll not choose to affront her *generous benefactor*. Remember the dog theory, Sir Matthew, they are all alike."

"I dare say you are right. But at any rate I had better keep out of that hateful brat's way, or rather take care that he keeps out of mine. But I shall bear the sight of him better if I make up my mind to send him to Deep Valley. That will wipe out old scores between us."

Having said this, Sir Matthew rose from the breakfast-table, seeming thereby to indicate that the conversation was at an end. Dr Crockley rose too; but, though he took up his hat and his riding-whip from the chair on which he had placed them, he lingered as he had still something to say before he took his leave.

Sir Matthew, however, seemed to take no notice of the hint, but stretching out his hand said decisively, "Good morning, doctor, good morning. Let us see you again soon."

Dr Crockley upon this stretched out his hand too, but instead of clutching that of the knight, he seized upon his button. "One word, Sir Matthew, one word. You are too much of a man of business to think me troublesome. Respecting that little appointment that you were talking about the other day; I should like to have it settled. Because, to say the truth, I shall consider myself as wearing your livery; or, to speak more fitly, to be fighting positively under your colours, when this is done; and of course you know we ought to understand one another completely."

"No doubt of it, Crockley. I said nothing that I do not mean to stand to. You shall have two hundred a year, paid quarterly, for attending to the health and wellbeing, and all that, you know, of the factory children. But as I don't want you to give them two hundred pounds' worth of physic, remember I shall expect that you will make up the deficiency in—in just saying round about the neighbourhood how remarkably well every thing goes on at Brookford Factory. I'll pledge you my word that every thing does go on capitally well there, Crockley, so you will have nothing on your conscience on that score."

"I am not afraid of that, Sir Matthew; I know I may trust you. But I should like a bit of a memorandum about my own business, if you please."

"Quite right, quite right, sir. I am too much a man of business to object to that. Draw up the engagement, such as you wish it to be, and I dare say I shall make no objection to signing it."

After this a cordial hand-shaking was exchanged and the friends parted.

XII

An unfortunate rencontre—An adventure—
Miss Brotherton grows wiser every day

MRS TREMLETT'S INQUIRIES PROVED SUCCESSFUL. Jim Sykes, the weeding-boy, knew perfectly well where widow Armstrong lived and after he had repeated his instructions three times, Mary Brotherton and her unresisting chaperon set off on their expedition. On one point only did the self-willed heiress yield to the judgment of her companion. Mary, who knew, that though she seldom went beyond the shelter of her own park-paling, she often walked without fatigue within it for two or three hours together, wished to set off for Hoxley-lane on foot; but Mrs Tremlett talked so much of the fatigue, that the good-natured girl consented to let the carriage convey them to the point at which the lane diverged from the high-road. This yielding, however, was wholly from consideration for her companion. For herself she believed the precaution quite needless; and she was right. However much her temper might have been endangered by the series of spoiling processes she had undergone, her health had been taken good care of, and few girls of her age in any rank, had greater power and will for exertion than herself.

Nevertheless, before she had driven half a mile, she heartily rejoiced at having sacrificed her own inclination to that of her good nurse; for the road to Ashleigh was the favourite ride of the officers quartered in the neighbourhood, and had she been seen on foot, it is probable that before reaching Hoxley-lane she would have been surrounded by a body-guard of military. So greatly did this danger appal her spirits, that the first moment she found herself free from a white-gloved hand either at one window or the other, she stopped the carriage, and ordered the coachman to go far enough down the lane to permit her to get out unobserved by any persons passing by the road.

But poor Mary was this day doomed to disappointment; and the indignant, and almost passionate beating of her heart under it, made her more conscious, perhaps, than she had ever been before, how deeply the business upon which she was engaged had entered into her soul.

Soon after Sir Matthew Dowling had dismissed his breakfast companion, he strolled out towards his splendid stables, and perceiving his son loitering among the grooms, and himself equipped for the saddle, he inquired whither he was going to ride. "Only to Ashleigh, governor," was the reply. "Then wait five minutes, Augustus, and I will ride with you."

Whether the youth approved the proposal or not, he was fain to submit to it, and the evil star of Mary Brotherton contrived to bring them to the top of Hoxley-lane at the moment her carriage was about to turn into it.

"Stop!" cried the young lady, accompanying the word with a very energetic pull at the check-string. "Go on to Ashleigh," was the order that followed

"Was ever any thing so provoking, nurse? Do you see who those hateful men are?"

"Why 'tis Sir Matthew, my dear," replied the gentle old woman.

"The wretch!" muttered Mary between her teeth at the very moment that Sir Matthew on one side, and his languishing son on the other, besieged her carriage.

"Not for my right hand would I have him guess where I am going," thought she, as with a face suffused with the deepest carmine that agitntion could produce, she forced her lips into an unmeaning smile in return to their salutation.

The father and son came to exactly the same conclusion, and at the same moment. There was but one cause that it was possible to assign for her evident emotion. She was deeply in love with Augustus,—more deeply than even the young man himself had imagined. The thing was plain, no doubt remained, no not a shadow of it on the mind of either father or son, but it was the elder gentleman only who at once determined to push so fine a game to its close, with as little delay as possible

Feeling quite sure that there was no liberty he could take at this moment which would not be welcome, he made a sign to the coachman to stop and deliberately dismounting he threw his reins to his groom, told Miss Brotherton's footman to open the carriage-door, and stepped in with the assumed air of a partially loved friend, who knows that no leave need be asked.

Mary shrunk back into her corner with considerably more disgust than if a reptile had possessed itself of the seat opposite.

"This is not quite as it should be, is it?" said Sir Matthew, with a leer. "Perhaps some other may have a better right here than I?" And a very expressive smile accompanied the words.

"Sir?" said Miss Brotherton.

"Come, come, my dear child, you must not look vexed at any of my little jokes. You know how we all dote upon you! Dear creature! How beautiful that sweet blush makes you look! He, he! there goes poor Augustus looking very much as if he could wring his papa's neck off. But his turn, we will hope, may come by and by. And now, my dear, I'll tell you what I am come here for. We all want you, and your good Mrs Tremlett too, if she likes it, to come over to us quite *en famille* to-morrow. I don't know what love-powder you have been scattering amongst us, but there is not a single individual of the family who does not positively dote upon you. Tell me, my pretty Mary, do you feel a little kindness for some of us in return?"

An attempt to take her hand accompanied this speech; and Mrs Tremlett, who estimated pretty nearly her young lady's affection for Sir Matthew and his race, actually trembled for the consequences. But, to her great surprise, Mary answered, after the pause of a minute, "Oh, dear Sir Matthew! you are only laughing at me!" in a voice so exceedingly childish and silly, that it might, under similar circumstances, have made the fortune of a comic actress; and though she did not permit him to touch the hand he attempted to take, she placed it together with its fellow, so playfully behind her, that Sir Matthew could only laugh and call her, "dear pretty creature!"

Meanwhile the carriage proceeded to penetrate through the dirty dismal streets, which, in that direction, formed the suburb of Ashleigh.

"I must get out here," said Miss Brotherton, suddenly pulling the check-string.

"Here? Impossible, my dear child!"

"Nothing is impossible to me, that I choose to do, sir," said the young lady, springing to the ground the moment the door was opened. The knight was fain to follow, the animated Augustus threw himself from his horse at the same instant, and Mrs Tremlett held herself suspended on the step of the carriage to learn what she was required to do.

"I wish to know what is the matter with these miserable-looking children," said Mary, approaching a half-open door, at each side of which, crouching on the stone step, sat a pale and squalid-looking girl. The eldest might be ten years old, the youngest was certainly not more than six.

"Gracious Heaven! you are not going to speak to those creatures, Miss Brotherton?" exclaimed Sir Matthew, while his son instinctively backed his horse into the middle of the street.

"And why not, Sir Matthew?" said Mary.

"You are not aware of what you are doing; I give you my honour you are not. You have no conception what these sort of creatures are. My dear, dear Miss Brotherton, get into your carriage—get into your carriage, I conjure you!"

Mary looked at him, but said not a word in reply.

"What ails you, my little girl?" said she, putting her hand upon the shoulder of the youngest child.

"Billy-roller," answered the little creature.

"The billy-roller smashed her," said the eldest girl, " but 'twas falling asleep against the machinery as lamed me."

"Are you mad, Miss Brotherton!" exclaimed Sir Matthew. "Surely, Mrs Tremlett, you ought to prevent your young lady from exposing herself to such scenes as these."

"Good morning, Sir Matthew, do not let me detain you," said the heiress, suddenly assuming the tone and style of a woman of fashion who chose to have her own way. "These sick little creatures quite interest me. Besides, I must positively find out who Billy Roller is."

"It is an instrument used in the works, Miss Brotherton. You know not to what you are exposing yourself—fraud, filth, infection, drunkenness! I give you my sacred honour that I think you are very likely to be robbed and murdered if you approach the thresholds of such dwellings as these."

"I beg your pardon, Sir Matthew," replied the heiress, "but you must excuse me if I obstinately persevere in judging for myself; I know I am a spoiled child, neither more nor less; and as such you must either give me up or bear with me. Permit me to wish you good morning; I shall do more than approach the threshold of this dwelling—I shall enter it."

Having said this, she waited no further parley, but taking a ragged child in each hand set her little foot against the door which already stood ajar, pushed it open, and walked in.

Her first idea on looking round her, was that perhaps Sir Matthew was in the right. Filth she saw; infection might lurk under it; and who could tell if fraud and drunkenness might not enter the moment after, to complete the group?

But there was little of selfishness and much of courage in the heart of Mary Brotherton, so she presently forgot every notion of personal danger, and was thus enabled to see things as they really were.

On one side of the small bare chamber, and in some degree sheltered by the door which opened against it, stood a rickety machine once intended for a bedstead. Two of the legs had given place to brickbats, and instead of a bed the unsteady frame now supported only a thin layer of very dirty straw, with the body of a dying female stretched up on it. The only other article of furniture in the room was an old deal box without a cover, but having a couple of planks, each about three feet long, laid across it; serving either for table or chairs as occasion might require. The walls, the floor, the ceiling, and the remnant of a window, were all alike begrimed with smoke and dirt.

It took not long to make this inventory, and having completed it, the young lady, still holding in each hand a staring child, turned towards the inhabitant of this miserable den, and said,

"Are you ill, my good woman?"

The being she addressed raised her heavy eyes, and in a voice so low as to be scarcely intelligible, answered "Yes."

"Gracious
Heaven! You are
not going to
speak to those
creatures, Miss
Brotherton?"

"Have you no assistance, nobody to nurse you?"

"Nobody but these," pointing to the children.

"Has any doctor seen her?" demanded Mary of the eldest child.

"No ma'am," replied the little girl.

"And how long has she been ill?"

"Ever since she com'd from the mill."

"And how long is that?"

"A twelvemonth," said the little one.

"I don't know," said the elder.

"But, my poor children, you are not the only people that live with her, I suppose? Have yon got any father?"

"Yes."

"Where is he?"

"At the mill."

"Have you got any body else belonging to you?" said Miss Brotherton, shuddering.

"There's Sophy, and Dick, and Grace," replied the eldest child.

"Where are they all?" again inquired Miss Brotherton.

"At the mill," was again the answer.

"Are Sophy and Grace grown up?"

"Sophy is," answered the child, "and Grace, almost."

"Then why do they not stay at home, one of them at least, to take care of this poor woman?"

"'Cause they mustn't. I 'tends mother."

"You are not big enough to take care of her, my poor child: Why don't you go to the factory, and let one of the bigger ones stay at home?"

"They won't have me now, 'cause of this."—And as she spake, the child held up a little shrivelled right-hand, three fingers of which had a joint deficient. "I can't piece now, and so they won't let me come."

"And Sophy won't let me go, 'cause of this," said the little one, slipping her arm out of a bedgown (which was the only garment she had), and displaying the limb swollen and discoloured, from some violent contusion.

"My poor little creature! how did you do this?" said Mary, tenderly, taking the little hand in hers, and examining the frightful bruise.

"'Twas the billy-roller," said the little girl, in an accent that seemed to insinuate that the young lady was more than commonly dull of apprehension.

"But how did it happen, my child? Did some part of the machinery go over you?"

"No!—That was me," cried the elder, with a loud voice, and again holding up her demolished fingers. "'Twas the stretcher's billy-roller as smashed Becky."

"'Twas, cause I was sleepy," said the little one, beginning to cry, for she construed Mary's puzzled look into an expression of displeasure.

"They beats 'em dreadful ma'am," said the sick woman, evidently exerting herself beyond her strength. "She's a good little girl for work;

but they will fall asleep, all of 'em at times, when they be kept so dreadful long."

"But these bruises could not be the effect of beating," said Mary, again examining the arm, "it is quite impossible."

"Why, ma'am, the billy-roller as they beats 'em with, is a stick big enough to kill with; and many and many is the baby that has been crippled by it."

There was something so hollow, so sunken in the woman's voice, that Miss Brotherton felt terrified. The fact that a child of the size of the baby before her should have been beaten with such a weapon, and with such violence, seemed wholly incredible. Again she thought of Sir Matthew Dowling's warning, and wished that she were not alone.

"I am afraid that you are very ill," said she, "and I know not how I can help you. Money I can give, but there is nobody here to make use of it for you."

"Money!" murmured the sinking woman from her layer of straw. "Money, you can give money? Oh! give it, give it. Give it to her—give it to the child; she knows what it is, she knows I am dying for the want of it. It is too late for me, but give it, give it, and may God—" Here the miserable creature's strength wholly failed; her eyes closed, and to all appearance, she was already a corpse.

"Oh! this is very dreadful!" cried poor Mary, wringing her hands, "nurse will know better than me," and so saying, she turned eagerly towards the door.

"She be gone, mother, and haven't gived nothing," said the eldest girl, in a voice mournfully expressive of disappointment, that, spite of her alarm, Mary stopped to take half-a-crown from her purse, which she put into the child's hand.

She looked at the coin, and in a half-whisper ejaculated, "Oh!" Then creeping to the bed, she put it into the palm of her mother's hand, pressing the fingers down upon it, and in an accent of interrogation uttered the word "Bread?"

This Mary heard, but not the answer to it, for she had quitted the scene before it was uttered. On opening the door of the house, she started at seeing Sir Matthew Dowling still within a dozen yards of it;

he was standing beside the carriage, with one arm extended to keep the door of it open, and the other resting against the vehicle on the opposite side of the opening, while his head thrust forward within an inch of good Mrs Tremlett's nose effectually prevented her following her young lady, however much she might have wished to do so. He had, indeed, upon Miss Brotherton's disappearance reseated the good woman almost by force, and then addressed her in such a strain as was rapidly working her up to make an attempt to escape from the other side of the carriage, when the reappearance of the young lady released her from her thraldom.

"Mrs Tremlett!" he said, "are you aware of the awful responsibility which will rest upon you if any thing unfortunate happens to your amiable but most headstrong young lady? All the neighbourhood know, Mrs Tremlett, that she has, as it were, placed herself for protection in your hands, refusing all other counsel, and shutting her ears to all other advice, and it is thus that you perform your duty!"

"Good God, sir! what do you mean?" said the good woman, in great agitation. "Let me out if you please, sir. If my young lady is in any danger it is wicked to keep me sitting here. Let me out, sir!"

"I will let' you out, Mrs Tremlett," replied the knight, still firmly retaining the position which so effectually kept her in, "I will let you out; but first for her sake and your own, it is my duty to tell you in a few words the sort of place she has now thought proper to enter. Don't struggle, Mrs Tremlett, but hear me. It is not possible they can do her any personal injury as long as I am so near the door of the house as at present. Be very sure that from some hole or corner of the filthy premises, some spying eyes are at this moment watching us. There is no danger of her being murdered now, but as sure as you sit there, Mrs Tremlett, murdered she will be, if she goes without the protection of a powerful arm within such dens of sin and iniquity as she has entered now. One short moment more, Mrs Tremlett—one short moment, while I tell what the creatures are among whom she has thrown herself. The house is notorious as one of the very worst in Ashleigh. The man is an habitual drunkard, whom I, and my excellent servant Parsons, have endeavoured in every possible way to reform—but in vain. The moment he has got his wages, he goes to the gin-shop, and often and often he won't work at all, which of course prevents his family from being in the comfortable easy circumstances which they ought to be. If he happens to be in the house now, I dare say there is no species of indecent language to which your young lady will not be obliged to listen. As to the mother of the family, I believe she is dying in consequence of a life passed in all sorts of the most abominable wickedness. Indeed I believe she is now half mad, for I have been told by some of my people whom I have sent upon charitable visits of inquiry to her, that she lies in her bed inventing the strangest lies imaginable. Indeed some think that notwithstanding she is so near death she still drinks, and that it is nothing but drunken lies that she makes people listen to."

"Pray, pray let me get out, Sir Matthew! Being murdered, sir, is not the only thing from which I should wish to save Miss Brotherton."

"One word more, Mrs Tremlett, and I have done. The eldest girl is a notorious prostitute. Another, a year or two younger is going the same way. The boy is suspected of being an extremely skilful thief, and the two younger girls, for they all work at my factory, Mrs Tremlett, and I know them well, the two younger ones are such depraved little wretches, that for the sake of example we have been obliged to turn them out of the mill, though we are in great want of young hands to do the work. Now, madam, I have done, and I leave it with you to judge how far it will be right and proper for Miss Brotherton to continue such frolics as these."

Sir Matthew was in the act of pronouncing the last words of this speech as Miss Brotherton opened the door of the house, and stepped out into the street.

On first perceiving her, the knight appeared about to take her hand, for the purpose of replacing her in the carriage; but his attention was called to the sound of many feet suddenly turning the corner of a street which led from a neighbouring factory. It proceeded from the workpeople, who were rushing home in scrambling haste to snatch their miserable dinners.

Gentlemen in Sir Matthew Dowling's situation; and enjoying the species of influence which belongs to it, take little or no pains to avoid meeting the people they themselves employ. They look not in the young eyes to read what sort of blessing cowers there, nor heed the crippled gait, or pallid visage of those who exist but by the poisonous employment which he gives them. But such gentlemen seldom, if they can avoid it, expose themselves to the remarks of any gangs belonging to their neighbours, and no sooner did Sir Matthew become aware that the mill in the next street was pouring forth its fifteen hundred hands, than he turned from the young lady who had passed by without appearing to see him, and taking his horse from the hand of the groom who held it, sprung with great activity into the saddle, and galloped off the way his indignant son had galloped before him.

Mary Brotherton meanwhile was utterly unconscious of the approaching throng; and intent only upon getting Mrs Tremlett out of the carriage, turned her eyes neither to the right nor the left, but seizing her by the arm, exclaimed, "Come to me nurse, come to me!"

The good woman who was quite as desirous as herself of the reunion, required no second summons, but more quickly than it can be told, was first by the side of her young mistress in the street, and them entering with her the low door of the dwelling so fearfully described by Sir Matthew.

Had Mrs Tremlett possessed the power, most assuredly she would have turned the steps of her charge the other way, and for ever have prevented her from exposing herself to the contemplation of such depravity as she had heard described; but knowing perfectly well that such power was vested in her, the next wish she conceived, was to give all the assistance and support she could to the dear wilful girl to whom she had devoted herself.

Aware, as she entered the door, that many eyes followed them, nay, many steps were stayed, apparently, to watch the spectacle so rare in Ashleigh of well-dressed ladies entering the sordid dwelling of operatives, Mrs Tremlett herself closed the door as soon as they had both passed through it, and looking round upon the desolation of the chamber, trembled with an emotion made up of terror and compassion, at perceiving to what a scene the delicately-nurtured Mary Brotherton had introduced herself.

"This woman is very ill, nurse Tremlett," said the young lady, drawing her close to the bed. "For God's sake tell me what we had better do for her?"

"My dear, dear, Miss Mary come away, and send the doctor to her!" answered Mrs Tremlett, positively shaking from head to foot, as she contemplated the ghastly countenance of the woman, the filthy rag that imperfectly covered her, and the scanty straw upon which her stiffening limbs were stretched. "This is no place for you, Miss Brotherton! come with me I say this moment, and we will send the doctor, and money, and clothes too, if you like it."

"If I like it!—Do you think I am amusing myself, Mrs Tremlett?—Feel her hand—feel her pulse! I believe she is dying!"

The words though spoken very quietly and deliberately, were uttered in a voice so unlike what she had ever heard from the young lady before, that the old woman became dreadfully alarmed.

"Oh, good God! she is losing her senses!" were the words she uttered as she threw her arms round the person of Miss Brotherton, and vainly attempted to remove her from the spot on which she stood.

"Fie upon you, Mrs Tremlett!" said Mary, sternly, "do you fancy that you are doing me any good? Be satisfied that I am not losing my senses, and let me request that you will make an effort to recover yours. This woman's head is too low. My dear mother asked for pillows." Here the steady voice faltered, but it was now only for a moment. "I want the cushions from the carriage, nurse Tremlett, will you get them, or shall I?"

Without answering a word the terrified old woman hastened to obey her, and did so in the best manner; for calling to the tall footman, who continued to stand beside the open door of the carriage, he obeyed the summons, which he supposed to be preparatory to his young mistress making her exit, by very unceremoniously thrusting right and left the curious group that still lingered on the threshold.

"Give me the cushions from the carriage, Jones," she said, "make haste, for God's sake!"

The man stared at her for an instant in utter astonishment, and then did as he was ordered.

"Now get upon the box and bid the coachman drive as fast as he can go, to the nearest doctor's—that's Mr Thomas, I think, in Cannon-street.—Tell him Miss Brotherton has sent for him, and desire him to get into the carriage directly."

Having uttered these commands as rapidly as she could speak, Mrs Tremlett carried a couple of the carriage cushions to the bed, and with the assistance of Mary and the elder child, managed to raise the woman into a position apparently less distorted and painful than before.

"Have you any thing to give her?" said Mrs Tremlett, addressing the child.

The little girl without answering, stepped to a sort of cupboard in the wall, and taking thence a pitcher without a spout, and a mug without a handle, contrived to tilt up the former so as to make it discharge a portion of its contents into the latter.

"It is water," said Mary, watching the operation. "It will not hurt her, will it?"

"Nothing can hurt her, my dear love!" replied Mrs Tremlett, her eyes filling with tears as she listened to the altered voice of her gay-hearted girl, whose smiles and frolics she had watched, and indulged, for so many years; but of whose deep feeling she had never conceived any idea till now. "I don't think any thing can hurt her now, Mary. Her pulse flutters, and her forehead is quite limp. I have sent for Mr Thomas, and he will probably be here immediately."

Mary's only answer was silently pressing the hand of her old friend as she took from it the broken mug of water, and then, kneeling on the sordid floor, she applied it to the pale dry lips of the sufferer.

The poor woman mode an effort to meet it, and swallowed a mouthful eagerly; and then, relieved probably by the change of posture, and refreshed by the cool liquid, she stretched out the hand in which she still held Mary's half-crown, and said, "Go Betsy, buy——"

The child she addressed, eagerly seized the money in the hand that had fingers to close upon it, and flitted through the door in an instant.

The poor woman had again closed her eyes; but her breathing was more tranquil, and Mary hoped she had fallen asleep. With this persuasion she stood perfectly still and silent beside her, her own hand locked, though she was not conscious of it, in the grasp of her deeply affected nurse, while her whole soul seemed settled in her eyes as she fixed them immovably upon what she felt to be the most awful spectacle that a mortal can gaze upon, namely, the passing of a human spirit from life to death.

The little girl whose swollen and discoloured arm still remained uncovered, probably because she feared the pain likely to attend the replacing it in the sleeve, stood close beside her mother's head, childishly contemplating the cushions which supported it, and apparently as unconscious as they were, of the heavy loss that threatened her.

But this still did not long remain uninterrupted. All the members of the family, who had been named as belonging to the factory, except the father, returned for the purpose of taking such rest and refreshment at one hour (nearly half of which was consumed by the walk to and from the mill) could permit. The latch was lifted by the eldest girl, a delicate featured, but dreadfully dirty creature of about seventeen with a sort of sharp eagerness, denoting the curiosity excited by the sight of the carriage stationed before their dwelling On perceiving the deathlike countenance of her mother, made distinctly visible by the noonday light, that streamed through the open door, she suddenly stopped, clasping her hands together, and uttering in tones that sounded like a shriek—"Oh! God, she is dead!"

"No! not dead!" said Mary solemnly, and without turning her eyes from the object on which they were rivetted. "Not dead!—she is sleeping—Hush!—Do not disturb her!"

Close following on the heels of the first, came a second girl, about a year her junior, but with a countenance much less prepossessing. Dirty she was too, if possible more so than the others, and there was a look of stolid stupidity about her that, but for the sort of reckless audacity which lurked in her eye, might have given the idea of an almost brutal want of animation. A thin consumptive-looking lad of about fourteen, followed after her, and closed the door behind him as he entered.

"Oh! Mother!" he exclaimed as her sunken face caught his eye, "I wish I was alongside of ye, and then we'd be buried together!" And without appearing conscious of the presence of the strangers, he suddenly threw

himself upon the tottering bedstead, and nestling his face close to that
of the dying woman, kissed her passionately again and again.

"My boy, you may hasten her going by that," said Mrs Tremlett, gently.
"Be still, be still all of ye!" But as she spoke, she, and Mary too, whose
hand she continued to hold, made way for the eldest girl, who now
eagerly, but silently pressing forward, dropped on her knees beside the
and throwing her two arms over the emaciated body, remained with
streaming eyes that rested piteously on the face of her mother. The
second girl looked on, till by degrees her heavy countenance appeared
to stiffen into horror, and she too drew near, but with distended and
tearless eyes, that seemed to speak more of fear than love.

Mrs Tremlett looked anxiously into the face of her charge. It was
deadly pale, and wore an expression of solemnity so new and strange,
that the good woman threw her arms around her in an agony of fond
anxiety, exclaiming, "My Mary, my dear, dear child! come away Mary,
Mary, come away! you can do no good. This scene is not a fit one for
you to witness."

"You mistake, nurse. It is fit for me. It is necessary for me. Do not
disturb me, nurse Tremlett! do not!" Then after a short pause, during
which her eyes were closed, and her hands crossed upon her breast, she
again whispered, "Could she not pray with me? Shall I not ask her to
pray with me?"

"My sweet girl, she will not hear you, I think," said the old woman,
while the tears streamed down her cheeks. "But you shall be satisfied
my darling," and approaching the bed, and leaning over the girl who
knelt beside it, Mrs Tremlett in a low but distinct voice pronounced the
words, "Shall we pray with you?"

She was evidently heard and understood, for the hands that for some
minutes had lain motionless, were with an effort brought together, and
clasped in the attitude of prayer. Mary who was eagerly watching her
every movement, suddenly stepped forward, and gliding in between the
eldest and the youngest girl, dropped on her knees beside them. Mrs
Tremlett following close behind her, knelt also, and then with trembling
lips, and faltering voice, but slowly, distinctly, and most reverentially, Mary
Brotherton uttered the last and most impressive of those sentences in our

litany which is followed by the solemn petition for deliverance. It was with a throb of pleasure at her heart, and an exclamation of thanksgiving from her tongue, that she heard the dying woman answer "Amen!"

Almost at the very instant she did so, the latch was again lifted, and Mr Thomas, one of the three medical practitioners of Ashleigh, entered. Miss Brotherton was not conscious of ever having seen him before; but he, like every one else in the neighbourhood, perfectly well knew the heiress by sight; and now, even now, in the awful chamber of death, bowed low before her.

It would not be easy to describe the feeling with which she turned away from this ill-timed demonstration of respect. Yet it was with no harshness; for the struggle so often going on within us between our better and our worser natures, was at this moment so decidedly in favour of all that was good in her young heart, that there was hardly place for any severer feeling than pity within it.

She had risen from her knees as he made his bow, and turning gravely towards him, said, "If any thing can be done sir, for this poor woman, let it not be delayed. I fear she is very ill."

"Certainly, ma'am—certainly, Miss Brotherton, my best attention may be depended on. But will you first, my dear young lady, give me leave to observe that I would much rather see you in your carriage than here. I really cannot answer for it. It is in point of fact impossible to say whether there may not be something deleterious, something noxious, in short, to your very precious health in the atmosphere of this room."

"I thank you, sir. Be sure I will take quite sufficient care of myself; but it is not for me that your services are wanted—it is here!"

Sophy, the eldest girl seemed unconscious of what was going on, for she remained perfectly motionless on the spot where she had first knelt down while the third sister, who had been sent on the poor mother's last errand for bread, and who had crept back unobserved into the room during the foregoing scene, occupied the space on her right hand, Mary Brotherton having knelt on her left, so that there was scarcely space for the approach of the smart apothecary.

"Move, my dear girls!" said Mary, gently laying a hand on the shoulder of each.

They both rose; while Mr Thomas, carefully storing the anecdote in aid of the gossiping part of his practice, looked and listened with astonishment to what seemed to him the very *unnatural conduct* of the rich young lady, and internally exclaimed, "A clear case of religious mania this, as I ever saw! She won't live long, probably. What a match!"

It required no very long examination of the poor patient, to discover that her last moment was rapidly approaching.

"Upon my word, Miss Brotherton, I really wish I could persuade you to come away," persisted the medical gentleman as he once more turned towards her. The air is becoming more mephitic every instant. This woman is at the last extremity."

"Nothing then, can be done for her?" said Mary.

"No, ma'am—nothing in the world. Not the whole college, if they were present, could keep soul and body together for another hour, I would venture to say."

On this Miss Brotherton put a fee into his hand, and bent her head in token that his business there was ended, and that he might depart. But he did not immediately obey the hint, for pocketing the unwonted golden prize, he seemed anxious to remain a little longer where such blessings abounded and returning to the bed, again took hold of the poor womam's hand, and then said in a voice of authority—"Let me have some water."

It was Mary only who seemed to understand his words, and she immediately obeyed them, placing in his hand the broken mug which she had set aside upon the floor. The apothecary put the water to the lips of the poor woman, and she again swallowed a little of it, after which they saw her lips move as if she was making an effort to speak to them.

Mrs Tremlett lent over her, and then, with a stronger effort she articulated—"Let me see William!"

"Who is William?" said Mrs Tremlett raising herself, "Is it one of the children?"

"It be father," said Betsy.

"Where is he to be found?" cried Miss Brotherton, eagerly. "Let him be sought for instantly—where is he likely to be?"

"At the gin-shop," replied the ungracious Grace.

"If you know where he is, go for him," said Mary, impressively, "and for God's sake let him not delay!"

The girl she addressed stared at her as upon something utterly incomprehensible: but she obeyed, and, in so short a time as to show that the gin-shop was at no great distance, returned with a man of an exterior as filthy as the rest of his race, wretchedly crippled in the legs, and a complexion that spoke both of ill health, and intemperance.

"What!—It is come to that, is it, already?" said the man looking wistfully at her from the bottom of the bed, but with a countenance whose lines seemed too fixed in the expression of hard indifference, to permit its exhibiting much feeling.

"She asked for you, father," said Sophy gently, then taking one of her mother's hands in hers she murmured, "Mother!—Dear mother—open your eyes upon us, father is here, and all of us," while large tear-drops fell upon the livid face as she hung over it.

The dying eyes were once more opened, and consciousness, and recognition of them all, were visible as she suffered them to rest first on one, and then on another. The boy only, from his position, she could not see; but even then, there seemed intelligence between them, and she certainly knew he was lying beside her, for her head rested against his, and she raised her left hand till her fingers touched his cheek. The youngest child also when the mother's eyes opened, was too much behind her, but she seemed aware of her vicinity, and pronounced the words "*Little one!*" probably her usual appellation, so distinctly as to make the child start, and instantly climb upon the bed to kiss her. The last movement was an effort to return this kiss; and the next moment Mrs Tremlett removed the child's clinging lips from a corpse.

A very awful interval of perfect stillness followed. "Can I be of any further service to you, Miss Brotherton?" from the lips of Mr Thomas, were the first words that broke it.

Poor Mary only shook her head, but Mrs Tremlett replied, "No, thank you sir, nothing more;" and with repeated bows, and rather a reluctant step, he departed; turning, however, to give another glance at the heiress, as he passed out, for he was not without hopes that she might fall

"Mother! Dear
Mother! open your
eyes upon us!"

down in a fainting-fit. Nothing, however, of the kind happened, and
he disappeared.

"You will go now, Mary dear?" whispered Mrs Tremlett, "and I will
come here to-morrow to inquire about them for you."

"Yes, I will go now," replied the young lady, "I cannot comfort them."
Then looking round upon the steadfast group, as if to discover which
of them appeared in the fittest state to be spoken to, she fixed upon the
little Betsy, and placing a couple of sovereigns in her hand, told her to

take care of them, and give them to her father presently, adding, "tell your sister Sophy to come up to my house. This," giving a card, "is the place where I live."

She then led the way to her carriage, Mrs Tremlett followed, and the next moment they were driving rapidly from the abode of the most abject misery, to a residence which every quarter of the globe had contributed to render luxurious.

It was evident that the heiress felt no inclination to converse; indeed, for by far the greater portion of the way her face was concealed by the handkerchief which she held to her eyes, and Mrs Tremlett had too much real feeling to disturb her. After driving, however, through the handsome lodge-gates, and sweeping up to the noble entrance of her mansion, where already, at the sound of her approaching carriage, two or three servants were seen waiting like a guard of honour to receive her, it seemed that her meditations had not been wholly confined to the deathbed scene she had witnessed, and that the sordid cabin, with its misery-stamped inhabitants, had made a deep impression; for the first, and for many hours the only words she uttered after her return, spoken to the ear of Mrs Tremlett as they walked arm in arm together through the hall, were these:

"I too am living by the profit of the factory house. Is the division just?—Oh, God! Is it holy?"

The old woman felt that she trembled violently, but knew not what words to utter that might compose her.

On arriving at the foot of the stairs, Mary withdrew her arm, and mounting them more rapidly than her companion could follow, reached her bedchamher alone, which she entered, closing and bolting the door after her.

XIII

Disagreeable meditations—A confidential interview with a faithful servant—Another interview, not quite so confidential, with a daughter—Martha and Michael take a pleasant walk together to visit the widow Armstrong—A consultation

IT WILL BE EASILY BELIEVED that Sir Matthew rode back to Dowling Lodge not in the very sweetest humour in the world. "Bring up a child in the way he should go," is an admirable proverb, and certain it is that when that "way" is agreeable, he does very rarely "depart from the same." Thus it happens that the young gentlemen and ladies, sons and daughters of the millocrats, who pile thousands upon thousands, and acres upon acres, by the secret mysteries of their wonderful compound of human and divine machinery, do rarely or never take their way into the dwellings that shelter and that hide the sufferings of their operatives. Nothing is so distasteful to a truly elegant mill-owner as any allusion, domestic or foreign, gossiping or professional, religious or political, to his factory, or his factory people; and the gay fatherly phrase, "Don't talk of that, for God's sake, my dear!—it smells of the shop," has turned away many innocent eyes from contemplating that, which had they looked upon it, could hardly have endured so long.

To know therefore that the wilful, whimsical, rich, and independent Mary Brotherton (while still too young to understand any thing whatever of the real nature of trade, and our glorious manufactures),— to know that she was beginning to thrust herself behind the scenes, and do Heaven knows what mischief among his devilish people, instead of minding her own business, and falling in love with his adorable son, was altogether too much to be borne with patience; and had it not been that the weather was so hot as to make him long for a draught of hock and iced water, a natural instinct would have made him turn aside from his park-gates, and pursue the by-path which led to his factory, where, as he knew by experience, the sort of temper he was then in could find great relief, without any body but the overlookers being in the secret.

As it was, however, Sir Matthew Dowling reached his home; and the first thing he heard from the man who threw wide its portals was, that Mr Parsons was waiting for him in his study.

"Bring me a biscuit, a bottle of Stein, and some iced water," said the knight in the accent of one not born to "enter the venerable presence of hunger, thirst, and cold," nor into that of heat or vexation either.

"What's the matter now, Parsons?" said he, throwing himself into a delicious arm-chair, and perceiving by one glance at the sour visage before him, that something or other had gone wrong. "The mill's not burnt down I suppose, is it?"

"And I'm not sure that would be the worst thing that could happen Sir Matthew, if it was," replied the confidential servant. "It is well insured you know, sir, and would bring in a famous sum, as sure as the bank, and that's more, I take it, than we can say of all our debts."

"Who the devil has been gossiping with you about the debts? What business is that of yours, I should like to know? Mind your billy-rollers Mr Parsons, and take care your hands keep up with your machinery, that's your work;—and I can tell you, if you don't know it already, that the success of the concern depends more upon that, than upon any other thing whatever. The building is paid for, and the glorious machinery is paid for—mind that, sir, and where's the interest of it to come from if you let the hands go to sleep over it? I tell you what, Mr Parsons, an overlooker is not worth his salt if he does not continually keep it in his head, that the more the machinery is improved the faster must the brats move to follow it. And you may rely upon it that where this is remembered early and late, day hours and night hours, the concern *will* answer, and every manager of it, master or man, will live well. But, by the Lord Harry where it is not, they are as sure to go the wrong side of the post, as you are to go to bed to-night. It stands to reason, Parsons. If one man knows how to drive, and another doesn't, the one man's team will pay, and the other's won't; and I will be much obliged to any man who will tell me how I am to help being undersold in the market, if I don't contrive to make my machinery go as fast, and as long too, as the best of 'em. That's the business you are to attend to, Mr Parsons, and I won't trouble you about any other."

"All true, Sir Matthew, every word of it. And I can't but say, though I scorn to be a boaster,—I can't but say, that I think I have given you reason to trust me. I am noted for being able to keep the children awake, and going longer than any other man in the mill. There isn't an overlooker in Ashleigh that can equal me with the strap or the billy-roller either, when I chooses to make 'em tell."

"I know all that, my good fellow, and I value your services accordingly. But I have been devilishly put out this morning, and that makes me snappish; besides, I am quite sure you have got something disagreeable to tell, by your face. So out with it, man, and make an end of it."

"Make an end of it, Sir Matthew?" replied Parsons, repeating the last words of the sentence with marked emphasis, "by the Lord, sir, that is exactly what I'm come to beg you to do. You must make an end of your charity job, Sir Matthew, for it don't answer in any way: we have lost one of the nimblest set of fingers we had, that wanted nothing but the strap to keep 'em going for six hours out of the four-and-twenty, and I wish you could just hear what gratitude you have gained in return for it. There is not a single day comes round that the rickety little Armstrong don't blubber over his work like a church spout. And I overheard him, the young villain, when he didn't think I was so near—I overheard him when the scavenger-girl, as was cleaning under the mules, looked up and asked, why for he cried, when his brother had got such good fortune—I heard him answer. And what do you think he said, Sir Matthew?"

"How the devil should I know?" replied the chafed capitalist. "Don't stand mumming there, but out with it."

"Neither more nor less than this, Sir Matthew: 'Don't talk of his good fortune, Bet,' says he, 'he's the most unhappiest boy in all the world,' says he."

"Pestilent little vermin!" exclaimed Sir Matthew through his closed teeth. "Infernal fool that I was to listen to that idiot woman and

Crockley too, who ought to know better, has been badgering me exactly with the same execrable nonsense. Never again as long as I live will I be persuaded to try any other scheme with the people than what we have always acted upon. Brutes and beasts they are, and like brutes and beasts they should be treated;—and so they shall by me, as long as my head's above ground."

"Well, sir, can't but say I am glad you are come back to your right mind, as one may call it. Such romantical goings on can never answer in a factory, Sir Matthew. It an't the way to do business, and business is what we have got to do. And so, sir, I hope you will send that scamp Mike back to the mill to-morrow morning, for they can't say no worse of it, let us pay him off as we will, than that he's the most unhappiest boy in all the world. And that's what they says already."

"It won't do, Parsons. That boy must be got rid of.—What do you stare for, you ass? Do you think I am going to get hanged for him?"

"Oh dear no, Sir Matthew—you know the value of your own life better than that, any how,—God forbid you should not. Only I did not overwell understand what you meant by getting rid of him."

"I must contrive to send him out of the way, at least out of this neighbourhood; and moreover, with his own consent and his mother's, too. That is what I meant, Mr Parsons."

"You must know best, Sir Matthew. But it seems to me you are taking a deal of trouble about him. If you'll just let me have him back in the mill, I think I'll venture to say that he shall never get within reach of plaguing you any more—and I'd get a pennyworth out of him into the bargain."

"For a tolerably sharp fellow, Parsons, you're devilish dull about this business. Can't you guess that I should not be taking all the trouble you talk of, about such a beggar's brat as that, unless I had reasons for it. There's that lord's daughter that got me into the scrape, won't she be ferreting and ferreting till she finds out that the sweet little master has not found himself comfortable here? And ten times worse than her,—ay, a hundred fold, is that obstinate headstrong girl of old Brotherton's. My Lady Clarissa might be troublesome from mere folly, and might perhaps be stopped short in any mischief she was doing, by a few words from me. But not the old one himself could stop Mary Brotherton if she got a whim in her head. You should have seen her just now, Mr Parsons, raving at me with her colour up and her eyes flashing, for all the world as if she had just escaped out of Bedlam, only because I cautioned her against going into Joe Drake's pigsty,—a pretty place wasn't it for a girl of her fortune to go visiting? But in she went, by heaven! and you may rely upon it, if such a girl as that, who cares for nothing, and nobody, once gets it into her head to go about among the factory people, she'll kick up more dust than we shall find it easy to lay again. I've been told already by one who I suspect wanted to put me on my guard, that this Mary Brotherton wished to have a little talk with Michael Armstrong. I can put two and two together as well as Miss Mary. She was at our cursed play last night, and I'll bet my life to a rotten egg that she wants to ask him what he cried for."

"Likely enough, sir," replied the overlooker with a grim smile. "I heard of the crying, I won't say that I didn't. You may guess, Sir Matthew, that it was a good deal talked about among the servants—and then t'other of 'em blubbering away at the mill, must give a pretty notion, mustn't it, sir, of your goodness to 'em?"

"Say no more about it, it makes me mad!" exclaimed the knight. "One or both of 'em shall be sent to Deep Valley mill, Parsons, if I die for it!"

"There's none but 'prentices taken in at the mill in the deep hollow, Sir Matthew, if you mean that."

"Yes, sir, I do mean that," replied Sir Matthew with a very ominous frown, "and there Master Michael Armstrong shall go, 'prentice or no 'prentice, or I'll give him up my place, and take his."

"That's all, then Sir Matthew," said the overlooker, preparing to depart. "I com'd to put you up to the boy's ingratitude, and have nothing further to say at present."

"You need not trouble yourself any more about that, Mr Parsons. I will take care of him," replied the knight. Whereupon Mr Parsons made a bow, and departed.

Sir Matthew Dowling had already taken one tumbler of hock-and-water. He now took a second, and then throwing himself back in his arm-chair, indulged for several minutes in very deep meditation. At the end of that time it seemed as if the good Rhine wine had done its office, for suddenly the knight's countenance became animated; the heavy gloom which had rested upon it disappeared, and springing to his feet he rang the bell with a sort of lively jerk which showed he had some project in hand that he greatly relished.

It was the lively Peggy who answered the summons; but though she entered almost out of breath from the eagerness with which she had traversed the passage which led from the kitchen to the study, and though she brought into immediate activity all the *agaceries* of which she was capable; a smiling nod was all the got in return, so eager did Sir Matthew appear to say, "Go to Miss Martha, Peggy, as fast as you can, and tell her to come here to me this very minute. Go, my dear, and make haste, there's a good girl."

Peggy was disappointed and angry, for she had a great deal to tell Sir Matthew about Michael Armstrong's ungratefulness, and all that the servants thought and said about it; but the command she had received was too peremptory to be trifled with, and though she very nearly slammed the study door in shutting it, she failed not to deliver her message, which was instantly obeyed with the most dutiful alacrity by Martha.

"Did you send Peggy for me, papa?" said she in entering.

"Yes, Martha dear, I did. How are you to-day, my dear girl? I have not seen you before this morning. Sit down, love, sit down; I want to talk to you, Martha. I have got something upon my mind that vexes me, and I am going to open my heart to you about it."

"Oh, my dear, dear papa!" returned Martha, "I should be so glad if I could be of any use to you!"

"You can, Martha—you can be of great use and comfort to me. In the first place you must be my father confessor, and let me confess my faults to you and I hope you will give me absolution if you can; for I really am very uncomfortable."

"What *can* you mean, papa?"

"Why, my dear, I mean that I have been foolish enough to put myself in a great pet, when I ought not to have done any such thing. It is always wrong to let temper get the better of one; but in this case it was particularly so. You know the fuss that has been made about this little fellow that I have taken out of the factory—I do assure you, my dear girl, that I really intended to be a very kind friend to him. But I got so provoked at his crying upon the stage last night in that beautiful speech that was written for him, that I cuffed him soundly for it when he came off—and I am sadly afraid that I frightened the poor little fellow so violently that he will never feel comfortable, and at his ease with me again. You cannot think how this vexes me."

"Oh! my dear papa, he will never remember it any more if you will please to forgive him." And Martha's heart bounded with joy as she spoke, to think how completely Miss Brotherton's opinion would be changed could she but hear her father speak thus amiably of what had passed.

"No, Martha, no; I cannot bear to see his frightened look. And besides, my dear, I shall never be sure of myself—you know how hasty I am!—I should live in perpetual terror lest any thing should tempt me to give him a cuff. There are other reasons too, my dear Martha, which induce me to think that I should be doing the little fellow and his family infinitely more service if I apprenticed him to some good trade, than he could ever gain by running about Dowling Lodge."

The excellent good sense of this observation struck Martha as very valuable, and she uttered the most cordial approbation of the wisdom and goodness from whence it proceeded.

"I am exceedingly glad you agree with me, my dear child," proceeded Sir Matthew, "for I have an idea that you could be very useful in making the arrangement. Do you happen to know where the little boy's mother lives, my dear Martha?"

"No, papa—but Michael could show me."

"Then you should have no objection to pay her a visit on this business, my dear?"

"Oh! dear no! I should like it so much!"

"Very well, my love—then you shall set out immediately if you will. Or stay—it would perhaps be better to get you the paper first that they will have to sign. You must remember to tell them, Martha, that I shall undertake to pay all the fees. It certainly is an excellent thing for a poor family like Armstrong's, to have a boy 'prenticed to a good trade. I trust the mother will not refuse her consent from any selfish notion, that she may lose the boy's help thereby, it would be really very wicked. You may tell her, my dear, that I shall continue to send her down nice and nourishing food, and that little Michael shall be taught to write, and be well instructed every way; so she may be quite easy about him, and he will be sure to send her a letter every now and then." The knight concluded with a smile of kindness, that perfectly enchanted his daughter. "Oh! my dear, dear papa!" she said, "how few people there are who know you as well as I do! Let me go and look for Michael now, papa, shall I? I should like to go down to his mother with him at once, and tell her of your great goodness. The papers could be sent afterwards, you know."

"Very well, dear, trot away then;—get your bonnet and parasol, find your little squire, and then come back here to me to receive my last instructions."

As soon as the happy-looking Martha had left the room the bell was again rung, and on this occasion answered by a footman,—the lively Peggy choosing to turn herself another way as soon as she heard it.

"Is Parsons gone?" demanded Sir Matthew of the servant.

"No, Sir Matthew, he is in the servants' hall," was the reply.

"Desire him to step here directly."

Though the overlooker was enjoying some very comfortable refreshment, he promptly obeyed the summons, and as soon as he had again entered the study, and shut the door behind him, his master said, "Do you know, Parsons, whether the woman Armstrong can read?"

"Yes, sir, I know she can—and that's one reason why she is so outdacious about the workhouse and every thing. There's nothing on earth does so much mischief among the mill people as making scholards of 'em," said the man.

"I know that well enough, who doesn't? But you may go now, I only wanted to ask you that one question," replied the master.

Once more alone, the knight again took to meditation. Profound as was the state of ignorance respecting all things beyond their own wretched dwellings in which the operatives at that time were kept, Sir

Matthew had some misgivings as to the possibility that the name and fame of Deep Valley mill, might have reached even Hoxley-lane. If it had, the sending to a woman who could read, indentures by which her child should become bound to that establishment till the age of twenty-one, was running a risk of more opposition than he wished to encounter. But he had a ready wit, and seldom remained long at a loss how to manage any business on which his mind had fixed itself. When Martha returned, therefore, he was quite ready with his last instructions.

"Have you found the little boy, my dear?" said he mildly.

"Yes, papa, he is waiting for me in the hall. Foolish little fellow! I believe he fears that you are very angry with him, and he looked so much alarmed that I would not bring him in."

"Poor child! you were quite right, my dear Martha. It is better not to harass him in any way. Now then, Martha, what you have got to do is this: Explain to the poor woman that it is my wish to keep my promise of providing for her boy; but that I am come to the persuasion that the apprenticing him to some respectable business will be better than letting him run about the place here learning nothing. You may talk to the little boy, you know; he is a sharp child, and I have no doubt will come to the same conclusion himself, if you state the thing to him properly."

"I have no doubt of it, papa," answered the innocent Martha; "I will do my very best to make him understand it. And what trade shall I tell Mrs Armstrong you have chosen for him?"

"Stocking-weaving, my dear, I really don't know a better; and we may be able to help him in that if he behaves well as he goes on."

"Well then, papa, now I may go?"

"Yes, my dear, now you may go—and you may just tell the woman, Martha, that if she approves the plan, I will call upon her myself some day with the papers. A pleasant walk to you! Good bye."

★　　★　　★　　★　　★

It was a very pleasant walk, for Martha was delighted with her companion. She opened to him kindly and clearly the plan for his being put apprentice to a respectable trade, and pointed out to his young but quick capacity the advantage this would give him in after life, and the power he might hope to possess, if he behaved well, of providing for his mother and brother.

"'Tis that what I should like best of all things," said Michael. "Because, please ma'am, I know I must help 'em, as they beant neither of 'em so strong as I be."

"You are a good boy, Michael, for thinking of them so much as you do. That is the reason I take notice of you, and love you."

The little fellow nestled closer to her side, as they walked on, and raising the hand that held his, he laid it upon his shoulder, and pressed his cheek upon it with very endearing fondness.

"What an affectionate little heart it is!" thought Martha, "and how very happy I shall be if I can help to get this business settled for him!"

Of course Miss Martha Dowling had never been in Hoxley-lane before; and notwithstanding her having so agreeable a companion, she speedily became aware that the region was as unpleasant as it was new.

"Is this the only road, my dear boy, by which we can get to your mother's house?" said she, almost mechanically enveloping her offended nose, in her pocket-handkerchief.

"It is here that we lives, please ma'am," said the child, pulling her onwards.

"How very foolish of me!" thought Martha, withdrawing her handkerchief, "of course poor people live in poor houses. But I cannot think why the place should smell so!"

No 12 was however soon reached, and the young lady carefully led by her little attendant through the largest gap in the hedge to the outer door of the back kitchen, in order that she might escape Mrs Sykes's crowded front one.

"Go in first, Michael, and tell your mother that I am coming," said the considerate Martha. The child did so, but in this case there was no means for preparation, and having named the unexpected visitant and given his mother a hasty kiss, he returned before Martha had recovered the sort of shock which the dirty and desolate spot on which she stood had occasioned.

In truth no person unaccustomed to approach the dwellings of the operatives in the towns of the manufacturing districts, can fail to be startled at the first near sight of them. In the very poorest agricultural village, the cottages which shelter its labourers have the pure untainted air of heaven to blow around their humble roofs; but where forests of tall bare chimneys, belching eternal clouds of smoke rear their unsightly shafts towards the sky, *in lieu* of verdant air-refreshing trees, the black tint of the loathsome factory seems to rest upon every object near it. The walls are black, the fences are black, the window-panes (when there are any) are all veiled in black. No domestic animal that pertinaciously exists within their tainted purlieus, but wearst he same dark hue; and perhaps there is no condition of human life so significantly surrounded by types of its own wretchedness as this.

Martha Dowling shuddered as she looked around her; and when Michael returned to lead her in, she felt half afraid of crossing the gloomy threshold.

But the widow Armstrong was, as usual, less dirty in her abject misery than, perhaps, any other inhabitant of Hoxley-lane, or its immediate neighbourhood, and the mild countenance and gentle voice with which she replied to the young lady's salutation removed all her scruples, and she seated herself in the chair placed for her by Michael, with the best disposition in the world to improve the acquaintance.

"I hope you are getting better, Mrs Armstrong?" said Martha, in that tone of genuine female softness which it is so impossible to mistake, "and that you don't miss little Michael as much as you did at first."

"You are very kind, ma'am, to take the trouble of coming to such a place as this," replied the poor woman, in a voice that indicated something like surprise. Upon which Michael, who had stationed himself near enough to enable him to slip his little hand into hers, said, with a tolerably expressive emphasis—"This is Miss Martha, mother."

"I wish, ma'am, I had strength and power to thank you as I ought, for all your condescending kindness to my poor boy!" said the widow, earnestly. "I never see him, that he has not some fresh story to tell me of your goodness to him. He can read a chapter in the Bible now as well as any boy of his age need to do. And oh! Miss—This is all owing to you—for never could he have given his time to it in the factory."

"There is more praise due to him than to me, Mrs Armstrong, I assure you. He is a very good boy at learning, and minds every word that is said to him. I suppose he has shown you his copy-book too, has he? I never saw a child that had so good a notion of writing."

"He was always a quick boy, Miss—but never can he be thankful enough to you for teaching him how to put his quickness to profit. It will be the making of him."

"I am very glad to hear you speak so earnestly about his learning, because that makes me think that you will be pleased at hearing the business I am come upon. My papa, who is very"—here poor Martha stopped short. She was going to add—"*kind to little Michael,*" but her honest heart would not let her pronounce the words; so she changed the phrase, and went on with "very desirous of being really useful to Michael, has commissioned me, Mrs Armstrnng, to ask you if yot do not think it would be more profitable and advantageous to him to be apprenticed to some good trade, the stocking-weaving for instance, than to run about our house any longer? Papa says, he fears it will give him habits of idleness which he may be the worse for all his life—and that would be quite contrary to his wishes, which have always been that he should benefit all his life long, by his good behaviour about the cow."

Mrs Armstrong's eyes which had been fixed on the countenance of Martha, every line of which spoke of truth and sincerity, fell upon the work she held in her hand as these words were uttered—and for a moment she made no answer. But feeling, perhaps, that this was both ungrateful and ungracious to her visiter, she looked up again and said, "I am sure, ma'am, we can never thank *you* enough for all your kindness."

There was the slightest emphasis in the world upon the word "*you*," but it was enough to heighten the colour of Martha, and for a moment she both felt and looked displeased.

"My power, of myself, to befriend your boy, Mrs Armstrong, is very little, I assure you," she said. "Of course it is natural that I should take more notice of him than a person like my father can, who has so many other things to attend to; but it is to his generosity and benevolence that you must look for any lasting advantage you may hope to gain for him."

"Indeed, ma'am, I would be happy to take your advice in the disposal of him any way; for I can't mistake your kindness, or your power to judge what is best, which of course must be greater than mine, notwith-standing your young age—and if Michael likes it, and you think it best, ma'am."

Martha saw that the mother's fear of having her boy parted from her, was combating the wiser hope for his future advantage; and fully conscious that the continuing his present mode of life could only be productive of mortification, she boldly answered this appeal, and in the confiding innocence of her heart ventured to say, "Perhaps, in this case, girl as I am, my judgment *may* be better than yours, Mrs Armstrong. I do not think it would be good or pleasant for Michael in any way, to continue living at the Lodge as he does at present; and I do think, that if put to a respectable trade, he may not only provide for himself, but be a help and comfort to you and his brother likewise. This is my opinion, certainly, and now ask his. He is still younger than me, to be sure, poor little fellow, and yet I think you ought to listen to his opinion."

"Well, Mike dear," said the widow, turning her head towards the child, "you hear what the young lady says; speak up, my dear, and tell us what you think about it."

"I be ready to go, mother, if she bids me, and you like it," replied the boy.

"You can judge, ma'am, that he knows his duty. That is just like him. From the time he was able to speak, dear creature, it was always the same—gentle, good, and reasonable. I won't say but what the parting with him will be a sore trial to me, but God forbid that I should set the wishes of my worn-out life against the hopes of his young one. How far away is it Miss, do you happen to know, where the master stocking-weaver bides, as he's to go to?"

Martha confessed her ignorance on this point; but added, that though she should be sorry to hear it was too far off for him occasionally to come home and pay her a visit, she should be more sorry still, were he to be placed in the town of Ashleigh. "It would be only putting him for ever in the way of temptation, Mrs Armstrong," said she; "and I am sure you are too sensible a woman, to wish that he should be were the doing his duty was likely to be a pain to him."

"Indeed, and that I would," said the poor woman, earnestly. "'Tis the seeing their poor young faces for ever so sad and care-worn, that is the worst trial of all."

"How true is what my clear father says about the factory people," thought Martha— "how wonderfully they do all hate work!"

This conviction of their epidemic idleness, however, in no degree chilled the good girl's desire at once to perform her father's will, and benefit a very interesting, though not, as she believed, a very industrious mother and son. So deeming it best to enter into no further discussion, but to accept the consent uttered by both as final and conclusive, she rose, and smiling good-humouredly at Michael said,

"Now you have taught me the way here, I think I shall be able to get back again by myself; and I dare say Michael, that you and your mother will like to have a little conversation together about this new plan for you. But remember, dear, that you are home by five o'clock to read your lesson and show me your copy-book; we were interrupted this morning you know." Then leaving in the poor widow's hand a welcome token of her visit, and promising that she would either bring or send the papers necessary for her to sign, before long, the excellent Martha Dowling departed, after having most innocently, but most effectually, lent her aid to the perpetration of as hateful a crime, as the black heart of long-hardened depravity could devise.

Having waited till the figure of the young lady had passed across the little window, the widow Armstrong pulled her boy towards her, and gave him a mother's kiss.

"To be sure thee dost look all the better, my Mike, for good food, and fine clothing. But I shan't be satisfied, unless you tell me that you like all these new favours that they are going to confer upon you."

"I like to go, mother, very much," replied Michael, stoutly.

"Thank God! then, my darling—you are provided for," she rejoined with deep sigh. "I have known a many stocking-weavers, Mike, exceeding well to do, and there was never one of them, I'll answer for it, that had a better will to work, and to do his duty, than you have—so I have no right to doubt but what you will do well, and I don't doubt it. But 'tis the parting with thee, my dear, dear child!—Oh! Mike, you have been a comfort to me ever since you was born—and how do I know, if—"

"Mother!" cried the boy, interrupting her, "I'll be a comfort to you still. I'll tell you what I've got in my head to do, and just see if it is not a good plan. I mean to be the very best boy that ever my master had, and when I've gone on working with him a bit, two or three months, perhaps, mother,—time enough for him really to find out that I am a good boy,—I will tell him all about you and Teddy, and make him understand that if he wants to keep me in good heart to work, he must let me trudge away home to pass a Sunday now and then with you two. I don't think he'll be able to say no, mother, when I tell him about Teddy's poor legs, and all you have done for us both, lying a-bed here."

Mrs Armstrong again kissed her boy, and after gazing at him with a look in which pride and pleasure were strangely blended with anguish, she said, "I do think you'll make your way, Michael—for you are a good boy, a very good boy. But I don't know how poor Edward will take it."

"That's the worst part of it, mother," replied the little fellow, beginning to cry. "Poor Teddy does look so very happy of a night when he sees me pop round the corner upon him, as he comes out of the factory!—But then I shall be able to help him, mother, all the better by and by. And when I come home of a Sunday, mother, I must teach him to write, and then think how beautiful to have a letter from one another! I know who'll give me a slate for Teddy, and me too, to learn with, and that's Miss Martha. And I shan't mind asking her, not the least, because she knows I am going away. And do you know, mother, I've got another notion, and that's no bad comfort neither. I should not a bit wonder, if Miss Martha was to turn out a right good friend to you and Teddy, when I am gone."

And so the little fellow ran on—each hopeful word he uttered begetting a new hope, till, by the time the hour of departure arrived, his poor mother had at least the comfort of believing that the prospect opening before him, was one that he looked upon with much less of pain than pleasure.

Meanwhile Martha found her way safely home, and gave her father such an account of the result of her mission, as induced him to give her a kiss, and declare that if she was not the handsomest of the family, she was out-and-out the most useful.

XIV

Mary Brotherton continues sick in heart and mind—But is roused and cheered by her own steadfast will—An o'er true tale

IT WAS NOT TILL THE second dinner-bell had rung, that Mrs Tremlett ventured to seek Mary in her chamber.

The worthy woman was perfectly aware that the naturally strong feelings of her young mistress had been violently affected by the scene they had witnessed, and though far perhaps from comprehending the effect it had produced on her mind, she was conscious that she should do no good by obtruding herself uncalled-for upon her retirement.

But when the signal that always brought them together had passed unheeded, she became uneasy, and availing herself of the privilege that long and well-requited affection gave, she knocked at her door and called upon her name.

Miss Brotherton answered the summons immediately; but her withdrawing the bolt of her door, as well as the unchanged appearance of her dress, showed that she had not been occupied in preparing for dinner.

"You are not aware how late it is, my dear child. The second dinner-bell has rung!" said Mrs Tremlett looking anxiously in her pale face.

"Has it?" replied the young lady; "indeed, I beg your pardon—but I will not keep you waiting, I will not dress to-day if you will excuse it."

"No, no, my dear, that won't do. Never mind about the dinner I will tell them to take it out again."

"Indeed I do not wish to dress," said Mary languidly. "Morgan will tease me by asking what dress I choose to wear and fifty questions besides. Let me go down as I am, nurse Tremlett."

"You shan't have Morgan at all dear. The dressing will refresh you my darling child; and it won't be the first time Mary, that I have done all that you wanted in that way. There—just sit down on the sofa for a minute, and I will speak about the dinner, and be back again."

It was very passively that Mary did as she was bid, and without another word of remonstrance sat down and awaited the return of her old friend. She was indeed completely exhausted, the scene she had witnessed had not touched only, it had wrung her heart; and the hours she had passed since, were, not such as to bring her spirits back to their ordinary tone. It was not alone, the melancholy spectacle of a fellow-creature passing from life to death, which had thus strongly affected her—it was the frightful degradation of the group of human beings who had gazed upon it with her. It was the horrible recollection of the dying woman's statement respecting the lacerated flesh of her child—it was the filth, the misery, the famine, and the vice that she had been warned of, and had seen, which had set her powerful, healthy, unprejudiced, and unselfish mind, to meditate upon the state of things which had produced it.

It was hardly possible for any one to be more profoundly ignorant upon the subject which had thus seized upon her heart, than was Mary Brotherton. On the question of negro slavery she had from her very earliest infancy heard a great deal, for her father was an anti-(black)-slavery man, who subscribed to the African society, and the missionary fund; drank Mr Wilberforce's health after dinner whenever he had company at his table; and while his own mills daily sent millions of groans to be registered in heaven from joyless young hearts and aching infant limbs, he rarely failed to despatch with nearly equal regularity (all booked for the same region) a plentiful portion of benevolent lamentations over the sable sons of Africa, all uttered comfortably from a soft arm-chair, while digestion was gently going on, and his well-fed person in a state of the most perfect enjoyment. On the slavery question therefore Mary really knew a great deal, and felt concerning it as every true Christian must feel. But as to every thing concerning the nature of the labour performed in the factories by whose chimneys her pleasant park was surrounded—the age, sex, or condition, of the labourers—the proportion of their daily existence devoted to toil—the degree of care bestowed on their immortal souls—or the quantum of enjoyment permitted to them by their earthly masters, while awaiting a summons to the presence of their heavenly one—of all this Mary Brotherton was as ignorant as the sleek lap-dog that dozed upon her hearth-rug. But this carefully-adjusted cloud was now passing away from her intellect for ever. If

"Where ignorance is bliss, it *is* folly to be wise,"

that folly had seized upon her; for no longer was she destined to taste the doubtful joy of luxury that had never looked upon the seamy side of existence, or dreamed that the means that supplied its exquisite, yet almost unnoted refinements, were earned by the agony of labouring infants. But though this, worse than fools paradise, was thus closed upon her for ever, she felt a power and energy of purpose awaked within her heart, that she thanked God upon her bended knees for giving, though she trembled as she received it. And never did sainted nun breathe purer or more earnest vows of self-devotion to heaven, than did this ardent-spirited girl to the examination, and, if possible, to the relief of the misery she had at length learned to know existed round her.

But like most other persons when occupied by a really profound emotion, Mary felt no inclination to talk about it. She had not indeed the slightest intention to conceal any thing she did from Mrs Tremlett, but on the contrary hoped eventually to gain much assistance from her strong practical good sense; but she could not discuss, she could not reason, she could not prate about it now, and she went through the business of the dinner-table so tranquilly, that her watchful companion felt rejoiced, though a little surprised, at her recovered composure.

Soon after they retired from table, Mary proposed a walk in the grounds, and as they wandered together through the richly-scented flower-garden, and then seated themselves where the cool breeze of evening brought the tempered fragrance to their senses more delightfully still, the feverish feeling of tightness across her forehead, seemed to relax, and as if to apologise for the silent fit that had seized her, Mary looked kindly into the face of her old friend, and then bent forward and kissed her.

"Bless you, my dear love! you feel better now, don't you?" said the affectionate old woman.

"Yes, dear nurse—much better. The air is delicious to-night."

"It was too much for you, my dear child, that dreadful scene this morning! My dear Miss Brotherton you must be reasonable, indeed you must, or instead of making me the very happiest being in the world as you do now, my life will become one of continual terror and alarm. You can do no good, my dear, in putting yourself in such places as we were in to-day."

Mary reflected for a moment before she answered her, and then said, "Are you quite sure, nurse Tremlett, that a young woman without any natural ties whatever, and with a fortune so large as mine, can do no good by making themselves acquainted with the condition of their poor neighbours?'

"Oh! no, Miss Mary dear, I never said that. You do a great deal of good by putting the gardener's, and under-gardener's children to school; and by all the help you give them and every body else that works about the place, and I dearly love to see you do it, and I have no doubt in the world, that it keeps many from sending their children to the mills, and it will bring a blessing upon your head, my dear. But that's nothing to do with poking yourself into such a place as you got into to-day. You never heard any thing so dreadful as what Sir Matthew Dowling was telling me about them, before you came ont the first time."

Mary shuddered, as she heard his name.

"You will promise me dear, won't you, never to go to such a horrid place again," resumed the old woman.

"We will not talk about that now, my dear Mrs Tremlett, I want you to tell me what you think I could do that would be most useful for those poor young girls. I know what it is to lose a mother, dear nurse, and it makes me feel for them."

"God bless your kind heart, my dear! That is just like you, and I wish with all my heart and soul, that you lived somewhere among the farm people, for there you would have some reward for your charity. But God help me! If one half of what Sir Matthew told me is true, these horrid girls are worse than it is decent to tell you, and the father's as bad."

"But don't you think my good friend, considering that I am more than come to years of discretion, and that you are a good deal older still, don't you think it might be as well for us, in a case of such import as this, to see and judge for ourselves, instead of taking Sir MatthewDowling's word for it?" said the heiress, while a slight frown contracted her brow.

"Why yes, Miss Mary—only it is so difficult to come at the truth," replied Mrs Tremlett.

"Surely there is one truth that it is easy enough to come at—I suppose you have no doubt upon your mind that these people are in dreadful distress?"

"Wicked people almost always are, Miss Mary."

"Then it is my duty Mrs Tremlett," replied Mary almost sternly, "to endeavour, at least in the case of such very young people, to amend, or prevent their wickedness. It would be a frightful sin—worse in me, burdened as I feel myself with riches earned by the labour of such miserable little creatures as those whom we saw to-day—if I should look upon such utter destitution, let it be mixed up with what frailty it may, and pass along on the other side. I will not do it, Mrs Tremlett, so never ask it more. At present all I know is, that I have seen misery. Its cause I have yet to learn—this may be the work of time, and I do not mean to wait till I have acquired such knowledge before I relieve the want and woe I have witnessed. I left word that the eldest girl was to come up to me. She will hardly delay doing so, poor creature, therefore I must again postpone my intended visit to Hoxley-lane, for I will not go out to-morrow till I have seen her."

All this was very contrary to Mrs Tremlett's judgment, for she had a very natural dread lest the warm heart of her young charge, should be imposed upon by the designing and depraved. Nevertheless there was a feeling of respect that came upon her involuntarily, and as it were unawares, as she listened to the firmly-spoken purpose of the young girl whom as yet she could hardly persuade herself was more than a child.

In pursuance of the resolution thus declared, Miss Brotherton did not stir from home during the whole of the following day. Lady Clarissa Shrimpton, Mrs Gabberly, and one or two more distant neighbours called, but she was denied to them all, from the fear that her anticipated interview with Sophy Drake, might be interrupted. But the precaution was unnecessary; the long morning wore away without the girl's making her appearance, and it was not till past eight o'clock in the evening, that a servant entered the drawing-room, and informed Miss Brotherton that a very dirty girl and two little children were at the gate, who said she had given them orders to call.

"It is very true," replied the young lady. "These are the people I told you to let in." The man retired in silence, but paid himself for his forbearance by the vehemence of his wondering commentary in the servants' hall.

Mary Brotherton was sitting at an open window, with the last light of evening falling upon her and the volume she held in her hand.

She had been making what proved but an idle effort to read, even when that light was stronger; but now, the volume hung listlessly from her hand, while her eyes, fixed on the brightly tinted vapours in the west, seemed to look athwart them, and like the worthy gentleman on the platform before Tilbury Fort, to gaze on many things, that were "*not yet in sight.*" Mrs Tremlett, with the happy indifference to the increasing twilight peculiar to the sisterhood of knitters, continued at another window to manœuvre her bright weapons, and vary the successive fronts of her phalanx with no louder note of command, than was occasionally produced by the gentle clicking of her needles against each other. It was nearly an hour since a word had been exchanged between them, but now as the footman left the room, Mary turned towards her, and said—"This is poor Sophy, Mrs Tremlett. Come and sit near me, will you? I want you to hear all she says."

Her old friend moved her place accordingly, and had just seated herself by the side of Miss Brotherton when the door again opened, and Sophy Drake, leading a little sister in each hand, entered the drawing-room.

It required no force of contrast to render the miserable, squalid, unhealthy appearance of these poor girls most painfully striking; if it had, the elegant apartment into which they now entered would have furnished it. Mary's heart smote her as she gazed upon them. "So young pretty too!" thought she, "and yet so painful to look upon!"

So young—so pretty, too, thought she—and yet so painful to look upon

The eldest of the three looked languid, weary, spirit-broken, and inanimate, hardly throwing a glance at the novel objects around her, and looking more fit to lie down and rest the aching limbs she slowly dragged along, than to indulge any feeling of curiosity. The little ones had the same unsteady tired gait, but they looked up with an expression of wonder, and almost of awe, on every object as they passed along

"How are you all, my poor girls?" said Mary kindly, as they drew near to her. The eldest girl dropped a courtesy but made no audible reply.

"It is so sad and hopeless a grief to lose a mother," continued Miss Brotherton, "that I can say not one word to check your grief. But if there is any thing that I can do to make you more comfortable, I shall be glad to do it. You seem all of you greatly in want of clothes. How comes that, when so many of the family work, and get wages?"

"The wages isn't enough to buy us bread, ma'am," replied the eldest girl, "and help pay lodging rent."

The statement seemed so very incredible, that Mary felt a painful conviction that the young creature before her was not speaking truth. She remained silent for a minute or two, and then said, "I suppose when you say bread, you mean food of all kinds?—and tea, and sugar, and butter, and so on?" said Mary.

"I have not had the taste of meat in my mouth for above these two years," replied Sophy colouring, and in a voice that seemed to indicate something like indignation— "and as to sugar in our tea, or butter on our bread, no factory child is brought up to it."

Mary coloured too. She longed to get accurate information respecting their manner of living, and the reasons why incessant labour failed to supply the necessaries of life; but she knew not well how to set about it.

"Do not be angry with me, Sophy," said she, "if I ask questions that seem unfeeling and very ignorant. I really know little or nothing about the manner in which poor people live, and I want to know. Not merely from curiosity, but because I should like to help them if I could."

"And God knows we want help bad enough, ma'am," replied the girl, while tears started to her eyes. "Father has got the money you gave yesterday, and we shall never hear any more of that."

"Is he a bad father to you then?"

"Not bad to beat us. But he drinks terrible."

"Then I suppose his wages go partly in that?"

"His wages, and our'n too, ma'am. He baint always able to get work. The old hands are often out, and then in course he takes our'n."

"Then if he was a temperate, steady man, you would do a great deal better?"

"In course we should, ma'am. But mother said he took to it, as most of the others do in all the mills, on account of hating to come home so, when we young ones comes in from work. I have heard mother say that father cried when I, that was the biggest, com'd home first beaten and bruised with the strap and the billy-roller."

"What *is* the billy-roller, Sophy," inquired Miss Brotherton, in an accent denoting considerable curiosity.

"It's a long stout stick, ma'am, that's used often and often to beat the little ones employed in the mills when their strength fails—when they fall asleep, or stand still for a minute."

"Do you mean, that the children work till they are so tired as to fall asleep standing?"

"Yes, ma'am. Dozens and dozens of 'em every day in the year except Sundays, is strapped, and kicked, and banged by the billy-roller, because they falls asleep."

"But, surely, parents are greatly to blame, to let children young enough for that, go to work at all?"

"They must just starve, ma'am, if they didn't," replied the girl.

"How many years have you worked in the factory yourself, Sophy?"

"Just twelve, ma'am, this last spring."

"And how old are you?"

"Seventeen, ma'am."

"Twelve from seventeen?—You mean to say that you began to work at the factory when you were five years old?" said Mary, with some appearance of incredulity.

"I was five years and three months, ma'am," answered the girl firmly.

Miss Brotherton looked at Mrs Tremlett, but perceived no appearance of incredulity on her countenance. "Is this possible, Mrs Tremlett?" said she.

"Yes, my dear, I believe that it is very common, replied the old woman. "I have often heard it spoken of among the servants."

"Have you ever been at school, Sophy?"

"Yes, ma'am. Afore father changed his mill and took work under Sir Matthew we all—father, mother, Grace, Dick, and all, worked for the great Quaker gentleman, Joseph Tell, and he had a school in the factory for Sundays."

"And you learnt to read there of course?"

"No, ma'am, I didn't;" replied the girl, shaking her head.

"Whose fault was that, my dear?—Surely if you were put to school you ought to have learnt to read?"

"I couldn't, ma'am, I couldn't—and it was not my fault neither," replied the girl with considerable agitation.

"We was often and often kept going till twelve o'clock on a Saturday night, and when the Sunday comed we couldn't sit down upon the bench, neither Grace, nor Dick, nor I, without falling dead asleep. 'Twas the only right good sleep we had, that before Sundays I mean, 'cause father was always obligated to wake us every other morning afore five o'clock, summer and winter, and earlier than that too, when we worked night-work. So keeping our eyes open Sundays wasn't possible, 'cause they didn't strap us."

"Then there is not one of you can read?"

"No, ma'am, not one."

"Can your father read?"

"Yes, ma'am, he can. That is he could, he says, when he was young but he has almost forgot now. He says, in his young days, the machinery improvements was nothing like what they be now, and that the piecer children hadn't not half so far or so fast to walk as they have now, and he learnt to read of his own mother when he comed home at nights."

"And why doesn't he do the same for his children, as his mother did for him?" said Miss Brotherton.

"Because we couldn't keep our eyes open for two minutes together when we comes home at night. I have seen poor mother, as is dead and gone, lay little Becky here, down upon the bundle of straw that she and I sleeps upon, 'cause she couldn't keep up to eat her supper when she comed from the mill—and I have seen her put the sopped bread in her mouth when she was so dead asleep, that she couldn't get her to swallow it—and how could she or the rest of us learn to read, ma'am?"

Mary made no reply, but sat for a moment or two, with her eyes fixed on the ground, in very painful uncertainty as to what she could say do, that could be of effectual service to the miserable group before her. She felt, that though poor Sophy might perhaps be telling not but the truth in this dismal description of her wretched family, it was not from her that any general information could be obtained. It was, as she thought, utterly impossible that it could apply to the hundreds of thousands whom she had heard it stated, as a matter of national pride, by some of her rich neighbours, were employed in the factories of England and Scotland. A moment's thought sufficed to convince her (as it has

done multitudes of amiable-minded ladies and gentlemen besides), that
it was perfectly impossible such horrors could exist on the glorious
soil of Britain, unless indeed, as in the case before her, the unhappy
drunkenness of the father plunged his helpless family into a degree of
poverty, which nothing, perhaps, but the unnatural degree of labour
described by this poor motherless girl, could avert.

"I must clothe them all," thought she, "and put the little ones to
school. Perhaps, too, I may find a place in my own kitchen for poor
Sophy. But as to learning from her any thing that can be depended upon
respecting the system by which the factory labour is regulated, that is
quite hopeless."

She felt, however, that the weary-looking group ought not to return
empty-handed after their walk, with no reward for it but her promises;
and turning to Mrs Tremlctt, asked her in a half whisper what she
could give them, that might be made immediately useful in the way of
clothing; their garments being in a condition that it was painful to her
to behold.

"You might give them that piece of dark cotton, my dear, that you
bought the other day for the coachman's children. There is no great
hurry you know about them, for they are not to go to school till next
month."

"Very true.—It is just the thing," replied Mary; and having rung the
bell and ordered her maid to appear, she gave orders to have it brought
to her.

"I do not exactly know how much there is of it, Sophy," said she,
putting it into her hand, "but enough, I think, for one or two of you, and
I will get more of the same sort when next I go to Ashleigh."

Sophy took it with a courtesy; but having held it for a moment said,
"Please, ma'am, this won't be no use to me, unless I may pawn part to
get the rest made."

"Can you not make a gown for yourself and your sisters, my good
girl?" demanded Mary.

"Please, ma'am, I never was learnt to sew," replied the girl, blushing.

More convinced than ever, that her first effort to assist the poor
operatives, had led her by an unlucky chance into a family whose

unthrifty habits made it almost hopeless to attempt doing them any essential service, Mary drew forth her purse, and giving half-a-crown to each of them, took the useless material back, saying, "I will send you some more decent clothes to wear, Sophy—and then we must think what further can be done for you and these poor little ones. But, indeed, my dear girl, I greatly fear that unless your habits are improved, and that you can be taught to use your needle like all other decent young women, in making and mending what is given you, it will be impossible for me, or for any one to do you much good."

Poor Sophy Drake looked both sorry and ashamed as she listened to this reproof,—but she attempted not to answer it, and again courtesying as she received the money, she turned away without again speaking, and left the room.

"This is very, very dreadful! nurse Tremlett," said Mary, as soon as they were alone. "I could not have believed that it was possible in such a country as England, to find human beings in a state of such degraded ignorance as that poor girl. Did you ever meet with any thing like it before?"

"I can't say, Miss Mary, that I ever before came within reach of hearing a factory-girl speak so much as I have heard to-day. But I can't pretend to say that I am a bit surprised. I told you, my dear, from the beginning, that you would only get yourself into trouble, and do no good. From the very first of my coming to this country, which was but a month before I came to live with your mamma, I always heard the same history of the factory folks. And you know, my dear, what every body says, must be true."

Mary, as she listened to this, looked harassed, puzzled and wretched. "But is it not something unheard of in the history of the world," said she, "that thousands and hundreds of thousands of people should exist, all labouring, young and, old, with unceasing industry to support themselves, and that this their painful labour should subject them to such habits of inevitable ignorance and degradation, that all decent and respectable persons must be taught to shun them?"

"It does seem very hard upon them, my dear, to be sure," replied her companion; "but as to why it is so, I am sure it is impossible for us to guess. It must be partly their own faults of course; but at any rate, my dear, I wish you would not go on, working yourself up so. I can't bear to see you, Miss Mary, looking vexed and miserable for what you can't help the least bit in the world. And besides, my dear, I must say, that it is nowise right for a young lady like you to run the risk of getting near very bad people indeed, whose ways I don't like to talk to you about. I know you can't abide Sir Matthew Dowling and I can't say I ever saw or heard of much to like in him; but for all that, there is not any good that I can see in disbelieving what he told us about these very people. He must know more about them than we can, and it was quite shocking I do assure you, Miss Mary, the things he told me. A great deal too bad to repeat, I promise you."

Mary burst into tears. "I am very unhappy, Mrs Tremlett," said she, "and it is not putting faith in Sir Matthew Dowling that can make me less so. That I may be led to do many things from my great ignorance, which were I better informed I should not do, is very likely; and it is therefore my duty to obtain information upon this tremendous subject as speedily as possible. Would to God, my good friend, that you could give it me! but as you cannot, we will cease to speculate together upon what we neither of us understand. I am sorry that our awful adventure yesterday, prevented my purposed visit to the poor woman in Hoxley-lane. We both agreed, you know, that I could get to harm there; and I have an object in view in making that visit that I am sorry to have delayed. We will go there to-morrow, nurse Tremlett,—and so early in the morning, as to run no risk of meeting any of the fine folks who love to show themselves on the Ashleigh road."

Mary Brotherton did go early the following morning to Hoxley-lane. But her visit was too late, by exactly twenty-four hours.

XV

*A tête-à-tête walk—Lively if not instructive conversation—The
rich visiting the poor—Misplaced confidence—Innocent sin*

THE FASHIONABLE AND LUXURIOUS SIR Matthew Dowling was not
usually an early riser, but on the morning of the day which
followed Martha's visit to Hoxley-lane, he almost outdid the lark. His
attorney having been sent for from Ashleigh with all speed within an
hour after he had received his daughter's report, all things regarding the
procuring indentures had been made easy, and he found himself when
he waked in the morning, in every sense ready for action.

Great, and very awful is the power of wealth in a bad man's hands; for
scarcely is there any barrier which the law can raise for the protection
of those who have it not, sufficiently strong to save them at all times and
seasons, from the aggressions of those who have it. How Mr Cantabury,
the attorney of Sir Matthew Dowling, contrived to get his part of the
business executed so speedily, it would be difficult to say; but certain it
is, that considerably before the knight's usual hour of breakfast on the
following morning this active friend and agent, arrived at the lodge with
documents, which only wanted the signature of the parties concerned,
to render them of sufficient power to bind little Michael during the
next eleven years of his life as apprentice to Mr Elgood Sharpton, *for the
purpose of learning the business of a stocking-weaver.*

The name of Deep Valley, by which Mr Elgood Sharpton's factory
was universally known, was not mentioned, but instead of this he was
described as Elgood Sharpton Esq., of Thistledown House, Derbyshire,

a designation most satisfactorily proving his honourable station, and, of course, his high respectability.

Sir Matthew perused the document, smiled, nodded his approval, replaced the red tape with which it had been tied, and lodged it in his coat-pocket, saying kindly to the judicious attorney as he did so, "Cantabury! we must get you made coroner at the next vacancy—or if we miss that, something or other else that may suit you, my good fellow. You deserve to be taken care of, and you shall."

Mr Cantabury expressed his gratitude and departed; whereupon Martha was again summoned to the presence of her father.

"What a capital good girl you are, Martha," said the knight, affectionately patting her cheek, "always up and about before any of the rest are out of their beds—I tell you what, Martha, you and I will have our breakfast comfortably together without waiting for any of them, and then I will walk down with you myself to see Michael's mother, and settle with her about the little fellow's destination."

Proud and happy was Martha made by this invitation, and gaily did she sally forth, when the cheerful meal was ended, for the rare pleasure of a *tête-à-tête* walk with the great man. Nothing could exceed Sir Matthew's good humour, he chatted, and joked, and talked of taking them all on a trip to Paris, and in short was hardly silent for a single moment. But amidst all this communicative confidential gossip, he never said a word more concerning the business they were upon.

Once or twice Martha began to say something intended to preface an inquiry as to the local destination of Michael, but some lively sally from her father always turned the conversation into another channel, till at length they entered the gloomy region of Hoxley-lane; after which, neither of them spoke again till Martha said—"This is the house, papa.—But I believe we had better go in the back way. Shall I step in first and say that you are coming?"

"No, no, my dear, there is no occasion to be so ceremonious, we will go in together."

Martha then lifted the latch, and they did go in together, causing the sick woman to start as if she had seen a spectre. It was nearly three years since Mrs Armstrong had last found herself in the overpowering presence of Sir Matthew Dowling; and the belief that this visit was for the express purpose of receiving her thanks, increased the embarrassment so startling a condescension was calculated to produce.

Martha saw her colour change from pale to red, and then to pale again, and gently approaching her, said, "Mrs Armstrong, my father, Sir Matthew Dowling, is come himself to talk with you about little Michael."

"It is very—condescending, miss," murmured the poor woman, "and I'm very grateful for this, and all favours."

"Very good, very good," said the knight, in return—not, however, looking very steadily in her face. "This young lady, who I suppose you know is Miss Martha Dowling, my daughter, paid you a visit yesterday I believe, and spoke to you, did she not, about your little boy?"

"Yes, sir," was the concise reply.

"And you approved, she tells me, of his being put to a good trade."

"In course, sir, I can't but approve, and be thankful for his being put in the way to help himself, and his poor crippled brother, too, when I am gone—but—I hope no offence, sir, I'd be right glad to know your honour's pleasure as to the place where he is to be."

"And that is a little more than I can tell you, my good woman," replied Sir Matthew, in a friendly familiar tone. "I can tell you where his master that is to be, lives. That," he continued, drawing the indentures out of his pocket, "that we shall find written down here—But he is one of the first in his line, and a capital trade it is, I promise you, so that he has got work-shops, I believe, in half-a-dozen places. However, I'll make it my business to learn whereabouts Michael is to be, and let you know."

As he said this, Sir Matthew opened the instrument and busied himself in unscrewing the top of his neat little portable ink-bottle.

"Then if it is all the same to you sir," replied the widow Armstrong, in rather an unsteady voice, "I should like well to know where it would be, before I put my hand to the binding him."

Martha looked up, more than half afraid that such cautious acceptance of the important service offered, might offend her hot-tempered father; but equally to her surprise and satisfaction she perceived that his countenance instead of expressing any thing of the kind, wore a look of more than usual good-humour, as he replied, beginning at the same time to replace the red tape round the papers. "That shall be just as it pleases you, my good woman, we won't say any thing more about it, just yet." Then turning to Martha, he said, in a sort of half-whisper. "I can't stay now, Martha, we must go, dear, because I expect to find some one waiting for me at home. But we must not deceive the poor dear woman either. She ought to know, Martha that this is a chance I may not have again, God knows when, if ever. Can't you explain to her, my dear, that this is a sort of thing that by no means happens every day. Sometime ago I had an opportunity of doing this gentleman a good turn about one of his principal hands for whom he was greatly interested—for he is like a father to them all, and he promised then to return it whenever I had any thing of the same sort at heart. So now, I have written to him about this boy, and he has answered me as kind as possible; only he tells me that he has got such quantities of applications from the people round him, that when he has a vacancy among the bound hands, he can't keep it open, and that he must have yes or no at once. I am afraid, therefore, that we must give it up, my dear."

This was "soft soder," as the inimitable Slick calls it; and the poor doubting, trembling, helpless bit of human nature, lying on the bed from whence she knew full well she should never rise, did not listen to it unmoved. She felt, as he intended she should, her heavy responsibility, and looked up into the face of Martha in a manner that very speakingly asked for counsel.

The good girl understood the appeal, and frankly answered it. "You hear what my father says, Mrs Armstrong," said she, leaning over the poor invalid.

"Yes, miss, I do," replied the anxious woman, "and, God help me!—I feel as weak and ignorant as a baby about what I ought to say in return."

"I don't know how that can be," said the innocent Martha a little reproachfully. "You know exactly how the case stands, and must certainly be able to judge what you think it right to do under these circumstances."

"I hope excuse, miss, if I seem over mothersome and foolish about him," replied the poor widow in a deprecating tone, "but he's a precious boy to me, and the binding him, comes upon me unawares like."

"Well then, there's nothing more to be said, I think," said Martha withdrawing herself from the bed. "It seems a matter of feeling, papa; and I don't think we ought to battle against it, for it is very likely she would be unhappy if we persuaded her, let it turn out as it would."

Instead of answering, Sir Matthew suddenly wheeled round, and looked out of the window, as if the bit of stony mould extending ten feet deep to the ditch that fenced it, contained something of peculiar interest and curiosity. During this interval, which lasted about a minute, the widow Armstrong again fixed her eyes upon the face of Martha, with an appealing look that seemed to implore assistance from her judgment, while it evidently expressed confidence in her kindness. When Sir Matthew again permitted his countenance to be visible to them, it expressed nothing but indifference; but Martha thought it was such an easy good-natured sort of indifference that there could be no danger in bringing him back to the subject, even though he said as he turned round, "Come, my dear Martha, I cannot stay another moment, I do assure you."

"I am quite ready, papa," she replied; "but don't you think it is almost a pity to let such an opportunity be lost for poor Michael?"

"Certainly it is, my dear," he replied in the most good-humoured accent imaginable. "But what would you have me do, my dear child? Depend upon it there is no real charity in assisting people against their will or in a manner in any way contrary to their inclinations. You know perfectly well, that it was my real and sincere wish that this good woman's child should be well provided for. An opportunity for doing this, better far than I could have hoped for, is now proposed but evidently does not meet her wishes. Unfortunately I must send the answer by to-day's post, and surely you would not recommend me to accept this situation for the boy, excellent as it is, against his mother's will?"

"No papa—only it seems to me that Mrs Armstrong has not quite made up her mind about it; and I thought perhaps that a few minutes' consideration might enable her to perceive how great a loss it would be to Michael were she to refuse it."

"Well, Martha!" returned the knight with a sort of jocose sigh, and at the same time seating himself on one of the widow's treasured rush-bottomed chairs, "I would rather make the person I expect wait at Dowling Lodge for an hour, than either disappoint your kind heart, or hurry this good woman into saying any thing that she does not really mean. What does the little fellow himself say about it?"

"He's grateful and thankful, sir, for what is offered to him, and willing he is to accept it.—'Tis only my poor weak sick heart that has got no courage left in it. You think, miss, he had better take it?" she added, turning her anxious eyes upon Martha.

For a moment Martha felt a repugnance to the taking upon herself, as it were, the responsibility of the transaction, but an exclamation from her father settled the business at once.

"Poor soul!" said he. "How natural is this weakness! Give her, by your advice, the strength she wants, Martha—it is the most valuable gift you can bestow!"

"Indeed papa is very right, Mrs Armstrong," said Martha cheerfully. "Michael will never forgive me if I let you throw away this golden opportunity."

"And I am sure I should never forgive myself if I threw away for him any thing that you could call so, my dear young lady,—I know full well all you have done for him, and been to him, and to doubt your judgment, would be a sin indeed. So if you please, miss, I am quite ready to sign."

Had Sir Matthew Dowling wanted any strengthening of the motives which actuated the deed he was about to perpetrate, he would have found it in this speech. The phrase, "I know what you have been to him," requiring no very forced interpretation, in order to suggest to him that it was probable she knew what he had been to him also. However, he felt no inclination to disturb the business which was proceeding so satisfactorily, and therefore again smiled very kindly as he said, "I am sure nobody can find fault with your conduct in this business, Mrs Armstrong. It has been exactly what it ought to be, and the better I think of you, the more anxious I feel to ensure this excellent situation for your boy. But stay a moment, I came down here in such a hurry, that I forgot the necessity of having a witness. Wait here for a moment,

Martha, and I dare say I shall find some of Mrs Armstrong's neighbours who may not only be able to witness these indentures, but also to give her their opinion upon the advantage of them."

So saying the knight arose, and walked out of the room; but, before an anxious inquiry from the poor woman about the possibility of writing to her boy could be answered by Martha, he returned again, followed by Parsons and another overlooker from one of his own factories, whom he found *accidentally* close to the premises.

"Here is a bit of good luck for us, Martha," said Sir Matthew, as he entered, "I should have been sadly put to it for time, if I had had to run about till I could find a man who knew how to write his name. I have asked two fellows already, but they both said, 'No.'—There is one comfort for you, at any rate, Mrs Armstrong, your boy will never be in such a state of ignorance as that."

Sir Matthew as he spoke, again untied the paper, and dipping a pen which had been stuck within his coat sleeve into the ink-bottle, he gave both pen and paper into the hands of Martha, saying, "There dear, you will hold it for her better than I shall—only make haste!—I hate to break an appointment."

Martha received the paper, and without a moment's delay, laid it before the pale and trembling woman, placing at the same time the pen in her right hand, and indicating with her own finger the place, to which Sir Matthew had pointed, as that where her signature should be.

The poor woman received both submissively; and after a moment's pause, looked up once more into the face of Martha who was bending over her. A kind and encouraging smile sat upon her plain but expressive features, and without further hesitation, the widow Armstrong signed her name.

"Here Parsons, sign away!" said Sir Matthew gaily, as he withdrew the document from the bed. The ready servant obeyed, and his fellow-driver followed his example, without waiting for any further instructions.

"Now then, Martha, let us be off!" cried the knight, moving towards the door as he pocketed the papers. But stopping suddenly before he opened it he said, "By the way, Parsons, as chance has brought you here, we may as well make use of you about getting a few necessaries for our little stocking-weaver. We must trust to you to get whatever may be wanted. He may take the clothes he has worn at the Lodge, for Sundays, but of course they would not be suitable for him to work in."

"Very well, Sir Matthew, I will see about it," replied the important overlooker.

"I must have no time lost, if you please," rejoined his master rather sharply; "for Mr Elgood Sharpton mentioned in his letter, that he should be having some of his people passing this way who might take charge of him, and I am sure I can't say when they may happen to come. So go directly into the town, Parsons, and buy whatever you think the boy may want, I dare say this will be very nearly the last expense, Mrs Armstrong," he added, "that I shall be put to for him and I assure you that I shall pay it very willingly."

With these words he left the room, and Martha pronouncing a shy but kind farewell, followed him. Soon after she had overtaken him and again passed her arm through his, she was startled by a violent burst of laughter, and on looking back, perceived at no great distance behind them, Parsons and his companion, making their way over a style that led by a short cut to Brookford factory. It was from them the hearty laugh had proceeded.

XVI

Miss Brotherton visits the widow Armstrong, and lays the foundation of a very lasting friendship—She then calls at Dowling Lodge, but fails of obtaining what she went for

AS SOON AS MISS BROTHERTON and Mrs Tremlett had finished their breakfast on the morning after the interview with Sophy Drake in the drawing-room at Milford Park, they set off together on foot to visit the widow Armstrong in Hoxley-lane.

"Nothing can happen to us worse than our adventure in the carriage the day before yesterday," observed the young lady; "you will confess, dear friend, will you not, that Sir Matthew's walking into the carriage was more terrible than any thing likely to befall us on the high-road without one?"

"Why, I suppose I must, my dear," answered the old lady; "for to tell you the truth, I don't think you could look more put out if a constable were to come up and arrest you."

"Decidedly not, Mrs Tremlett; and listen to the birds, and sniff the sweet air, and then tell me if we are not wise to walk?"

The old woman confessed that she really did enjoy it, and on they went with the gardener's boy for a guide, till in less than an hour they found themselves before the door of No 12, in Hoxley-lane. Probably their little pioneer was not one of the widow's visiters, for the pass through the hedge, leading to the back-kitchen door appeared unknown to him, and in answer to Miss Brotherton's knock for admittance, the principal entrance to No 12 was opened by the ragged mistress of the tenement.

"Does the widow Armstrong live here?" inquired Mary. "Yes, ma'am," observed the woman gloomily, continuing as she made way for the ladies to enter, "The widow Armstrong is a lucky woman—she has got but one child left to provide for, and yet the gent keeps coming to help her, but nobody thinks of me and my ten young ones."

The ready hand of Miss Brotherton was immediately in her purse. "That is a large family indeed, my good woman. Are they none of them old enough to help themselves?"

"The seven oldest have all been in the factory from a'most the time they could.stand, ma'am," replied Mrs Sykes, "and if they hadn't they must have been dead and buried long ago for want of bread. But though they have worked poor creturs, early and late, there's no more come of it, than that their bones be here instead of in the churchyard."

"But with so large a number, all receiving wages," said Miss Brotherton, gently, "I should have hoped that you might have found yourselves better off than you seem to be."

"And that's what we are told, ma'am, from year's end to year's end, and we must bear it, for there is no help. But 'tis a'most as bitter as the work that grinds us."

Neither the person or manner of Mrs Sykes were in any degree prepossessing; she was dirty, and in every way untidy in the extreme. She had on her feet the fragments of a pair of men's shoes, but no stockings, the rest of her clothing being barely sufficient to cover her. Her eye, voice, and complexion, furnished strong indications of her being accustomed to take spirits, while her frightfully thin limbs gave her the appearance of being half starved. In short, it was impossible to look at her without feeling that she was a degraded, as well as a suffering being. Mary Brotherton did feel this, and her heart sunk within her as she thought of Sophy Drake, of her drunken father, and of all Mrs Tremlett had told her respecting the vice, which like a wide-spreading and hideous epidemic, seemed to ravage in all directions the miserable neighbourhood in which fate had placed her. She shuddered as she contemplated the wretched being that stood before her, and till she had spoken the words given above, a deep feeling of the woman's unworthiness chilled the ready pity of her warm young heart. But both in these words themselves, and in the tone of quiet settle despair in which they were spoken, there was a frightful and mysterious allusion to some species of injustice and cruelty, under which accusation she seemed herself to be included.

The distaste and reprobation that were a moment before making hasty inroads upon her benevolence, seemed suddenly arrested as she listened; and she was about to repeat again the questions she had already so uselessly asked, as to whence this universal severity of judgment against the factory labourers arose; and wherefore, beyond all others, submitted to the sentence which dooms human beings to toil, these people should appear to loath their employment, and execrate as it should seem, the very means by which they lived. But ere her lips opened to demand the explanation to which she so eagerly desired to listen, a glance at the hard features of the wretched woman checked her. "It cannot be from such as these," thought she, "that truth and instruction can be reasonably looked for"—and as she silently gave her alms, and moved onwards towards the door which had been pointed to, as that of the widow Armstrong, something like a systematic project for making herself mistress of the knowledge she wanted, for the first time suggested itself to her imagination.

Mrs Sykes eyed the silver largesse, as it fell into her hand, with a glance that seemed to devour it, and the words of thanks she uttered were almost hysterical in their eager vehemence. After delaying a moment for the contemplation of this precious "drudge 'twixt man and man," she opened the door of communication and Miss Brotherton and her friend passed into the dwelling-room of the widow Armstrong.

Contrary to custom, her lame boy, Edward, was sitting on the side of her bed, and when Mary entered, he was holding her hand, and gazing in her face with an expression of countenance which appeared to both the intruders to be the most piteous they had ever looked upon. The poor child was looking, too, most wretchedly ill, and the first idea which suggested itself was, that he felt himself to be dying.

Notwithstanding the extreme poverty of the widow Armstrong, there was an air of decency and decorum about her that might in any situation have commanded respect; but when contrasted with the appearance of her neighbour, seemed to indicate a claim to more observance than her visiters were showing by this sudden and uninvited entrance.

"I beg your pardon, Mrs Armstrong" said Mary, gently, "for breaking in upon you so abruptly; and I fear our doing so may have startled your sick child.—This little fellow is very ill, I fear."

"It is long since he has known health ma'am," replied the widow; "but is not that which makes him look so white and trembling now. We have lost what was dearer to us both than all the world beside—and though I don't think as this one will ever look up again, I can't find a word in my heart to comfort him!"

"What, then, has happened to you?" said Mary, with much interest—"Nothing bad to your son Michael, I hope?"

"You know Michael, ma'am?" said the poor woman, anxiously.

"I have seen him at Sir Matthew Dowling's," she replied.

"I wish you never had, ma'am!" rejoined the widow, bitterly—"We were only starving before, but now we are worse than that."

"Do explain to me what you mean, Mrs Armstrong," said Mary.

"I ought to do it, ma'am, for you speak kindly; and that's a claim poor folks can seldom withstand.—But how can I tell you the matter, ma'am? I know nothing—and that's the reason why poor Edward and I are so miserable."

"But that is a bad way to get into, my good Mrs Armstrong," said Mary, cheerfully. "Don't fret yourself about fancied evils, which perhaps do not exist. Little Edward here should know better than that."

The pale, brokenhearted boy looked at her with black eyes, but said nothing.

"Are you uneasy because Michael has not been down to see you lately?" resumed Miss Brotherton.

"He never failed to come, ma'am, till he was carried away from us!" replied the widow, with a sob, that seemed the result of strength exhausted, and weakness that could struggle no longer.

"Carried away from you!" cried Mary, changing colour. "What do you mean, Mrs Armstrong? who has carried away Michael from you?"

"Sir Matthew Dowling, ma'am, has had him taken away," and another sob followed the words.

"Do not think I torment you thus from idle curiosity," pursued Mary, bending over her; "but I entreat you to explain to me fully what you mean. I am greatly interested for your little boy."

"I thank you for it, ma'am," returned the poor mother, mournfully; "but I can tell little that you, or any grand lady, the friend of Sir Matthew, would think to the purpose. Yet the parting with him without one blessing, or one kiss, is hard to bear, though we don't justly know that any harm's to come to him."

"I am no particular friend of Sir Matthew Dowling's," replied Mary, with an accent which perhaps spoke more than her words.

"Then I will tell you about Michael!" exclaimed the lame boy, coming round the bed to the place where she was standing, and looking into her face as if he thought he could read all her thoughts there. "You have seen poor Mike when he was living there, ma'am?"

"Yes, I have, my dear boy," she replied, gazing with deep feeling at his pale, but beautiful countenance; "I have seen him there more than once, Edward, and I am quite sure he was not happy, though he was dressed so fine."

"He was more unhappy ten times over," replied Edward, "than when he was as ragged as me."

"Was he unkindly treated?" demanded Mary.

"He was beaten, kicked, and spit upon!" cried Edward, bursting into tears; "and then he was told to laugh, and look merry."

"A wretched, wretched, sort of cruelty!" she replied, "of which I can well believe Sir Matthew capable. But you surely do not suppose that he has run away from it without telling you or his mother that he had such an intention?"

"If you knew Mike better, ma'am, you wouldn't think that he could do such wickedness," said the mother. "He has stood beating with strap and stick for years, ma'am, young as he is; and never asked to stop from the mill a day, though he has been bruised almost to a jelly;—and worse than that, too, poor lamb! a hundred fold, with such a heart as his, he has seen his lame brother there, that was always dearer, a great deal, to him than himself—he has seen the cruel stripes fall on his poor shoulders too; and though he has come home with his little face warmed with tears from it, he didn't think of running away."

Mary saw that she had given pain, and hastened to atone for it by expressing her sorrow for supposing such a thing possible; and then repeated her request, that she might be told what it was that had happened.

The widow then related more succinctly than might have been expected, all that had passed between herself, her boy, and Miss Martha Dowling on the morning which followed the theatrical representation at Dowling Lodge. And before she proceeded further, Edward bore testimony to the spirited and courageous willingness with which his brother had adopted the proposed scheme. He had, it seemed, as usual, watched Teddy's return from the factory—told him what Sir Matthew proposed doing for him, and declared, that hard as it would be to part with him and "mother," he was ready and willing to start and was quite determined to be the best boy that ever was 'prenticed, and to be workman enough to maintain them both as soon as his time was out.

Here the widow again resumed her narrative, and related very accurately the scene of the following morning; dwelling much on the young lady's kind manner, and on her own putting it to her whether she advised that the child should go, or not.

"And Martha Dowling counselled you to let him go?" demanded Miss Brotherton.

"Yes, again and again, she did," replied the poor mother.

"You quite sure it was Miss Martha?"

"Oh, yes! ma'am; my Mike took care to make me understand that, the day they came together."

"Then be quite easy in your mind, Mrs Armstrong," said Mary, eagerly. "I have no great liking for Sir Matthew Dowling. I do not think well of him, nor have I much to say in favour of any of his family. They seem to me to be cold-hearted, selfish people. But for this one, this Miss Martha that you speak of, I will undertake to answer for it that she has never deceived you, and that if she advised you to let Michael go, it was because she thought the doing so would be advantageous for him."

"Bless you for ever and for ever, ma'am!" cried Mrs Armstrong, seizing the hand of Mary, and pressing it to her lips. "There is truth, ma'am, in your voice, and in your eyes. Do as I do, Edward, dear! look at the kind face of this young lady, and see if you can't find comfort from what she says? I did think, myself, ignorant as I am, that the young lady had an honest face. But, oh! ma'am, let it be as it will, and make the very best of it, 'tis cruel to have our darling taken away in this fashion, without one word of take-leave and blessing!"

"Indeed it is!" replied Mary; "and your being ignorant of the place of his destination increases this anxiety. But on this point, at least, I think I shall be able to set your mind at rest. Before this time to-morrow, I will take care to see some part of the family at the Lodge, and shall certainly not scruple to inquire every particular respecting your boy. Keep up your spirits therefore, both of you; and for the future, let this little fellow here look to me for his wages. I won't have him go to the factory any more. What sum has he been receiving for his work?"

Astonishment very literally rendered the widow Armstrong dumb, on hearing this most extraordinary proposal. Poor soul! a few short days ago it would have been sufficient to make her forget her weakness and her want, and have put her in a state of mind that queens might envy; for she would hardly have been able to remember that it was possible to have another wish; but now the first use she made on recovering her speech, was to exclaim, "Oh! Michael! Michael! why beant you by to hear this?"

"He shall hear it, Mrs Armstrong," said Mary, in a voice of such cheerful confidence, that the terrors of both mother and son seemed to vanish before it. Mrs Tremlett, too, ventured to add an encouraging commentary upon Mary's promised visit of inquiry at the Lodge, observing, that it was altogether out of probability that they should want to make any mystery as to where the little fellow was gone.

Mrs Armstrong, as she listened, seemed almost too happy to credit the evidence of her own senses; but in the deep-set melancholy eye of Edward, there was still an expression of suffering and of fear that looked as if misery had taken a hold upon him that could not be relinquished.

"Now I must go!" said the young lady, rising, "or I shall hardly have time to keep my promise. But I must settle with you first, my dear boy. What was the amount of your wages by the month?"

"Six shillings, ma'am," replied Edward, looking at her, as she drew out her purse, with an eye that seemed to doubt what it beheld. "Six shillings!" cried Miss Brotherton, as she put the pitiful wages of a long month's agony into the little trembling hand. "And have you lost your health and liberty for this?" Tears started to her eyes, as she contemplated the look of wonder and delight expressed by the countenance of the poor widow; yet that look was not turned upon her. Stretching out her arms to the boy, she caught him to her bosom, and held him there, much as if she had suddenly beheld him snatched from the fangs of some devouring monster. The face of the child himself, she could not see, but his whole frame trembled, and they fancied he was shedding tears.

"God bless you both!" she said, "to-morrow you shall see me again." And so saying she took the arm of her friend, and again through the dwelling-room of Mrs Sykes. The woman had now three little dirty creatures round her, to whom she was giving bread.

"Heaven keep you, ma'am! This is your treat!" she said, as Mary and her friend passed through, "It is the first time for many a week that I have fed 'em so freely, poor creturs."

Miss Brotherton's heart was too full to answer—she nodded her head and passed on. Their homeward walk, up Hoxley-lane, across the London road, and along a pretty shaded bridle-road that led to a gate in her own park-paling, was performed almost entirely in silence. There is a state of mind in which ideas come with too much violence and rapidity to be told off in words. When this happens from an excess of happy imaginings, no condition can be more delightful: but when, as in the present case, it arises from the remembrance of painful realities, it is greatly the reverse. The misery around her was no longer a matter of doubtful speculation, but of most frightful certainty. Neither was it any vice in little Edward Armstrong, which drove him to offer up his sickly suffering frame to ceaseless labour at the rate of threepence for each long, painful day. She felt oppressed, overwhelmed and almost helpless. Yet at that time Mary Brotherton knew not, guessed not, dreamed not, of the hundredth part of what the unhapppy class who had thus roused her human sympathies, were daily and hourly suffering around her.

The first words she spoke on entering her house were to order her carriage and having gone so far in the performance of the task she had undertaken, she turned with tender kindness to her old friend, and gave as much care to her comfort and refreshment, as if the relative situation which they had borne to each other in days of yore was just reversed, and that Mary was the nurse, and Mrs Tremlett the nursling.

"You shall do nothing more before dinner, my dear good soul, but lie down upon the sofa, and get cool. Not even Mrs Gabberly, I suppose, could see any thing particularly dangerous and improper, in my going alone to pay a visit to Martha Dowling."

And alone to Dowling Lodge the heiress went, pretty steadfastly determined not to leave it, till she had learnt exactly at what point of the earth's surface Michael Armstrong might be found.

She inquired for Martha, and was shown as usual into my lady's morning drawing-room, where to her extreme annoyance she found her ladyship, Sir Matthew, Lady Clarissa Shrimpton, and Miss Mogg.

If Lady Dowling could have been glad to see any pretty young lady, it would have been Miss Brotherton, and she did exert herself, more than usual, to be civil; while, on the contrary, Sir Matthew both felt and evinced considerably less satisfaction at the sight of her, than he had ever done since the fact of her heiress-ship had become matter of unquestionable notoriety to the whole neighbourhood. But if his reception was cold, that of Lady Clarissa was warm, for she actually threw her arms round the young lady, reproaching her at the same time very tenderly for not having sent to say she was going to drive to Dowling Lodge. "I should have liked your carriage, my dear, so much better than my broiling little phaeton!"

It was hardly possible at that moment, that either one of the four persons present could have said any thing to her sufficiently interesting to fully awaken her sense of hearing; unless, indeed, Sir Matthew had led the conversation to Michael Armstrong. But this he did not do; and, therefore, having endured Lady Clarissa's embrace, and answered her mechanically, she knew not what, Miss Brotherton walked up to the sofa where the lady of the mansion as usual sat enthroned, and said, "Will you be so good, ma'am, as to let Miss Martha be told that I am come to call upon her?"

The surprised eyebrows with which her ladyship listened to this speech would, probably, under other circumstances, have given birth to an exceedingly comical caricature, but at this moment Mary Brotherton had no fun in her thoughts, and not immediately receiving an answer, she said, loud enough for Sir Matthew to hear, "Will you give me leave to ring the bell, and ask for the pleasure of seeing Miss Martha?"

Lady Dowling still remained silently staring at her; but not so Sir Matthew. He reached the bell almost as soon as the young lady herself, and fully persuaded that this most unaccountable request could only proceed from some little manœuvriug project at that moment labouring in the fair Brotherton's head, which had, somehow or other, his son Augustus for its object, his countenance resumed all its former affectionate urbanity towards her, and taking her hand too suddenly for any contrivance to prevent it, he said—"Martha?... Do you want to see Martha, my dear?—To be sure you shall. She is a Dowling, Miss Brotherton, though not quite like the rest of us. But where is the Dowling, young or old, male or female, who would not fly from the farthest corner of the world to see you?"

"I only want to see Miss Martha just now, sir," replied Mary, half smiling.

"And Martha you shall see, my dear, without a moment's delay. Desire Miss Martha Dowling to come here instantly!" he continued, as the door opened and a servant appeared at it—adding, when the door closed again, "You do her an honour, my dear Miss Brotherton, in thus asking for her, that more than one of her family, perhaps, might feel inclined to envy." But as Miss Brotherton made no answer at all, and Lady Clarissa began to hem, and fidget, and walk towards the window, all which the observant knight well knew were pretty lures, meant to recal him, he contented himself with gallantly drawing forward an arm-chair for the heiress, at no great distance from Lady Dowling, and then strode across the apartment to sooth the irritation of his noble friend.

Martha never suffered a summons from her father to remain a moment unanswered. The message had been delivered, to her in his name, and she entered almost immediately. Miss Brotherton, who was in no humour to make small talk for her ladyship, instantly rose, and went forward to meet her. "I took the liberty of sending for you, my dear Miss Martha," she said, "to request you would let me speak to you alone, for five minutes.—Will you take a parasol, and let us walk into the shrubbery together?"

Martha, who certainly liked Miss Brotherton, notwithstanding the late painful scene, produced by her indiscretion, and who, moreover, at this moment joyfully recollected how charming an anecdote she had now to relate concerning her father, acquiesced in this proposal with a ready smile, and saying that her parasol was always in the hall, the two young ladies left the room together.

No sooner did she find herself beneath the sheltering trees of the extensive shrubbery, and ascertained, by looking round, that they were really alone, than Miss Brotherton, passing her arm through that of her companion, said, "My dear Miss Martha, I cannot help feeling great interest in the welfare of the little boy whom we saw performing the other night—little Michael Armstrong, I mean. Will you have the kindness to tell me where he is now?"

Instead of giving a direct answer, Martha eagerly exclaimed, "I am so glad, Miss Brotherton, that you asked to see me, for I have quite longed to tell you all particulars about that little fellow—and all that papa has been doing for him. I do assure you, Miss Brotherton, that notwithstanding what you saw the other night, papa has been, and still is, most excessively kind to him. Only he was very troublesome about the acting, and papa's temper is hasty. *That,* as you must be aware, Miss Brotherton, is the case with many people; but there are very few who have courage and candour to own it, as my father does. In justice to him, I must tell you what happened the morning after the unfortunate play. My father sent for me, and said, that he was perfectly miserable in his mind on account of the anger he had shown towards Michael. He told me, as frankly as possible, that he had beat him, and that in consequence of this, the boy was evidently so afraid of him that he had no enjoyment when in his presence. And he went on to say that such being the case, he was determined to apprentice the child to a good trade, where he might learn to maintain himself comfortably, and assist his family besides. So you see, Miss Brotherton," concluded Martha, in an eager voice, and with heightened colour, "you see that if papa loses his temper, he knows how to atone for it."

Miss Brotherton listened to this statement with the most unbroken attention; and had she not been previously aware of the kind and excellent nature of Martha Dowling, she would have become so then. Her hopes too, that all was fair and right concerning the disposal of the little boy, were strengthened; and in full confidence of receiving a satisfactory answer, she said, "I am very much obliged to you, Martha, for telling me all this, because I truly feel an interest in the little fellow. And now I hope you will tell me also to what part of the country he has been sent."

"I would tell you in a moment, if I knew, my dear Miss Brotherton, but I do not. His departure at last was very sudden; owing, I believe, to papa's having found some particularly good opportunity of sending him."

"I wonder you should never have asked where he was sent to, Miss Martha," said Mary, gravely.

"I did ask, Miss Brotherton," replied Martha; "but papa said he could not recollect the name of the place."

Mary changed colour, as she remembered the promise she had given to the child's mother; but after a moment's reflection, said, "Perhaps he may have recollected it, since, my dear—I wish you would run and ask him to come to me for a moment."

Martha seemed to hesitate. "I am sure," said she, after a hesitation, "that papa would be delighted to come here to talk to you, Miss Brotherton—only Lady Clarissa might—"

"Nay, then, I'll go to him myself," said Mary, rather abruptly. "There is no particular objection, I suppose, to Lady Clarissa's being let into the secret of little Michael's abode." And immediately turning her steps towards the house, she re-entered the drawing-room, followed by Martha.

They found Sir Matthew engaged in exhibiting a portfolio of splendid engravings to her ladyship, who was descanting upon them in rapture; though the application of a near-sighted glass to her long-sighted eye, while the other was effectually closed, rendered them pretty nearly invisible to her.

"I beg ten thousand pardons, Sir Matthew," said the heiress, placing herself at the opposite side of the loo-table, and thereby commanding a perfect view of his countenance; "but you are too goodnatured, I am sure, to be angry with me, even though I do interrupt you. Will you have the kindness to tell me, sir, while Lady Clarissa is lost in admiration of that enchanting Venus, where little Michael Armstrong has been sent to?"

The question was too unexpected for even Sir Matthew's sturdy self-possession, to receive it as he would have wished to do. His bold eye, which had been gaily fixed on the young lady, as she spoke to him, fell before her keen, inquiring glance, and he turned the page of Lady Clarissa's adoration with rather unseemly rapidity, as he replied, "To a tradesman—that is, to a manufacturer, some miles further north, Miss Brotherton. I have just been telling Lady Clarissa," continued the knight, recovering his audacity, "I have just been telling her all the little fellow's adventures. The love of novelty seemed to have superseded all other love in his young heart, for he was delighted to go."

"But he could not have liked going without taking leave of his mother and brother, Sir Matthew. I have just seen them, and they are in a perfect agony about him—in fact, I am come here on purpose to ask where he has been sent."

"Fairest of messengers!" exclaimed the knight, with a tender smile, "how utterly miserable shall I be if I cannot answer you!—I think it is to Halifax, I am almost sure that it is either to Halifax or Wakefield that he is gone."

"You have bound the little fellow apprentice, you do not know where?" said Miss Brotherton, with undisguised astonishment.

"I do not say that, my dear young lady, I know he is apprenticed to an excellent good man, who is a stocking-weaver; but he has two or three large concerns belonging to him, and I protest to you that at this moment I really cannot say to which this little fellow has been sent."

"I am quite shocked to give you so much trouble, Sir Matthew," returned Mary, "but I should be exceedingly obliged if you would learn the name of the place, and let me know it. I ventured, sir, to promise the boy's mother that I would learn this for her, and I am quite sure that you will not let me disappoint her."

"Most assuredly not! I will call or send to-morrow at the latest, my charming Miss Brotherton! How I adore your benevolence! No wonder you are such friends, Lady Clarissa! Your hearts are made upon the same model!"

To this satisfactory assurance Miss Brotherton made no answer; but telling Sir Matthew that she should remain at home on the morrow for the purpose of receiving his promised information, took her leave.

With increased dislike of Sir Matthew, perhaps, yet with no very serious fears about the fate of little Michael, Miss Brotherton boldly determined to brave all the wonder which the act might occasion, and ordered her carriage to stop at No 12, Hoxley-lane, Ashleigh.

As it happened, however, she escaped all her military admirers, and reached the widow Armstrong without interruption; the absorbing mills were in full activity, and few of the inhabitants of the miserable region through which she passed were left to gaze on the unwonted spectacle. The answer she brought was received by the widow and her boy with breathless attention; but it was quite evident that it did not altogether remove the sort of vague terror which seemed to have taken hold of them. Mary's cheerful assurance, however, that she should soon bring them more satisfactory intelligence, could not be listened to without good effect; and she left them at last so infinitely happier than she had found them, that spite of Sir Matthew's unsatisfactory reply, and more unsatisfactory manner, she still blessed her morning's work.

XVII

A journey, begun in very good style, but ending not quite so well—A faithful description of a valley in Derbyshire— Michael makes some new acquaintance

AND WHERE WAS LITTLE MICHAEL? The indentures, when duly signed and executed, did not remain two hours in Sir Matthew Dowling's possession before he began to put in action the power they gave him. Mr Joseph Parsons perfectly understood the nature of the *"few necessaries"* which he was commanded to procure for the young stocking-weaver; and accordingly, by the time Sir Matthew had taken leave of Martha in the hall, after their walk back from Hoxley-lane, his confidential agent was ready to attend him in his study.

"Now, Mr Parsons, I flatter myself that you will allow I have managed this business tolerably well. My excellent friend, Elgood Sharpton, will owe me a good turn—for, thanks to the meddling of old Sir Robert, 'prentice-boys are not so easily got as they used to be—and you and I, Mr Parsons, have got rid of a most infernal spy. Now then, to business. How soon can you set off with him?"

"As soon as a horse can be harnessed to the jockey-cart, Sir Matthew."

"The jockey-cart!—the devil! What a fool you are, Parsons! Have you really no more wit in you than to propose setting off, willy-nilly, with this young cur, that yelped at the rate he did the other night, before all the fine folks in the county, in an open jockey-cart? Fie, Mr Parsons, fie!—I really had a better opinion of your understanding."

"I thought he was going to set off, at any rate, by his own free will, Sir Matthew," replied the superintendent, "and I knew when we got among the moors, it wouldn't much matter to me, if he did sing out."

"You are an excellent fellow, Parsons—true to the backbone, and as firm as a rock—but don't you ever undertake to carry through such a pretty little kidnapping scheme as this, where every thing is to be done according to law, unless you have got the help of a little such stuff as this," and the knight touched his own forehead expressively as he spoke.

"There's few men as wouldn't be the better for a little of that, Sir Matthew," returned the judicious Parsons with a submissive nod, "but I'm ready and willing to do your bidding, be it what it may, and that's the best way of putting your honour's wit to profit."

"You are right there, my good fellow—one captain is always better than two. But, however, as to master Michael, Parsons, we must neither let him stay loitering here till his dainty mother has questioned all the gossips who will come to prate with her about her boy, and about all the nonsense current concerning Squire Elgood Sharpton's, of Thistledown House; nor yet must we carry him off at noonday in an open jockey-cart without permitting him to kiss mother and brother, and uncle and aunt, and the devil knows who beside, from one end of Ashleigh to the other,—all ready perhaps to tell him some amusing anecdotes concerning his future master."

"But what be the indentures good for, Sir Matthew," shrewdly inquired Mr Parsons, "if they don't give you power over the chap, let him hear what he will?"

"Fair and softly, Mr Parsons—there is a when and a where in all things. It has cost me some pounds, and a d—d deal of trouble to get up a cry hereabouts concerning my goodness and charity to these Armstrongs. Once get the boy off, and you and I between us, can make folks talk as loud of the great preferment he is come to, as mother Armstrong can about her doubts and alarms. There is no fear of that—I have more than one friend who will swear a thing or two for me. But once get up a screaming bout at the widow's, and a struggling scene in taking off the young gentleman, and we never shall hear the last of it. So, if you please, Mr Parsons, we will just get the young gentleman to take a ride before he is an hour older. But not in a jockey-cart though. I believe you know the road and the baiting-place?—By Jove! Parsons, now I think of it, there would be no better joke than taking him in my own carriage for the first few miles, and letting you drive on, as far as Wood-End or there about, and wait till our coming. You know I have taken him out in the carriage lots of times, so he will think nothing of that—and I will have Crockley go with me to make the party agreeable. So off with you to Wood-End as fast as you can go. But it must be in the covered cart remember—and a trifle of cord must be in the way in case he gives trouble."

Within an hour from this time, Sir Matthew Dowling's carriage was proceeding at a dignified and leisurely pace along a cross-country road which led to a lane, which led to a moor, across which was a track which led by another lane to Mr Elgood Sharpton's factory in the desolate hollow, known by the name of "Deep Valley."

The party, as arranged by Sir Matthew, consisted of himself, his friend Dr Crockley, and Michael Armstrong. The little fellow had been repeatedly honoured by a seat in the same stately vehicle before, for the purpose of being shown off at various houses in the neighbourhood, and had a notion that he was now taken out, in order to hear the remainder of his great fortune announced. That this final proof of Sir Matthew's benevolence should have for its object the sending him far away from Dowling Lodge would have been, but for the dreaded parting with his mother and brother, a source of unmixed joy to the little apprentice; and, even with this drawback, the distant hopes of his young heart might have been read in the contented meditation of his eye, as he rode silently along in front of his jocose companions, who amused themselves the while in talking very mystically concerning him, and his very useful and judicious destination.

At length the carriage reached the point at which Sir Matthew intended his airing should terminate, and he looked out to reconnoitre the opening of a lane to the left where he expected to see the covered cart. Nor was he disappointed; a covered cart, with an excellent stout horse in it, was drawn up close to the bank to take advantage of the shade of a thick elm-tree that grew upon it. As the carriage approached, the occupant of the humbler vehicle peeped out, and Sir Matthew recognised the punctual Parsons.

"Pull the check-string, Crockley," said the knight, "We will get out here. That is, you may if you will, there is no occasion, I suppose, for me to trouble myself, is there?"

"Oh! dear no," replied Dr Crockley, cheerfully. "Here comes Parsons, good man and true. Get out master Michael. Jump, jump, and enjoy it, my fine fellow! Perhaps you won't have much time for jumping when you begin learning your trade."

Without thinking it needful to reply to what he did not very clearly understand, Michael did as he was bid, and sprang from the carriage to the ground. The well-known figure of Parsons greeted him as his feet touched the turf, and the next instant he felt his hand suddenly seized by him.

"Shall you want me, Mr Parsons?" said Dr Crockley, putting his head out of the carriage.

"Not at all, sir," replied the superintendent, leading Michael forward. "Then shut the carriage-door, John," said Sir Matthew, "and order the coachman to drive home."

"Please sir! Please sir!—" uttered the plaintive voice of Michael, as he turned his head, and attempted to disengage his hand. "Please sir, is Mr Parsons to take me away?"

"Yes, my boy, he is," replied the knight, loud enough for the footman to hear. "He is going to take you to your new master, and you may give my compliments to him, my dear, and tell him, that I have sent him a very good boy. Good bye!—Good bye!—Home!"

So ended the colloquy; the carriage turned round and drove off by the way it came, and Michael Armstrong was left alone with Mr Joseph Parsons. He need not, however, have held the little fellow's hand so tight, for there was no rebellion in his heart, nor any thought of escape in his head. He knew his companion too well to hope for any explanation from him respecting this sudden manner of sending him off, and child as he was, he had no inclination to weep before him; but, on the contrary, his young heart swelled with a proud determination to behave well, and to set about his new employment with a stout spirit. Nevertheless, when he arrived at the cart he paused for a moment, before he obeyed the orders of Parsons to "climb up," and ventured to say, "Please sir, beant I to see mother any more?"

"Climb up! I tell you," said the brute, clenching his fist at him, "and if you bother me with any more questions, I'll just give you this in your mouth to stop your jabbering."

Had Michael counted twenty years instead of ten, he could not more resolutely have screwed his spirit to endurance than he did as he now clambered up, and placed himself, as he was directed, in the back part of the vehicle, not another syllable passed his lips. For four hours the slow but sore-footed cart-horse, jogged on through a lane, that would have made any pace beyond a walk, intolerable. At the end of that time, the cart stopped before the door of a lonely public-house that formed a corner, round which the road turned off at nearly a right angle, and stretched across one of those wild and desolate moors which are, perhaps, only to be found in such perfection of dark and stoney ruggedness in Derbyshire. Michael, as he descended from the cart, looked out upon the unlimited expanse of dreariness, and shuddered: but his mind had not been sufficiently filled with the remembrance of brighter objects, to give the scene as full effect upon him, as it might have produced on others.

The "Mucklestone Moor," haunted by the black dwarf; was a pleasant spot compared to it; for there the barren heath was only strewed with fragments of stones around one certain spot whence rose, doubtless with some pretence to picturesque dignity, "a huge column of unhewn granite." But on the Ridgetop Moor of Derbyshire, no object reared itself above the rest, either to attract or relieve the eye. As far as sight could reach, the wild heath was encumbered with a crowded layer of large and shapeless gray stones, defying the air of heaven to nourish vegetation among them, and making any effort of man to remove the congregated mass, desperate and unavailing. Arid, rugged, desolate, was the desert that spread around; and to those who knew the nature of the operations carrying on in every direction near it, no great stretch of imagination would have been necessary to suggest the idea of fitness, and sympathy between the district, and the most influential portion of its population. This is, indeed, a fitness that seems often found. Where towering mountains scale the heavens the hardy natives show a spirit pure and clear as the sweet air by which they live. In the rich valleys of the East the lazy peasant eats his rice, purchased with easy labour, and is content to dream away his being in the sultry shade. And in the flinty region of our northern moors, the race of Millocrats batten, and grow fat, as if they were conscious of, and rejoiced in the local sympathy.

A stunted elderly lad of all work, came forth on hearing the rumbling of the wheels. "Ask the dame if she has got two beds in one room!" said Mr Parsons, descending from the driving-seat, of which he had had quite as much as he desired. The message brought out a hideous crone, whose sharp visage looked as if it had drawn itself up into points and angles while battling with the rough blasts that roared, whistled and moaned about her dwelling.

"And who be you?" was her first salutation. To which Mr Parsons only nodded graciously in reply.

"Dear me! Be it you, sir?" exclaimed the woman. "I ax your pardon, for not knowing your honour at a glance. Beds? Ay, ay, plenty of beds, sir.—Please to walk in. Who is this fine young'un? He can't have nothing to do with the mills, any way."

"This a fine holiday suit, dame, that Sir Matthew has been pleased to bestow upon him," replied Mr Parsons, "and if he had behaved himself a little better, he might have lived like a prince to the end of his days; but he is an untoward chap, and chose to cry, when he should have laughed. And so, you see, the fine folks at the Lodge got tired of him."

"What then!—This be the boy, be it, as we have had so many talking about? He was to be made a gentleman of by Sir Matthew Dowling? And so he is turned off, is he?"

This was said as the old woman led the way to the receiving-room, that is to say, the kitchen of the mansion, and here, though the season was still warm elsewhere, a large fire was burning. That its warmth was welcome might be gathered from the fact, that the only persons in possession of the room were sitting or standing close beside it. The guests, before the arrival of the new comers, amounted only to three, namely, a young woman pacing her way to a distant service, a stout lad, her brother, who travelled with her, to carry her box and guard her from harm; and a venerable looking man with gray hair, but having withal bright eyes, and a florid skin, and bearing in his dress and demeanour, the appearance of a thriving agriculturist.

It was with so bustling a movement, that the landlady pushed back the little round table on which stood the farmer's mug of beer, and there was so much of respect in the manner with which she wiped the chair brought forward for Mr Parsons, that the fact of his being a person of consequence, became notorious to all. The farmer quietly pushed back his chair, to follow the table, the young woman modestly squeezed herself very closely into the chimney-corner, and her brother fairly bolted, standing with eyes and mouth widely opened, to gaze at ease upon the distinguished society into which it had been his chance to fall. Mr Parsons took his place among them, as such a great man ought to do. That is to say, he looked neither to the right nor to the left, but made himself comfortable without taking the trouble of considering whether any other person were present, or not. Michael crept in after him, and when the more important part of the company had arranged themselves, he was observed standing alone in the most distant part of the room.

"What dost stand shivering there for, my boy?" said the old farmer, in north-country dialect, so broad as to be dangerous for south-country folks to spell, "I could be after thinking there was some mistake here. Surely you ought not to be standing, while some other folks are sitting."

This observation, though the genuine result of the old man's notions of vulgar, and the reverse, might not have been so bluntly spoken, had he not felt himself affronted by the unceremonious style in which his place before the fire had been taken from him. Michael probably did not understand the full meaning of the remark, nevertheless he looked dreadfully terrified, and fixed his eyes upon the back part of Mr Parson's august head, his face being fortunately turned from him, with an expression of desperate fear, that semed to puzzle the good farmer.

"Well now, don't he look like as well-behaved and pretty a young gentleman as one would wish, to see?" continued the farmer, turning to the young girl, "and yet there's no mistaking that t'other's his master."

"Fine feathers makes fine birds, for them as can see no farther," cried Parsons contemptuously, and turning one of his threatening scowls upon the old man. "But wait a bit, Goodman Goose, and you'll find out perhaps, as all is not gold as glitters."

"Poor little fellow!" exclaimed the farmer, on meeting the superin-tendent's ill-omened eye. "I wish, with all my heart, master, that nobody cared no more for your ugly looks than I do."

"Fine feathers makes fine birds, for them as can see no farther."

"Dame Pritchard," said Parsons, without appearing to hear him, "Let the boy and me have a bit of supper, d'ye hear. Spite of his fine clothes, however, which were but a gift of charity, the boy is neither better nor worse, than one of our factory children."

"I would not have thought it!" said the old man, apparently satisfied, and turning to his mug.

"No, I dare say," retorted Parsons, with a sneer. "Such chaps as you, seldom finds out what's what, or who's who, before they are told."

From this moment no further interest was expressed about little Michael. *He was a factory boy*, and what good was there in asking any further questions? So a thick slice of bread, and a scrap of bacon were set before him, and as soon as the more elaborate supper of Mr Parsons was concluded, he with great affability took the little fellow by the hand, and preceded by Dame Pritchard and a candle, conducted him to a pallet bed in the same chamber as his own.

For the first moment after he was left alone with the boy, the superintendent felt a strong inclination to make him pay for the affronts he had been the cause of his receiving below. But the same wisdom which had cut short his indignation there, checked him now; and having locked the chamber door, and given Michael a stimulating kick to haste his undressing, he carefully packed in a bundle the Dowling Lodge suit which he took off, leaving in its place beside the bed, the result of his hasty shoppings at Ashleigh.

When roused from his slumbers at day break the following morning, Michael found these new garments ready for him, and for a moment his heart sunk at the change, for though new, they were of the very lowest kind, and formed as strong a contrast as was well possible with the dress he had laid aside on preparing for his night's rest. But the human mind will often show symptoms of philosophy even at ten years old; which truth was made evident by the manner in which the young apprentice invested himself in his new suit, cheering his spirit as he did so, with the recollection that a person going to be bound to a trade like that of stocking-weaving, would look very ridiculous in such a dress as had been just taken away from him.

Early as it was, Mrs Pritchard was ready in the kitchen with a pot of hot tea for Mr Parsons; Michael received a fitting hunk of bread, the covered cart was brought up to the door, and the ill-matched pair set off again upon their journey.

It might seem paradoxical to say, that the temper of Mr Parsons was irritated by the patient, unsuspicious, and submissive demeanour of his helpless charge; yet such, nevertheless, was the fact. It was many years since the bones of Mr Parsons had been exposed to any conveyance more rough and rude than Sir Matthew's jockey cart, which was constructed with excellent and efficient springs; the movement, therefore, of the covered vehicle which had brought his aching joints to the "Crooked Billet" on Ridgetop Moor, was equally unwonted and disagreeable; and now that the peaceable demeanour of his little companion had convinced him that it was altogether unnecessary, he felt ready to twist his neck round, as an atonement for all he had endured.

Ere they had advanced a mile further, however, his spirit found a species of consolation that was perfectly congenial to it. The drear dark desert that spread before them, dimly visible as far as the eye could reach through the chilling mist of the morning, was just such a region as his heart desired for the dwelling of the young plague who had caused him so jolting a journey; and here too the covering of the rough machine was far from unwelcome, so that Mr Parsons, as he drove slowly and cautiously onward amidst the deep ruts, and rumbling stones, looked out upon the bleak desolation of the scene, with a feeling that almost approached to complacency.

At length the moor was passed, and for a few miles their joints enjoyed the luxury of a turnpike-road. The country too, seemed softening into a species of wild beauty, that might, in some degree, atone for its bleakness. But ere this had lasted for more than a couple of hours, the horse's head was again turned aside from the main road, and by a steep and very tough descent, they gradually approached the level of a stream, running through so very narrow a valley, as in many places to afford barely space enough for the road, between the brook and the precipitate heights which shut it in.

On reaching this level, the road, which for the last quarter of a mile had seemed to be leading them into the little river itself, turned abruptly, and by an angle so acute, following the indented curve of the lofty hill, that they speedily appeared to be shut in on all sides by the towering hills that suddenly, and as if by magic reared themselves in every direction round. It is hardly possible to conceive a spot more effectually hidden from the eyes of all men, than this singular valley. Hundreds may pass their lives within a few miles of it, without having the least idea that such a spot exists; for, from the form of the hills it so happens, that it is possible to wander for hours over their summits, without discovering it; one undulation rising beyond another, so as to blend together beneath the eye, leaving no opening by which this strip of water-level in their very centre, can be discerned.★

★ The real name of this valley (which most assuredly is no creation of romance) is not given, lest an action for libel should be the consequence. The scenes which have passed there, and which the few following pages will describe, have been stated to the author on authority not to be impeached.

For about another half mile, the narrow cart-road runs beside the stream without encountering any single object, except its lofty barrier and the brook itself, more remarkable than here and there a reed of higher growth than common, or a plant of Foxglove, that by its gay blossom seems to mock the desolate sadness of the spot. Another turn, however, still following the wavy curvings of the mountain's base, for mountain there it seems to be, opens another view, and one that speaks to many senses at once, the difference between the melancholy caused by nature, and that produced by the work of man. A wide spreading cotton-factory here rears its unsightly form, and at one glance makes the happy wanderer whose foot is free to turn which way he will, feel how precious is the power of retracing his steps back again along the beguiling path that has led him to it.

This was a joy for which our little Michael sighed in vain. On jogged the cart, and nearer it came at every jolt to the object which he most hated to look upon. But then came also the cheering thought, that he was no longer a mere factory boy, but about to become an apprentice to a good and profitable trade, in which hereafter he might expect to get money enough for himself, for mother, and Teddy too! Nevertheless, he certainly did wish, at the very bottom of his heart, that the stocking-weaving business was not carried on in a building so very like a cotton factory! But though Michael saw this hated cotton factory he as yet saw but a small portion of the horrors which belonged to the spot he had reached. His position in the vehicle made it impossible for him to look round, and perceive how completely all the acts that might be committed in that *Deep Valley*, were hid from the eye of every human being but those engaged in them. Neither could he recognise in the dismal building detached, yet connected both with the manager's house and the factory, the *Prison Prentice-house* which served as HOME to hundreds of little aching hearts, each one endowed by nature with light spirits, merry thoughts, and fond affections; but all of whom rose to their daily toil under circumstances which rendered enjoyment of any kind both morally and physically impossible.

The gradations by which all the misery that awaited him was disclosed, were, however, neither lingering nor uncertain. The cart stopped, Parsons got out, and then calling forward his companion, seized him roughly by the arm, and swung him through the door which opened to receive them.

"Soh! This is the chap you are going to bestow upon us, is it, Mr Parsons?" said a fellow, whose aspect must have withered hope in the gayest spirit that youth and joy ever produced between them. "Has he nimble fingers?"

"He can move 'em quick enough when he've got a mind for it," replied Parsons. "But you must not spare the strap, I can tell you, for a more obstinate hard-skinned little devil, never crossed the threshold of a factory."

"Never mind, Mr Parsons, we know how to manage all those matters, you may depend upon it. We possess many advantages over you, sir. No parents here you know, to come bothering us about bones and bruises. Here they all count at what they are worth, and no more. Children is plenty, Mr Parsons; and that's about the best thing we have got in our favour; for it can't be denied but we all of us, at times, finds that we have managed to complete more work than 'tis easy to dispose of."

"No doubt of that, Mr Woodcomb. But you had better hand off the boy, if you please, and then we'll settle our little matter of business, and I'll be off. Your roads are none of the best, sir, and I must make my way back to the Crooked Billet to-night."

"Not till you have had a bit, and a drop with us, Mr Parsons. They are at supper in the Prentice-house now, and our young master shall be handed in at once."

So saying, the scowling manager opened a door in the farther corner of the room, and made Michael a sign that he was to pass through it. The child obeyed, but he trembled in every joint. Feelings of deeper terror than had ever reached his heart before, were creeping over him. His lips moved not, but his very soul seemed to whisper within him, "Mother! Mother!"

Yet at that moment the unhappy boy knew not what was before him; the influence under which he cowered thus, was like that produced by the leaden dimness of a coming storm upon the birds, who droop their pinions and seem ready to fall to the earth, even before a single hailstone has touched them.

A long low passage led to another door, which was again opened by the condescending hand of Mr Woodcomb; through this he thrust the poor Michael, and having either by a word or a sign made known to the governor of the Prentice-house, that he had brought an accession to his wretched crew, he retired, closing the door behind him.

Michael heard the door close, and looked up. The room he was in was so long as almost to appear like a gallery, and from one end to the other of it a narrow deal board stretched out, having room for about two hundred to sit down at once. The whole of this table was now occupied by a portion of the apprentice children, both boys and girls, belonging to Deep Valley Mill, and their appearance might have wrung the heart of any being who looked upon them, however blessedly wide his own destiny might lead him from the melancholy troop. But to Michael, the spectacle was appalling; and, young as he was, he seemed to feel that the filthy, half-starved wretches before him, were so many ghostly representations of what he was himself to be. A sickness like that of death came over him, and he would have given a limb, only for freedom to stretch himself down upon the floor and see no more. But the master of the ceremonies at this feast of misery bore a huge horsewhip in his hand, without which indeed, it is said, he seldom appeared on the premises, and with it an eye that seemed to have the power of quelling with a single glance, the will of every little wretch it looked upon.

The place that Michael was to take at the board was indicated to him, and he sat down. The food placed before him consisted of a small bowl of what was denominated stir-pudding, a sort of miserable water and a lump of oaten cake, of a flavour so sour and musty, that the little fellow, though never accustomed till the fatal patronage of Sir Matthew fell upon him, to any viands more dainty than dry bread, could not at this first essay persuade himself to eat it. The wife of the governor of the Prentice-house, a help meet for him in every way, chanced to have her eye upon the stranger child as he pushed the morsel from him, and the smile that relaxed her features might have told him something, had he chanced to see, and understand it, respecting the excellent chance there was of his having a better appetite in future.

A girl nearly of his own age sat on one side, and a boy considerably older on the other; the first who had as much of beauty as it was perhaps possible for any human being to have after a six month's residence at Deep Valley Mill, looked up into his face with a pair of large blue eyes that spoke unbounded pity, and he heard a soft little voice whisper, "Poor boy!" While his lanky neighbour on the other side made prize of the rejected food, venturing to say aloud, "Any how, it is too good to be wasted."

The wretched meal did not last long, and for a few minutes after it was ended, the governor and his wife disappeared. During this interval, those who had strength and inclination moved about the room as they listed, but by far the greater number were already dropping to sleep after a day of protracted labour, during which they had followed the ceaseless movements of the machinery, for above fifteen hours. Among the former was the hungry lad who had appropriated the oat-cake of Michael, and no sooner were the eye of the master and mistress removed, than he turned to the new-comer, and in a tone that seemed to hover between good-humour and ridicule, said, "So you could not find a stomach for your supper, my man?"

"I did not want supper," replied Michael, dolefully. "You didn't want it, didn't you? That speaks better for the living as you have left, than I can speak of that as you'll find," returned his new acquaintance. "Don't you say nothing to nobody, and, to-morrow morning, after the lash have sounded through the room to wake us all, just you start up, and jump into your clothes, and when we goes to pump, I'll show you where we gets our tit-bits from."

Michael was in the act of nodding assent to this proposal, when the woman, who five minutes before had left the room, returned to it, and by a very summary process caused the ragged, weary, prayerless, hopeless multitude to crawl and clamber, half sleeping and half waking, to their filthy beds. They were divided by fifties in a room, but notwithstanding the number, and the little space in which they had to stow themselves, the stillness of heavy sleep pervaded every chamber, ere the miserable little inmates had been five minutes enclosed within the walls. Poor Michael lay as motionless as the rest, but he was not sleeping. Disappointment, fearful forebodings, and excessive nausea, all conspired to banish this only blessing that an apprenticed factory child can know.

He had already laboured, poor fellow, for nearly half his little life, and that under most hard and unrelenting masters; but till now, he had never known how very wretched his young thoughts could make him. His mother's fond caresses, and his brother's fervent love, had in spite of toil, and sometimes in spite of hunger, cheered and comforted the last moments of every day. The rude bed also, on which the brothers lay, was too clean, notwithstanding all the difficulty of keeping it so, to be tainted with the loathsome scent of oil, or sundry other abominations which rendered the place where he now lay, almost intolerable. Yet to this den, far, far away from the only creatures who loved and cherished him, he was come by his own consent, his own express desire! The thought was almost too bitter to bear, and the bundle of straw that served him for a pillow, received for the first hour of the night a ceaseless flood of tears.

It was, as his young companion had predicted, by the sound of a flourished whip, that he was awakened on the following morning. In an instant he was on his feet, and a minute or two more sufficed to invest him in his clothes; this speed, however, was the effect of terror, for he remembered not the invitation of the preceding evening. But hardly had he finished the operation of dressing, when Charley Ford, the boy who gave it, was by his side, and giving him a silent hint by a wink of the left eye, and a movement of the right elbow that he might follow him, turned away, and ran down stairs.

Michael did so too, and presently found himself with a multitude of others in a small paved court, on one side of which was a pump, to whose spout every child came in succession to perform a very necessary, but, from lack of soap, a very imperfect act of ablution.

Neglecting to watch his turn for this, and not permitting Michael to do so either, Charles Ford made his way to a door that opened upon another part of the premises, and pushing it open, disclosed to the eyes of Michael a loathsome and a fearful spectacle.

Seven or eight boys had already made their way to the sort of rude farm-yard upon which this door opened, one and all of whom were intent upon purloining from a filthy trough just replenished for the morning meal of two stout hogs, a variety of morsels which, as Michael's new acquaintance assured him, were "dainty eating for the starving prentices of Deep Valley mill.

"Make haste, young'un," cried Charles, good-naturedly, "or they won't leave a turnip-paring for us." And on he rushed to the scuffle, leaving Michael gazing with disgust and horror at the contest between the fierce snouts of the angry pigs, and the active fingers of the wretched crew who contested with them for the offal thus cast forth.

Michael Armstrong was a child of deep feeling; and it was, perhaps, lucky for him, that the burning sense of shame and degradation which pervaded every nerve of his little frame, as he looked on upon this revolting spectacle, come upon him while yet too young for any notion of resistance to suggest itself. He felt faint, sick, and broken hearted; but no worm that ever was crushed to atoms by the foot of an elephant, dreamed less of vengeance than did poor Michael, as the horrid thought came over him, that he was going to abide in a place where little boys were treated with less care and tenderness than pigs!

He turned away shuddering, and feeling almost unable to stand—and then the image of his mother seemed to rise before him—he felt her soft gentle kisses on his cheeks, and almost unconsciously pronounced her name. This dear name, lowly as it was murmured, came upon his ear so like the knell of happiness that was never to return, that the hard agony of his little heart melted before it, and sitting down upon a bundle of fagots that were piled up against the wall, he rested his burning head against the bricks, and burst into a passion of tears. At this moment he felt a hand upon his shoulder, and trembling from head to foot, he sprung upon his feet, and suddenly turning round beheld, instead of the savage features of the overlooker which his fancy had conjured up, the meekest, gentlest, loveliest little face, that ever eyes look upon, within a few feet of him. It was the same little girl who had been placed next him at the miserable supper of the preceding night, and whose low murmur of pity for all the sorrow he was come to share with her, had reached his ears and his heart.

"You'll be strapped dreadful if you bide here," said the child. "Come away—and don't let them see you cry!" But even as she spoke she

"Make haste young'un or they
won't leave a turnip paring for us."

turned from him, and ran toward the door through which the miserable
pilferers of the pig-trough were already hurrying.

Perhaps no other warning-voice would have been so promptly
listened to at that moment by poor Michael, for it was something very
like the numbing effect of despair that seemed to have seized upon him,
and it is likely enough he would have remained in the attitude he had
taken, with his head resting against the wall, till the brutal violence of
his task-master had dragged him from it, had not this pretty vision of
pity appeared to warn him of his danger.

He rose and followed her so quickly, that by the time she had reached
the crowd of children who were still thronging round the pump, he was
by her side.

"Thank you!" whispered Michael in her ear, "It was very kind of you
to call me—and I shouldn't have come if you hadn't—for I shouldn't
care very much if they killed me."

"That's very naughty!" said the little girl.

"How *can* I be good?" demanded Michael, while the tears again burst from his eyes. "'Twas mother that made me good before, and I don't think I shall ever see her any more."

"I never can see my mother any more, till I go to Heaven," replied the little girl—"but I always think every day, that she told me before she died, about God's making every thing come right in the end, if we bear all things patiently for love of him."

"But God can't choose I should be taken from mother, and that's why I can't bear it," said Michael.

The little girl shook her head, very evidently disapproving his theology.

"How old are you?" said Michael.

"Eleven years old three months ago, and that was one week after I came here," answered his new acquaintance.

"Then you are more than one whole year older than me?" said Michael; "and I dare say you know better than I do; and I'll try to be good too, if you'll love me, and be kind to me always, like poor Edward. My name is Michael—What's your name?"

"Fanny Fletcher," replied the little girl, "and I *will* love you and be kind to you, if you'll be a good boy and bear it all patiently."

"I would bear it all patiently," said Michael, "if I knew when I was to get away, and when you was to get away too. But perhaps we are to stay here for ever?" And again the tears ran down his cheeks.

"That's nonsense, Michael," said Fanny. "They can't keep us here for ever. When we die, we are sure to get away from them."

Michael opened his large eyes and looked at her with something like reproach. "When we die?" he repeated sadly. "Are we to stay here till we die?—I am never to see mother and Teddy any more then?"

" Don't cry, Michael!" said the little girl, taking his hand—"We shall be sure to get out if God thinks it right. Don't cry so!"

"I wish I was as old as you," said Michael, with an accent expressive of great respect. "I should bear it better then."

As Michael ceased speaking he felt the little girl shudder. "Here he is!" she whispered, withdrawing her hand from him—"we mustn't speak any more now."

"Off with you, vagabonds!" roared the voice of the apprentice-house governor, from behind them. "Don't you see the factory-gates open?"

The miserable little troop waited for no second summons, well knowing that the lash, which was only idly cutting the air above their heads, would speedily descend upon them if they did; but not even terror could enable the wasting limbs of those who had long inhabited this fearful abode, to move quickly. Many among them were dreadfully crippled in the legs, and nearly all exhibited the frightful spectacle of young features pinched by famine.

★   ★   ★   ★   ★

Let none dare to say this picture is exaggerated, till he has taken the trouble to ascertain by his own personal investigation, that it is so. It is a very fearful crime in a country where public opinion has been proved (as in the African Slave Trade), to be omnipotent, for any individual to sit down with a shadow of doubt respecting such statements on his mind. IF they be true, let each in his own little circle, raise his voice against the horrors detailed by them, AND THESE HORRORS WILL BE REMEDIED. But woe to those who supinely sit in contented ignorance of the facts, soothing their spirits and their easy consciences with the cuckoo note, "*exaggeration*," while thousands of helpless children pine away their unnoted, miserable lives, in labour and destitution, *incomparably more severe*, than any ever produced by negro slavery.

★   ★   ★   ★   ★

It was with a feeling certainly somewhat akin to comfort, that Michael found himself thrust into the same chamber with his gentle little monitor, Fanny. The mules they attended, were side by side, and though no intercourse was permitted, that could by possibility interfere with the ceaseless labour of piecing, nevertheless, a word when their walk brought them near enough to each other to be heard, was often exchanged between the children, and the effect of this on Michael, was most salutary.

Superlatively, and above all others, wretched as are the miserable young victims apprenticed to factory masters, it is not unusual to find among them some helpless creature, whose first impressions were received under more favourable moral circumstances, than those in which the children of the manufacturing districts are placed. For it is from a distance from those unblessed regions, that the great majority of apprentices are furnished, and the chances are, therefore, greatly in favour of their having first opened their eyes amidst scenes of less ignorance, degradation, and suffering, than those born within reach of the poisonous factory influence.

Such was the case with Fanny Fletcher. It was not till mother and father we both dead, that she had ceased to hear the voice of love, and the precepts of religion. For three years she had, indeed, been supported by the labour of a poor widowed mother; but being her only child, Fanny had wanted nothing, had never been exposed to the hearing of coarse language, or the witnessing of vicious habits, and all her little studies had been so thoroughly mixed up with religious feelings, that by the time she was ten years old, it would have been almost impossible to eradicate them, or rob her entirely of the gentle courage, and patient endurance, such feelings invariably lead to. When her mother died, all the world—her little world, consisting of a score of poor bodies of her own class, exclaimed, "Poor Fanny Fletcher!" But there was not one among them rich enough to save her from the workhouse and to the workhouse therefore she went, whence within three months she was sent, with many others, as apprentices, to Deep Valley factory, ostensibly, and as doubtless the parish authorities believed, to learn a good trade, but in truth, to undergo a species of slavery, probably the most tremendous that young children were ever exposed to in any part of the known world, civilized or uncivilized.

That the desolate little creature suffered fearfully, both in body and mind, cannot be doubted; yet at the time Michael first saw her, there was still that beautiful look of innocent patience in her eyes, which shows that the spirit, though bending under sorrow, is neither reckless nor degraded. Herself, and her companions from the workhouse to which she had been consigned at her mother's death, were the latest arrivals at Deep Valley when Michael reached it, and were still considered by the rest of the inmates as new-comers, who did not yet know the full misery of incessant labour, with strength daily failing for want of pure air and sufficient food. Fanny was by nature a slight delicate little creature, with an elastic sort of vitality about her which seemed to set fasting at defiance. That is to say, her sweet eye had not yet lost its brightness, but her beautifully fair cheek was very pale, and her delicate limbs most deplorably thin, though they had not yet reached that shrunk and wasted condition which was nearly general among her companions. Michael looked at her as she bent over her threads, and repaired the incessant breakings among them with her white little hands, with a degree of love and pity which while it wrung his heart, softened the hard despair that had nearly seized upon him, by making him feel, that though his mother and his brother were lost to him for long long years, during which he was to taste of nothing but misery, still there was somebody who might grow to love him. This was a timely solace! Young as he was, he perceived at once, that instead of being brought to Deep Valley to learn a trade, he had been beguiled to enter there bound and helpless, for more years than he dared to count, and with no prospect of learning any thing beyond the same slavish process of waiting upon the machinery, which had painfully occupied his daily existence, and that of his dearer brother, as long as they could remember to have lived. Under these circumstances, it was truly a great blessing to have found somebody of whom he might make a friend, and so strongly did the poor little fellow feel it, that when the miserable band were led to their morning meal, he told Fanny as he walked beside her, that he thought he should grow to behave better than he had done that morning, if she would always talk to him about good things, and let him talk about mother and Teddy to her in return.

"There's a good boy!" replied Fanny, soothingly. "I will talk to you, Michael, whenever I can—and never mind," she added, as they sat down again side by side at the long dirty board that formed their breakfast table, "never mind not having what's good to eat, it won't taste so nasty by and bye, when you grow used to it."

"I won't mind it!" replied Michael, manfully, as he supped the musty-flavoured watery mess. "But I wish I had got a bit of good bread for you, Fanny!"

XVIII

An explanatory epistle, which does not prove satisfactory—
Plans for the future, followed by active measures to carry
them into effect—A morning visit to Mrs Gabberly

DURING THE WHOLE OF THE day which followed Miss Brotherton's expedition to Hoxley-lane, that young lady remained waiting at home, not very patiently, for Sir Matthew Dowling's promised communication. But still it came not, and when, at an hour too late to hope for it any longer, she at length retired to bed, it was in a state of irritation and anxiety that left her little chance of quiet slumber.

Pale, harassed, and fearing she knew not what for the little fellow, for whose safety she had undertaken to answer, Miss Brotherton joined her good nurse at the breakfast-table, incapable of thinking or speaking upon any other subject. But it was in vain that the gentle-spirited Mrs Tremlett again and again declared it to be "impossible, and quite out of all likelihood, that Sir Matthew should mean any harm by the boy;" Mary, though weary of conjectures could by no means end them by coming to the same conclusion; nor did the following letter handed to her while she still sat before her untasted breakfast greatly tend to tranquillize her. It was from Sir Matthew Dowling himself, delicately enveloped, highly scented and sealed with prodigiously fine armorial bearings on a shield, almost large enough to have adorned the panels of a carriage. But all this perfection of elegance was lost on poor Mary, whose heart, indeed, seemed to leap into her throat, as she tore open the important despatch. It contained the following lines:

"My charming Neighbour!

"If you knew, or could at all guess, how fervently I admire the beautiful benevolence you have manifested, in trying to quiet the fidgetty spirit of poor widow Armstrong, you would be better able to appreciate the vexation I feel, at not yet being able fully to answer your inquiries concerning her boy. Think not, my dearest Miss Brotherton, that I neglected this business yesterday, on the contrary, I do assure you I gave my whole attention to it; nevertheless, I have by no means succeeded in learning what you wish to know. The facts of the case are these. A most respectable stocking-manufacturer, with whom, however, my foreman is better acquainted than myself, employs a multitude of young hands, most of whom are apprentices, in the different branches of his business. It was to this person, that the weak and wavering poor woman for whom you are interested, agreed to intrust her boy. Indentures were accordingly prepared, and I gave my superintendent orders to have the little fellow supplied with all necessaries, desiring that no time might be lost in getting him ready, as I knew that people belonging to this stocking-weaving establishment were likely to pass through Ashleigh in a day or two, and I wished, if possible, to avoid having the trouble of sending to his destination myself. Now it unfortunately happened, that my man, Parsons, obeyed this order much more literally than I intended; for meeting in Ashleigh the persons I had named to him the very next day, he immediately mentioned the circumstance to them, and finding that they had a comfortable van, and every thing convenient with them, the whole business was arranged and done before I returned from a visit I had been making at Netherby. This was certainly being more prompt than was necessary, but it would have mattered little, comparatively speaking, had he not been such a goose as to let the van drive off, without even asking to which of the manufactories of the establishment it was going. Yet, although this is vexing, my dear Miss Brotherton, I should think it could not be very important. I have told Parsons to write about it immediately, and he shall wait upon you with the information you wish for, as soon as he receives it.

"Will you, my fair friend, join us in a little picnic party, projected by our young people for Thursday next, under the green-wood tree in

Blackberry wood? Lady Clarissa is, of course, to be one of our society, and she will communicate all particulars respecting place and time.

"Ever, my dear Miss Brotherton,
"Very faithfully yours,
"MATTHEW DOWLING."

Having read this letter to the end, she turned the sheet, and began a reperusal of it, without uttering a word, and when she had again reached its conclusion, she put it into the hands of Mrs Tremlett, still without speaking a word. Before, however, that excellent, but not rapid lady, had got half through it, poor Mary's agitation broke forth—

"What do you think of it, nurse? for Heaven's sake, give me your opinion without delay! I am quite sure, that the poor creatures in Hoxley-lane, whom I have beguiled with my presumptious promises, will pine themselves to death with this uncertainty. Tremlett! for mercy's sake finish reading it, and tell me what I can do more!"

It might not have been very easy for any one to have satisfactorily answered this inquiry; but the good Mrs Tremlett was altogether incapable of forming any opinion worth hearing on the subject, for in truth she neither shared, nor fully comprehended the vague fears, that were tormenting her young mistress.

Having, however, at length, despite of Mary's interruptions, contrived to reach the end of the epistle, her first words were—

"Don't, my darling Miss Mary!—Let me beg of you to refuse at once. There is nothing in the whole world so dangerous and cold catching, as these foolish parties on the damp grass. And besides, the evenings are drawing in now, and I'm sure"—

"Oh! Nurse Tremlett! Nurse Tremlett!" interrupted Mary, more angry with her than she had ever been in her whole life before, "How can you be so cruel as to trifle thus? Why won't you try to think a little for me about this strange mysterious business, and give me your opinion?"

"Lord bless you, Miss Mary, if you were to kill me, I could no more help thinking of you first than I could fly," replied Mrs Tremlett. "And, indeed, my dear, I don't see what you should put yourself into such a fuss for. What can you think is going to happen to the little boy? You'll just spoil that poor sickly body, my dear child, if you encourage her in having such tantrums, because her boy set out upon his journey a day, may be, earlier than she expected."

"Then you really and truly do not believe it possible, nurse, that Sir Matthew Dowling should have smuggled the boy away, without intending to let us know where he has sent him?" said Miss Brotherton.

"Good gracious, no, Miss Mary," replied her friend.

For a moment this opinion brought some consolation with it, simply from the decision with which it was uttered; but the next, all her anxiety returned again, for though she felt that there was, perhaps, something improbable and exaggerated in the idea of the child's being kidnapped in the face of day, and as it were before a hundred witnesses, there was at least no delusion as to his unhappy mother's state of mind respecting him, nor in the fact of her having in some sort pledged her own word, that the poor woman and her lame boy should receive tidings of him.

A little further conversation with Mrs Tremlett, convinced her that her opinion on the subject could be of no great value, inasmuch as it was founded solely on the notion, that "it was not likely, Sir Matthew Dowling should want to hide away the little boy."

"No!" thought Mary. "Nor was it likely he should have acted, looked, and spoken as I saw him do, when his poor girl lost her senses from agony at my having witnessed it. If I misdoubt him unjustly, I will be careful that it shall not injure him. I will await his own time for information. If it comes, no one will be the worse for the impatience with which I shall have waited for it. But, if it comes not, I can be doing no wrong by taking every means of seeking it."

In conformity with this resolution, Miss Brotherton not only waited with tolerable external composure herself, but continued in a great degree to tranquillize the spirits of the widow Armstrong, likewise; and during a whole week, Sir Matthew Dowling was permitted to remain unmolested. Miss Brotherton, indeed, did not meet him under the greenwood-tree, pleading an indisposition, which was not quite imaginary, as her excuse, but she troubled him with no more questions.

On the day fixed for this *al fresco* meeting of nearly the whole neighbourhood, Edward Armstrong was appointed to pay his first visit to Milford Park. During her almost daily visits to his mother, she had remarked that, though he uttered not a word in contradiction of the reasonings, by which she sought to show the improbability that any mischief could have befallen Michael, his speaking features expressed no confidence in them, and wishing upon this day of general riding and driving, to remain within her own gates, she determined to take the opportunity of conversing with him alone.

She was by herself in her pretty boudoir when he arrived, and perceiving that his pale face was flushed by heat and exercise, she made him sit down on the sofa, beside her.

There was something singularly sad in the utter indifference with which his young eye wandered over all the striking and unwonted objects that surrounded him. When bad to sit beside the young lady on her silken couch, he obeyed without seeming at all conscious that the rest he needed was now afforded in more dainty style than usual, and all the intelligence of his soul seemed settled in his eyes as he looked into the face of Miss Brotherton, and faintly murmured—

"Is there any news of him?"

"No, Edward, there is not," replied Mary, firmly; "but surely, my dear boy, this delay cannot justify the look of misery it produces on your countenance. Tell me, Edward, what is it that you fear for Michael!"

"I do not know myself," replied the boy. "And yet I think it over in my head day and night only to find out what is the very worst possible they can do to him."

"But is that wise, Edward, or is it right, think you, while your poor mother has only you left to comfort her, that you should only strive to fill your own head and hers with the very worst thoughts your fancy can conjure up?"

"I do not fill mother's head with them," replied Edward. "I have never told her one single word of all my dismal thoughts."

"Then you are a good boy, and I love you for it. But what are your dismal thoughts, Edward? You may tell them to me."

The boy hesitated for a moment, and then said—"I think Sir Matthew Dowling is a wicked, cruel man; and I think that he would be more likely to be wicked and cruel to Michael than good to him."

"What is it has made you think Sir Matthew cruel and wicked, Edward?" demanded Miss Brotherton.

"Because he is hard and unjust to those who labour for him—and because I have seen him laugh and make sport of the tears of little children."

There was something in the accents of the boy that startled Mary.— She felt inclined to exclaim—"How much more older art thou than thy looks!" so thrilling was the tone, and so profound the feeling with which he spoke.

"Yet still," she replied, "it is difficult to see that he could gain any advantage by ill-using Michael in any way bad enough to make you look so miserable, Edward."

"If he keeps him from me is not that enough?" said the pale boy, looking reproachfully at her.

"But, Edward, you knew that he was going to leave you; and your mother, at least, consented to it."

"Yes, she did consent to it. Poor, dear mother! She did consent to it. But had I been true, as I ought to have been, she never would," said Edward, clasping his hands and closing his eyes with a look of intense suffering.

"Explain yourself, my dear boy," said Mary, kindly. "In what have you been otherwise than true?"

"We agreed together—poor Michael and me agreed together, never to let mother know how bad we were served at the mill—and, above all, we agreed that she should never know how miserable Michael was at the great house, 'cause we was sure she'd have him away, and so lose the bit of comfortable food she has been having. But it was wrong and wicked to deceive her. We should have told her all, and then Michael would have never gone!"

"You acted for the best, my dear boy, and must not reproach yourself," replied Mary; "and so far am I from thinking it wrong to keep her mind easy in her present state of health, that I strongly advise her being still comforted as much as possible by our manner of talking to her. Fear not, Edward, that I shall neglect the safety of Michael, because you will not hear me talk of his being in any danger. I will not rest till I know what has become of him."

Mary said this in a tone that left no doubt of her sincerity; and it was then for the first time that Edward seemed to remember her greatness. He stood up before her with a look of tender reverence inexpressibly touching, and said solemnly—"Then God will bless you for it!"

"And he will bless you, my dear child!" replied Mary, with tears starting to her eyes. "He will bless and comfort you for all your duty and affection. Keep up your spirits, Edward, and, above all things, never be idle. It is for your mother's sake as well as your own that I am so anxious you should learn to read and write, dear Edward—and by degrees we shall get you on to ciphering, and who knows but we may make a clerk or accountant of you, and so enable you to get money even if your health is not very good."

The boy smiled languidly as he replied, "I should like it very much, if I was to live long enough."

"You will get stout and well, Edward," said Mary, cheerfully, "now that you have no hard work to do. And you shall come up to the same school that all my boys and girls go to here—and when school is over, you must come every day to my kitchen with a little basket for our mother. You understand, Edward? And once every week you must come up into this room to me with your books, that I may see your writing and hear you read a little."

A gleam of hope and joy kindled in the boy's beautiful eyes as he listened to her, and a bright blush mantled his pale cheeks; but it was like the flitting sunshine of April chased by a heavy cloud almost before its warmth could be felt or its beauty seen. "Oh! if Michael could but hear that!" he exclaimed, while tears, for the first since the conversation began, burst from his eyes. "*That* was what poor Michael always wanted. If I could but learn, and so get my bread without mill-slavery, Mike always said he would not mind working himself, 'cause he was so strong. But now that very thing is come; and he, maybe, will never know it!"

Heavy and fast the drops fell from beneath the hand which he had raised to conceal his face, till Mary, as she watched him, wept for company. This, however, was not the way to help him, and conquering a weakness so every way unwise, she spoke to him with affectionate but steady firmness of the exertion it was his duty to make at a time when his mother had none but him to comfort her. She had touched the right string—the little fellow's nerves seemed braced, and every faculty awakened by the words she uttered; and if he took back to his mother no tidings of poor Michael, he brought to her support a young spirit strong in endurance, and an intellect that, for the first time, had whispered to its owner hopes, promises, and aspirations, which seemed to make the life he had often loathed a new-found treasure to him. Mary saw not all that passed in the young mind she had rescued from the listless languor of despair; yet she perceived enough to satisfy her that she had done him good, and that, however vain her hopes of benefiting the miserable Drakes might be, there could be no doubt that, in this case at least, her efforts would not prove wholly abortive.

It is wonderful what an energy and renewed impetus this conviction gave to her spirits! No mildew can blast more surely, or bring a more lamentable feeling of withering over the heart, than that caused by the cold and false philosophy which would check every effort to do good, lest, by possibility, success might not attend it.

The remainder of this day was by no means spent unhappily by the warm-hearted little heiress. The schoolmistress was made to expect Edward on the morrow—and the cook was made to expect Edward on the morrow. One Mercury was despatched to the town for a choice collection of slates, copies, spelling-books, and the like, and another to Mary's tailor in ordinary, with instructions to call on the widow Armstrong, and take measure of her son. All this business, and a good deal more tending the same way, having been satisfactorily got through in the course of the day that kept all the Ashleigh world safely entangled in the thickets of Blackberry wood, Mary Brotherton lay down to rest, and slept exceedingly well, though not urged thereto by having shared in their pleasant fatigues.

She rose the next morning with a sort of pleasant consciousness of increasing power to walk alone in this busy world, and gaily announced at breakfast to Mrs Tremlett her purpose of immediately making a visit of speculation to Mrs Gabberly, in order to ascertain if any gossip was yet afloat respecting the disappearance of Sir Matthew Dowling's far-famed *protégé*. The distance from Miss Brotherton's mansion to Mrs Gabberly's cottage was not great, and the heiress traversed it without having any fear of officers before her eyes, or any other protection than her parasol.

She was, of course, received with expressions of unmitigated astonishment at her absence from the gala of the preceding day.

"What on earth, my dear child, could have kept you away?" said the animated lady.

"Perhaps I was afraid of taking cold, Mrs Gabberly. Mrs Tremlett took care I should remember how short the days are growing."

"Mrs Tremlett!—Nonsense!—Well now, I can tell you that you just lost the most delightful day that any body ever had. Such a dinner!— Game of all kinds—almost all in savoury jelly too! Think of that! So wholesome, you know, with the spice; and eating it in the open air, and all. Depend upon it, my dear Miss Brotherton, that if you suffer yourself to be boxed up by that ignorant old woman, you will very soon lose your health altogether. And do you know I can't help thinking that you do look rather feverish to-day—your eyes have that sort of brightness. I wish to goodness you would let me feel your pulse."

"Nothing will do my pulse so much good, my dear Mrs Gabberly, as your telling me all the news you heard yesterday," said the young lady good-humouredly shaking the hand that was extended to ascertain her state of health.

"Well now, my dear, I am sure I have no objection in the world to tell you, and certainly one does pick up a vast deal of information at such party as that. Will you believe it? two of the Simmonses are going to he married."

"Really! That's very good news, I suppose. Had you a great many people there?"

"Oh! Every body, just every body, but your own dear self; and I can truly say that if you had been there, it would have been quite perfect!"

"You are very kind; but a person so very much afraid of taking cold, is a troublesome on these *al fresco* occasions. Lady Clarissa was there, of course?"

"Of dourse, my dear. And *such* a flirtation with Sir Matthew! God knows, I ain't over strict in any way; I despise it, because it shows such ignorance of life and good society. But I must say, I do think they carry the thing a little too far. Of course, a lady of rank and title like Lady Clarissa, is not to be judged altogether like common people. I am quite aware of that, and nothing can be more thoroughly vulgar than forgetting this. And I certainly have lived too much in first-rate good society, not to know it. But, nevertheless, you know, there is reason in roasting eggs, and even an earl's daughter *may* get talked of."

"Was Lady Dowling in presence?" inquired Miss Brotherton, smiling.

"No, my dear, thank God she was not, or we should have had sour looks with our sweetmeats, I can tell you."

"Did Sir Matthew bring his little favourite with him? The little boy he adopted you know?"

"Oh! dear, haven't you heard all that yet? Well now, upon my word, Mary Brotherton, it will *not* do, your shutting yourself up in this way. Catching cold, indeed! As if I, the daughter of my own poor dear father, wasn't likely to know more than Mrs Tremlett about catching cold! Why, my dear, the little boy has been sent away I don't knew how LONG, with a monstrous premium, paid by Sir Matthew, to get him entered at one of the first commercial houses in Europe. Dr Crockley was exceedingly agreeable and attentive to me all day yesterday. And, indeed, so he was, I must say, to every body. We do sometimes differ about spinal complaints, and I think he is a great deal too speculative. But it is impossible to deny that he can be very agreeable when he chooses it, and it was he that told me all about this last noble act of Sir Matthew. To be sure he is an honour to the country if ever there was one, Sir Matthew, I mean. It is such men as that, Miss Brotherton, that brings wealth and prosperity to our glorious country. To think only of the hands he employs! Fifteen hundred children taking all his mills together, he told us yesterday, besides several women and men. Oh! it is glorious to be sure! However, Dr Crockley did just whisper to me, but I don't believe he meant it should go much farther, he did certainly hint, that poor cross Lady Dowling did not like to have the little fellow in the house, and that was one reason why good Sir Matthew was in such a hurry to place him."

"Did you happen to hear to what part of the country the boy had been sent, Mrs Gabberly?"

"Why, no! my dear, I can't say I did. But that makes no difference you know. Every body is aware that it is a noble situation for him, and that's the main point of course."

"Oh! certainly. I only asked from idle curiosity. And I suppose, Mrs Gabberly, that it is because I am so idle, that I do often feel curious about things that nobody else seems to care about. Do you know I am dying to get into a factory, and see all these dear little children at work. It must be so pretty to see them all looking so proud and so happy, and all enjoying themselves so much! I really must get a peep at it," said Miss Brotherton.

"Law! my dear! What a very queer notion," replied Mrs Gabberly.

"Perhaps it is," said Mary smiling, "as nobody else in the whole neighbourhood ever talks about it; but if I have such a fancy, there can be no reason why I should not indulge it, can there?"

"Why, good gracious, my dear child! only think of the dirt! You would be downright poisoned, Mary."

"Poisoned? How can that be, dear Mrs Gabberly, when every body agrees that it is such a blessing to the country, to have brought such multitudes of children to work together in these factories?"

"Nonsense, my dear!" replied Mrs Gabberly, knitting her brows. "This is some of Mrs Tremlett's vulgar ignorance, I am very sure. How can a girl of your good understanding, Miss Brotherton, speak as if what was good and proper for the working classes, had any thing to do with such as you. Fie! my dear! Pray never let any body in the neighbourhood hear you talk in this strange wild way, I do assure you, that there is nothing that would do you so much injury in the opinion of all the first families hereabouts. And nobody knows this neighbourhood better than I do."

"I am quite aware of that Mrs Gabberly," said the young lady very respectfully, "and that is one reason why I wish to talk to you about this notion of mine. Is it really true, Mrs Gabberly, that none of the ladies in the neighbourhood ever go into the factories?"

"To be sure it is. Why should they go, for goodness sake?"

"Oh! I don't know exactly.—But I cannot see why they should not—if they wish it," replied Miss Brotherton, modestly.

"Well now, but I do, my dear. And I do beg and entreat that you won't talk any more about it. I am quite sure, Mary, that some body or other has been talking nonsense to you, about all this. If you had got any friends or connexions towards Fairly now, I should think they had been telling you all the romantic stuff that has been hatching there about factory children, and God knows what beside. But I don't believe you have ever gone visiting that way, have you, my dear?"

"And who is there at Fairly, dear Mrs Gabberly, who would be likely to talk to me on such a subject?" said Mary, colouring to the temples, with eagerness to hear the answer. "Good gracious! my dear, did you never hear tell of that poor wrong-headed clergyman, George Bell? Such a difference to be sure between one man and another. My dear good Mr Gabberly never in his life breathed a word that could hurt the feelings of his neighbours. He visited them every one, and was on the best and most friendly terms with them all, which is what I call living in the true spirit of Christian charity. Whereas this tiresome, troublesome, Mr Bell, has taken it into his head to find out wrong, where every body else sees nothing but right: and God forbid, my dear, that you should take it into your dear innocent head to follow any of his mischievous fancies; I wonder what he'll get by it? Great goose he must be, to be sure, not to see that he is going exactly the way to set every body that can be of the least use to him smack against him in all things!"

"What is it he does, Mrs Gabberly, that is so very wrong?" demanded Miss Brotherton.

"What is it he does? Why just every thing he ought not to do, my dear, that's all. You would hardly believe, perhaps, that a clergyman should actually encourage the poor to complain of the very labour by which they live? And yet I give you my word and honour that is exactly what he has been doing. It's incredible, isn't it, almost? He positively says, loud enough for all the country to hear him, that the labour in the factories—such a blessing as it is to the poor—he actually says that it is bad for the children's health. Such stuff, you know my dear, as if the medical men did not know best; and there's numbers of 'em that declare that it's quite impossible to tell in any way satisfactory that it can do 'em any harm at all. And, upon my word, I don't know what poor people will come to! It's quite out of the question to attempt pleasing 'em. If they've got no work they are perfectly outrageous about that, and ready to tear people to pieces just to get it; and no sooner is there enough to do, than away they go bawling again, swearing that the children are over-worked; isn't it provoking my dear?"

"Mr George Bell," said Mary, very distinctly.

"Yes, my dear, that's the name of the foolish man who seems to take a pleasure in making people fancy they are not well enough off, when I'm sure, by all I can hear and understand, these very identical people may consider themselves first and foremost of the whole world for prosperity," replied Mrs Gabberly.

"Fairly?" rejoined Miss Brotherton, interrogatively.

"Yes, my dear, Fairly's where he lives, if I don't mistake."

"Good morning, Mrs Gabberly," said the young lady, rising some what abruptly; "I am very glad you had such a pleasant day yesterday. Good by." And without permitting the stream of Mrs Gabberly eloquence to well forth upon her afresh, the heiress slipped through the parlour door, and escaped.

XIX

A voyage of discovery—A plain statement, leading to the conviction that even where ignorance is not bliss, knowledge is not always happiness—A hasty friendship that may nevertheless prove lasting

To ORDER THE CARRIAGE, AND to give Mrs Tremlett notice that she wished her to make all speed in preparing to accompany her in it, was to Miss Brotherton the work of a moment. As the business she was upon might, however, take some hours, she urged her old friend to eat luncheon as if certain of having no dinner; and having given time for this, and interrogated her coachman concerning distance and so forth, the hopeful, animated girl, sprung into her carriage as the clock struck two, determined not to re-enter her mansion till she had lost some portion of the ignorance which had of late so cruelly tormented her.

The roads were good, and by the help of a short bait, Miss Brotherton and her companion reached Fairly turnpike a little after four. Here she made inquiries for the residence of Mr Bell, and having learned in what direction she should find it, repeated the instructions to her coachman, and bade him drive on.

"Are the horses to be put up there, ma'am?" demanded the coachman.

"Yes—no, James, not there I suppose—that is, not at the clergyman's house; but of course you will be able to find some place quite near, you know; and William must wait—no, not wait, but come back as soon as he knows where you put up, that I may send for you when I am ready."

To these, not over-clear, instructions James answered, "Yes ma'am," and drove off.

In obedience to the directions received at the tollbar, the carriage soon left the high-road, and proceeded down a grassy lane, which harvest carts for the time had rolled into smoothness. Less than a quarter of a mile of this, brought the wanderers to another turning, that in five minutes placed them before the gates of an edifice the aspect of which made Mary pull the check-string.

"That looks like a parsonage-house! Does it not?" said Miss Brotherton.

And before Mrs Tremlett could answer, William had already opened the door, and let down the steps. It was very easy to get out, and very easy to inquire if Mr Bell were at home; but when answered in the affirmative, Miss Brotherton felt that it was not very easy to decide in what manner to explain the cause of her visit to the object of it. She had by no means settled this point to her satisfaction, when the door of a small parlour, lined with books, was opened to her, and she found herself in the presence of the gentleman she had so unceremoniously come to visit.

There was much in the countenance of Mr Bell to reassure a more timid spirit than that of Mary Brotherton; nevertheless she stood before him for a minute or two in some embarrassment, not so much from fear of him, as of herself. Did she fail to make him at once understand the motive of her inquiries, he could not avoid thinking both them and herself impertinent, and this consciousness caused a much brighter glow than usual to mantle her cheeks, as she stood before him, with her eyes fixed timidly, and almost beseechingly, on his face.

Although Miss Brotherton had not quite the easy and (*tant soit peu*) assured air of a woman of fashion, there was enough in her appearance to indicate her claim to observance, as well as admiration, and Mr Bell opened the conversation by earnestly requesting that she would sit down.

His aspect had done much towards giving her courage, and his voice did more.

"You are very kind sir," said she, "to receive so courteously a stranger who has in truth no excuse whatever to offer for thus intruding on you. Nevertheless, I am greatly tempted to hope, that if I can succeed in making you understand the object of my visit, you will forgive the freedom of it."

"And I," returned Mr Bell, smiling, "am greatly tempted to believe that let the object of this visit be what it may, I must always feel grateful to it. Is there any thing, my dear young lady, that I can do to serve you?"

"There is indeed, Mr Bell!" she replied, with great earnestness of voice and manner. "I am come to you for instruction. Though you do not know me, you probably may know the place at which I live. My name is Mary Brotherton, and my house is called Milford Park."

"Certainly, Miss Brotherton, both your name, and that of your residence are known to me—on what subject can I give you any information that may be useful?"

"Circumstances, Mr Bell, have lately directed my attention to a subject which my own situation in life, as well as the neighbourhood in which I live ought to have long ago made thoroughly familiar to me—such is not the case, however; I am profoundly, and I fear shamefully ignorant respecting the large and very important class of our population employed in the factories. I am in possession of a large fortune wholly amassed from the profits obtained by my father from this species of labour, and I cannot but feel great interest in the welfare and prosperity of the people employed in it—especially as I understand a very large proportion of them are young children—and moreover, that from some cause or other, which I can by no means understand, the whole class of 'the factory people,' as I hear them called, are spoken of with less kindness and respect by those who have grown rich upon their industry, than any other description of human beings whatever. I am told, sir, that it would be *unsafe, improper*, and altogether *wrong* were I to attempt making myself personally acquainted with them, as I would wish to do—and having accidentally, Mr Bell, heard your name mentioned as a person who took an interest in their concerns, have come to you thus unceremoniously, in the hope that you would have the kindness to give me more accurate information on the subject, than I have found it possible to obtain elsewhere."

Mr Bell, who had placed himself immediately opposite to her, looked in her young face, and listened to her earnest voice as she spoke, with the deepest attention. It soon became sufficiently clear that he considered not this intrusion as requiring apology, but that on the contrary his very heart and soul were moved by her words. He paused for a moment after she had ceased speaking, as if unwilling to interrupt her by his reply; but when he found that she remained silent, he said,

"The subject on which you are come to converse with me, my dear Miss Brothertun, is assuredly the very last I should have expected to hear named by a young lady in your position—for it is one from which the rich and great of our district turn away with loathing and contempt. Yet is it the one of all others to which I would if possible direct their best attention, involving as it does both their interest and their duty beyond any other. But I fear I cannot enter upon it without wounding many prejudices which of necessity you must have imbibed, and proving to you that much which doubtless you have been educated to consider right, is on the contrary most lamentably wrong. Can you bear this my dear young lady?"

"I hope I could, in a search after truth, Mr Bell, even if my mind were in the condition you suppose," replied Mary. "But this is not the case. You will not have to remove many false impressions I think.—It is the total absence of all knowledge on the subject, which I am bold enough to ask you to remedy."

"And most willingly will I endeavour to do so, to the very best of my ability," replied Mr Bell.—"But to me it is a beguiling subject, and if I detain you too long, you must tell me so."

"Fear not," replied Mary, smiling. "I shall be more willing to hear, than you to speak."

"You are of course aware, Miss Brotherton," resumed the clergyman, "that the large proportion of young labourers to whom you have just alluded, are calculated to amount, in Yorkshire and Lancashire alone to upwards of two hundred thousand."

"Is it possible?" exclaimed Mary. "Alas! Mr Bell you must not think that '*of course*' I know any thing—had you named two thousand as the number, my surprise would have been less."

"But so it is, Miss Brotherton. Above two hundred thousand young creatures, including infants among them, counting only five years of life, are thus employed in the counties I have named; and they surely form a

class, which both from their numbers, and their helplessness are entitled
to English sympathy and protection?"

"Unquestionably!" cried Mary, eagerly, "I always feel that the
labouring poor have great and unceasing claims upon the sympathy and
assistance of the rich.—But this claim must be equally great I should
suppose amongst all the labouring classes. Is it not, Mr Bell?"

"I feel it difficult to answer your question by a negative," he replied,
"because taken in its broadest sense, it most assuredly demands an
affirmative. Nevertheless it is unquestionably true that at this moment
there is no race of human beings in any portion of the known world—
the most wretched of negro slaves not excepted, Miss Brotherton—who
require the protection and assistance of their happier fellow creatures, in
the same degree as the young creatures employed in our factories."

Miss Brotherton looked at him, not doubtingly, but with considerable
surprise and timidly replied, "But the negro slave, Mr Bell, has no choice
left him—he is the *property* of his master."

"Neither has the factory child a choice, Miss Brotherton. He too is *a
property*; nor is it the least horrible part of the evil which noiselessly has
grown out of this tremendous system, that the beings whom nature has
ordained throughout creation to keep watch, and ward over the helpless
weakness of infant life, are driven by it to struggle with, and trampled
down the holiest, and dearest of human ties—the love of a parent for its
offspring. Picture to yourself a bleak winter's morning, Miss Brotherton,
when the mother of factory children must be up hours and hours before
the sun to rouse her half-rested little ones; and nervously watching
her rude clock till the dreaded moment comes, must shake the little
creatures, whose slumber the very beast of the field might teach her to
watch over and guard, till they awake, and starting in terror from their
short sleep, ask if the hour be come? The wretched mother, and the
wretched child then vie with each other in their trembling haste to seize
the tattered mill-clothes, and to put them on. The mother dreads the fine
of one quarter of the infant's daily wages, which would be levied, should
it arrive but a minute too late, and the poor child dreads the strap, which,
in addition, is as surely the punishment for delay. Miss Brotherton, I have
seen with my own eyes the assembling of some hundreds of factory

children before the still unopened doors of their prison-house, while the lingering darkness of a winter's night had yet to last three hours. I shall never forget one bitter morning, last January twelvemonth! The last piteous summons from a dying parishoner had left me no choice but to exchange my pillow for the bitter blast of Howley-common and the path across it leading me within a hundred yards of a large cotton-factory, I witnessed a spectacle which to my dying day I shall never recall without a shudder! There was just moon enough to show me all the dreary sternness of the scene.—The ground was covered deep with snow, and a cutting wind blew whistling through the long line of old Scotch firs which bordered an enclosure beside the road. As I scudded on beneath them, my eye caught the little figures of a multitude of children, made distinctly visible, even by that dim light, by the strong relief in which their dark garments showed themselves against the snow. A few steps further brought me in full view of the factory gates, and then I perceived considerably above two hundred of these miserable little victims to avarice all huddled together on the ground, and seemingly half buried in the drift that was blown against them. I stood still and gazed upon them—I knew full well what, and how great was the terror which had brought them there too soon, and in my heart of hearts I cursed the boasted manufacturing wealth of England, which running, in this direction at least, in a most darkened narrow channel, gives power, *lawless and irresistible* to overwhelm and crush the land it pretends to fructify. While still spell-bound by this appalling picture, I was startled by the sound of a low moaning from the other side of the road, at a short distance from me, and turning towards it perceived a woman bending over a little girl who appeared sinking to the ground. A few rapid steps brought me close to them, and I found on examination that the child was so benumbed and exhausted as to be totally incapable of pursuing her way—it was her *mother* who was urging her forward, and who even then seemed more intent upon saving a fine, than on the obvious sufferings of her sinking child. I know, poor wretch, that little choice was left her, and that the inevitable consequence of saving her from the factory, and leading her gently home to such shelter as her father's roof could give, would be to watch her perish there for want of food."

"Alas! alas! is it thus my wealth has been accumulated?" exclaimed Miss Brotherton, shuddering. "Is there no power in England, sir, righteous and strong enough to stay this plague?"

"Miss Brotherton!" returned the clergyman, "such power, and such righteousness, must be found, or this plague, as you well call it, will poison the very life blood of our political existence; and long ere any serious danger is likely to be dreamed of by our heedless rulers, the bloated wealth with which this pernicious system has enriched a few, will prove a source of utter destruction to the many. Never, my dear young lady, did the avarice of man conceive a system so horribly destructive of every touch of human feeling, as that by which the low-priced agony of labourine infants is made to eke out and supply all that is wanting to enable the giant engines of our factories to out-spin all the world! But you must see it, Miss Brotherton, you must watch it with your own eyes, you must follow the hateful operations of this atrocious system into the thousands of sordid and forgotten huts which cover its miserable victims, ere you can possibly understand its moral mischief. There is no strength, no power in words to paint it."

"Its moral mischief," said Mary, eagerly; "explain that to me, Mr Bell, for it is the point I find most puzzling—why is it that these poor factory-people, because they labour more unremittingly, as it should seem, than all the world beside, why, for this reason, instead of being honoured for their industry, are they invariably spoken of with contempt and obliquy?"

"Your question, Miss Brotherton, involves by far the most terrible portion of this frightful commercial mystery," he replied; "but, as I have told you, nothing except personal investigation can enable the inquirer to arrive at the whole truth respecting it. Were a patient, accurate, and laborious detail of all the enormities committed, and all the sufferings endured, under the factory system, to be presented to the public, it would be thrown aside by some, as greatly too tedious for examination, and by others as a statement too atrocious to merit belief. Yet, England MUST listen to it, and that soon, or she may mourn her negligence when it is too late to repair it. That marvellous machinery of which we make our boast, Miss Brotherton, is not more perfect in its power of

I was startled by the sound of a low moaning, and perceived a woman bending over a little girl, who appeared sinking to the ground.

drawing out the delicately attenuated thread which it is our glory to produce, then the system for reducing the human labour necessary for its production to the lowest possible price is, for degrading the moral nature of the helpless slaves engaged in it."

"That the system has such a tendency I cannot doubt, after the repeated assurances which have reached me, that so it is," replied Mary. "Nevertheless, I am still unable to comprehend why it should be so."

"You have only to take advantage of your residence near Ashleigh, Miss Brotherton, the dense population of which subsists almost wholly by factory labour, in order to understand, but too well, why this terrible result is inevitable. You are as yet too young a lady for me to expect that you should have very deeply studied the nature of the human mind, or made yourself fully aware how greatly the habits and character of all human beings depend upon education, and the circumstances in which they are placed. Nevertheless, if you turn your attention to the subject, you will not, young as you are, be long incapable of detecting the dangers which beset the hearts and souls of those whose unhappy destiny have made them factory labourers. The dark little circle in which they move from birth to death, from father to son, from mother to daughter, is so uniform, that almost any average individual case may fairly serve as a specimen of the whole class. Boys and girls, with few exceptions, labour indiscriminately altogether in the factories. While still almost children, they form connexions, and are married. Having worked in the mills, probably from five years old to the hour of their unweighed and thoughtless union, the boy assumes the duties of a husband with little more knowledge of moral or religious responsibility than the animal brute that labours with a thousand times less degradation in the fields; while the childish wife comes to her important task ignorant of every earthly usefulness, save what belongs to the mechanical drudgery in which throughout the whole of her short, sad life, she has been made to follow the uniform and ceaseless movements of machinery. She cannot sew, she cannot cook, she cannot iron, she cannot wash. Her mind is yet more untaught and undisciplined than her hands. She is conscious of no responsibility, she knows no law by which to steer her actions, or regulate her spirit, and becomes a mother as she became a wife, without one single thought of duty mixing itself with her increasing cares. By degrees, both the husband and the wife find employment in the factory less certain. It is for children, children, children, that the unwearied engine calls, and keenly does the hungry father, and the mother too, watch the growth of the little creatures to whom they have given birth, till the slight limbs have firmness enough to stand, and the delicate joints are sufficiently under the command of the frightened will to tie threads together under the potent inspiration of the overlooker's strap. There comes a state of deeper degradation still. The father is idle, for often he can get no work, and it is to the labour of his little ones that he looks for bread.. Nature recoils from the spectacle of their unnatural o'erlaboured aspect as they return from their thirteen, fourteen, fifteen, hours of toil.

He has not nerve to look upon it, and creeps to the gin-shops till they are hid in bed. The mother sees it all, and sternly screws her courage to the task of lifting their bruised and weary limbs upon their bed of straw, putting into their mouths the food she has prepared, their weary eyes being already closed in sleep, and preparing herself to wake before the sun on the morrow, that with unrelenting hand she may drag them from their unfinished slumber, and drive them forth again to get her food. This is no varnished tale, Miss Brotherton, but the bare, naked, hideous truth. And can you wonder that beings thus reared and ripened should form a degraded class? Can you wonder that all others should turn from them, as from a race with whom they have nothing in common? If some sad accident, preceding birth, disturbs the beautiful process by which nature prepares the noble being she has made to be lord of all, and an abortive creature comes to life, curtailed of all its fair proportions, both of mind and body, all within reach of the hapless prodigy shudder as they mourn, and the best and wisest among them pray to God that its span of life be short. But believe me when I tell you, Miss Brotherton, that the effect which the factories of this district is producing upon above two hundred thousand of its population, is beyond all calculation more deplorable, and many a child is born amongst them whose destiny, if fairly weighed against that of such a one as I have described, would appear incomparably more terrible."

"Can such things be, and the rulers of the land sit idly by to witness it?" cried Mary shuddering.

"It seems as if the rulers of the land knew little, and cared less about it," replied Mr Bell. "The profoundly ignorant opinion that there is some connexion between our national prosperity, and the enormous fortunes amassed by some score of North-country manufacturers has, I believe, produced much of the lamentable non-interference of which the disinterested few complain, who are near enough to look upon the frightful game. So individual voices have been most gloriously raised on this tremendous theme, and if they will be steadfast and enduring, they must and will prevail—for human nature, with all its vices, is not framed to look coldly on such horrors, and permit them. But the remedial process is so slow—it is so difficult to arouse the attention, and awaken the feelings of busy men concerning things at a distance, whose connexion with all that they deem important they are too ignorant of, or too preoccupied to trace, that the keenest observers, and those who would the most deeply deprecate any remedy but a legal one, begin to fear that mercy will be clamoured for with very dangerous rudeness, before the parliament of England shall have roused up its wisdom to the task of affording it."

"And in what way, Mr Bell, is it wished, or hoped that the legislature should step forward to cure this dreadful evil? Is it proposed to abolish the use of machinery?"

Mr Bell smiled and shook his head.

"You perhaps think," said he, "that there is a great disproportion between my strong sense of the vice and suffering produced by the factory system, and the measure for its mitigation to which I now limit almost my wishes. But it would be vain to look back to the time when steam engines were not, and there would indeed be little wisdom in addressing our lamentations to their introduction. It is not the acquisition of any natural power, principle, or faculty, that we should deplore; all such, on the contrary, should be hailed as part and parcel of our magnificent birthright, and each new use we learn to make of the still much-unknown creation around us, ought to be welcomed with a shout of praise, as a fresh fulfilment of the supreme command 'replenish the earth and *subdue* it.' It is not from increased, or increasing science that we have any thing to dread, it is only from a fearfully culpable neglect of the moral power that should rule and regulate its uses, that it can be other than one of God's best gifts."

"But how," demanded Mary, "how, if machinery continues to be used, can any Act of Parliament prevent the necessity of employing children to wait upon its operations instead of requiring the strength of men, as heretofore, to perform what the steam-engine does in their place?"

"No Act of Parliament can be conceived capable of inducing a manufacturer to employ the weaker, and at the same time the more costly agent, preference to a more powerful and cheaper one," replied Mr Bell. "No reasonable man would ask this, no reasonable man would desire it, and assuredly no reasonable man would attempt to enforce such an absurdity by law. No, Miss Brotherton, this mighty power, as surely given for our use as is the innocent air that fans the woodbine yonder, has at length, after some few thousand years of careless overlooking on our part, been revealed to us. But let us not fly in the face of benignant nature, and say like Caliban,

> "You taught me language; and my profit on't
> Is, I know how to curse."

"If used aright there cannot be a doubt that this magnificent power might, in all its agencies, be made the friend of man. It requires no great stretch of ingenuity to conceive that it might be rendered at once a source of still increasing wealth to the capitalist, and of lightened labour to the not-impoverished operative. But that, as things are at present, this great discovery, and all the admirable ingenuity with which it is applied, acts as a ban instead of a blessing, upon some hundred thousands of miserable victims is most true, while all the benefit that can be shown as a balance to this horror, is the bloated wealth of a small knot of master-manufacturers. But so monstrous is this evil, that its very atrocity inspires hope, from the improbability that when once beyond all reach of contradiction its existence shall be known by all men, it should be permitted to continue."

"Then why is it not known?" demanded Mary, her colour heightened as she remembered her own entire ignorance upon the subject a few short weeks before, "surely it is the duty of all lookers-on to proclaim it to the whole world."

"Alas! Miss Brotherton! It is more easy to raise a voice, than to command attention to it. Loud and long must be the cry that shall awaken the indifferent, and rouse the indolent to action. But this loud, long cry, will be uttered, and by the blessing of God it will be listened to at last."

"But tell me Mr Bell," resumed his deeply interested auditor, "what is this moderate enactment in mitigation of these wretched people's sufferings, which you say would content you?"

"All that we ask for," replied Mr Bell, "all that the poor creatures ask for themselves, is that by Act of Parliament it should be rendered illegal for men women and children to be kept to the wearying unhealthy labour of the mills for more than ten hours out of every day, leaving their daily wages at the same rate as now."

"And would *that* suffice," demanded Miss Brotherton with astonishment, "to effectually relieve the horrors you have been describing to me?"

"Miss Brotherton it would," replied the clergyman. "I would be loath to weary you with details," he continued, " but a few items may suffice to make you see how enormous are the benefits which would follow such an enactment. At present, if a large demand for manufactured goods arises, instead of being, as it ought, a blessing to the industrious hands that must supply it, it comes upon them as a fearful burden, threatening to crush the very springs of life in the little creatures that are chiefly to sustain it, while the golden harvest that it brings is not for them, but for masters. For the miserable need of an extra penny, or sometimes three halfpence a day, the young slaves (who, observe, have no power of choice, for if they, or their parents for them, refuse, they are instantly turned off to literal starvation—no parish assistance being allowed to those who resist the regulations of the manufacturers), for this wretched equivalent for health and joy, are compelled, whenever our boasted trade flows briskly, to stand to their work for just as many hours as the application of the over-looker's strap, or billy-roller, can keep them on their legs. Innumerable instances are on record of children falling from excess of weariness on the machinery, and being called to life by its lacerating their flesh. It continually happens that young creatures under fifteen years of age, are kept from their beds all night. Fifteen, sixteen, seventeen, hours of labour out of the twenty-four, are cases which recur continually, and I need not say with what effect upon these victims of ferocious avarice. Now not only would all this be mended, the positive bodily torture spared, and as far as is consistent with constant in-door occupation, the health of the labourers preserved, were it made unlawful to keep them at positive labour for more than ten hours of every day; not only would all this follow from the enactment, but innumerable other advantages, some of them more important still, would, beyond all question, be its consequence. In the first place, were there no power of executing great and sudden orders by irregular exactions of labour, the recurrence of those fearful intervals when the starving operatives are thrown out of employ by the accidents which cause a deficiency in the demand, would not happen—for in that case the capitalists would find themselves obliged to be beforehand with the demand, even though some portion of their enormous wealth should for a time lie idle. From this would also follow the necessity of often employing adult hands, where now the cheaper labour of children, forced from their very vitals through the day and night, may be had for the sin of demanding it. Then would the unnatural spectacle of a stalwart father idly waiting to snatch the wages from the little feverish hand of his o'er-laboured child be seen no more. Then would there be strength and spirits left in the young to profit by the Sunday-schools now so often ostentatiously opened in vain, because the only way in which a little piecer can keep holiday is by lying throughout the day stretched upon his straw in heavy sleep. Then too, the demoralizing process by which the heart of a mother is rendered hard as the nether mill-stone, by the necessity of goading her infants to their frightful toil, would cease. Boys and girls would no longer have to return to their homes at midnight—there would be time and inclination then, for those comfortable operations of the needle and the shears, which

'Make old clothes look amaist as weel as new.'

Then would not the disheartened ministers of God's church strive in vain to make the reckless, joyless, worthless race listen to his words of faith and hope. Then, Miss Brotherton, they would arise from that state of outcast degradation which has caused your friends to tell you that it would be 'unsafe, improper, and altogether wrong,' for you, and such as you, to make personal acquaintance with them."

"And do you really think all this mighty, this glorious good, would follow from an enactment so moderate, so reasonable, so every way unobjectionable?"

"I have not the slightest shadow of a doubt, Miss Brotherton, that such good would follow it, and more, much more, than I have named—more than any one could believe or comprehend who has not, like myself, been watching for years the misery, the vice, the degradation, which have resulted from the want of it."

"Then why, Mr Bell, have not such representations been made to the legislature as must ensure its immediate adoption?"

The good clergyman shook his head. "It is a most natural, question, my dear young friend—allow me so to call you. All are my friends who feel upon this subject as you appear to do. It is a most natural and a most obvious question. Yet would my reply be any thing rather than easy of comprehension were I to attempt to answer it directly. I sincerely hope I shall converse with you again on this subject. Documents are not wanting, my dear Miss Brotherton, to prove that all, or nearly all, that private individuals can do, in the way of petition and remonstrance, has been already tried; nor are we yet without hope that good may come of it. But it must be long, and perhaps the longer the better, ere your young head and innocent heart, can conceive our difficulties. You would hardly believe the ingenious devices to which frightened avarice can have recourse in order to retard, mutilate, and render abortive a measure having for its object a reduction of profits, with no equivalent save the beholding smiles instead of tears, and hearing the sounds of song and laughter instead of groans!"

"But while you are still waiting and hoping for this aid from our lawgivers," said Mary, "is there nothing that can be done in the interval to help all this misery, Mr Bell?"

"Nothing effectual, my dear young lady," he replied mournfully. "I may, with no dishonest boasting say, that my life is spent in doing all I can to save these unhappy people from utter degradation and despair. But the oppression under which they groan is too overwhelming to be removed, or even lightened, by any agency less powerful than that of the law. Nothing, in fact, can so clearly show the powerful oppression of the system as the total inefficiency of individual benevolence to heal the misery of those who suffer under it. Its power is stupendous, awful, terrible! Nature herself, elsewhere so omnipotent, here feels the strength of unchecked human wickedness, and seems to bend before it. For most certain is it, that in less than half a century, during which the present factory system has been in operation, the lineaments of the race involved in it are changed and deteriorated. The manufacturing population are of lesser and of weaker growth than their agricultural countrymen. The development of the intellectual faculties is obviously becoming weaker, and many whom we have every reason to believe understand the physiology of man as thoroughly as science can teach it to them, do not scruple to assert, that if the present system continues the race of English factory operatives will dwindle and sink in the strongly-graduated scale of human beings, to something lower than the Esquimaux."

"Gracious Heaven!" cried Mary, clasping her hands with an emotion that almost amounted to agony, "and all these horrors are perpetrated for the sake of making rich, needlessly, uselessly rich, a few obscure manufacturing families like my own, This is very dreadful sir," she continued, while tears burst from her eyes. "I have gained knowledge but not peace by my visit, and I must leave you with the sad conviction that the hope I had nourished of making my fortune useful to the suffering creatures among whom I live, is vain and idle."

Mr Bell listened to this melancholy assertion, and sighed because he could not contradict it. "Yes;" said he, at length, "it is even so; and if any proof were wanted of the depth and hopelessness of the wretchedness which the present system produces, it might be found in the fact, that despite the inclination I feel both for your sake, and that of the poor operatives, to encourage your generous benevolence, I cannot in conscience tell you that it is in your power effectually to assist them. That you may save your own excellent heart from the palsy of hopeless and helpless pity, by the indulgence of your benevolence in individual cases of distress, I need not point out to you; but that any of the ordinary modes of being useful on a larger scale, such as organising schools, founding benefit societies, or the like, could be of any use to beings so crushed, so toil-worn, and so degraded, it would be idle to hope."

Miss Brotherton now rose to depart—but as she extended her hand, and began to utter her farewell, it occurred to here that it was possible her new friend might, by conjecture, at least throw some light upon the destination of little Michael, and avoiding as much as possible the making any direct charge against her rich neighbour, she briefly narrated the facts of Michael's adoption, dismissal, and unknown destination, with little commentary on either, but concluded by saying,

"The mother of the child is in great anxiety about him, and though I cannot conceive it possible any harm can have befallen the boy, I am in some sort a fellow-sufferer with her in the anxiety which this mystery occasions, from having almost pledged myself to learn the place of his destination. Can you, dear sir, suggest to me any means by which this information can be obtained?"

"Some part of this history has reached us already," replied Mr Bell. "It has been somewhat industriously bruited through the neighbourhood, that Sir Matthew Dowling, notoriously one of the most tyrannical millocrats in the whole district, has been moved to kindness in behalf of some poor widow's son, and taken him to be reared and educated with his own children—I trust I am excusable, knowing what I know, for misdoubting the disinterested benevolence of any act of Sir Matthew Dowling's. Nevertheless it is certainly not easy to perceive why after having so ostentatiously distinguished the boy, he should kidnap him, as it were, from his own house, in order to get rid of him. If, instead of being the object of especial favour, the little fellow had fallen under the rich knight's displeasure, Miss Brotherton, I should think it by no means improbable that he might have consigned him as an apprentice to some establishment, too notorious for its severity to make it desirable that his selection of it should be made known. But of this there seems neither proof nor likelihood."

Miss Brotherton turned pale as she listened to this suggestion.

"Nay, but there is both truth and likelihood in such a suspicion," she exclaimed with considerable emotion, and after a moment's consideration, added, "I know no reason why I should conceal the cause I have for saying so—if you know not all, how can you give me counsel?"

Hurriedly, and as briefly as possible, Miss Brotherton then recounted the scene she had witnessed in the green-room of the Dowling Lodge theatricals, but there was an unconscious and involuntary fervour in her manner of narrating it, which rendered it impossible to listen with indifference, or not to feel at the recital some portion of the indignation she had felt when it occurred.

"It must be looked to, Miss Brotherton," replied her warm new acquaintance. "The boy must be traced, tracked, found, and rescued! I think there are few of these wretched prison-houses of whose existence I am ignorant, and it is probable I may be able to help you in this. Should I obtain any hint likely to be useful in the search, I will call upon you, if you will give me leave, to communicate it."

Most earnestly and truly did the heiress assure him that it was impossible she could receive a visit more calculated to give her pleasure, adding that whether the hint were obtained or not, she trusted the acquaintance she had so unceremoniously began, would not drop here and that by returning her visit, he would prove to her that he was not displeased by it.

It rarely happens between right-hearted people who meet for the first time, if one of the parties conceives a liking for the other, that it fails to prove mutual; and it was with a cordial sincerity, as genuine as her own, that Mr Bell expressed his hope that their acquaintance would ripen into friendship.

Too intently occupied by all that had passed, to remember her own arrangements, Mary forgot that her carriage was not at the door, and while these parting words were exchanged, walked forth, expecting to find it. It was Mrs Tremlett who first recollected that the coachman had been ordered to put up his horses at the nearest inn, but this was not till they had traversed the little garden, and were already in the lane; for though the good nurse had been little more than *personnage muet* during the foregoing scene, she had taken a deep interest in it, and it was much with the air of one awaking from a dream, that she said, "My dear Miss Mary! you have forgot that the carriage is sent away."

"Indeed have I!" said Mary, laughing, "and no wonder. But there stands our faithful William, he will tell us in what direction we may find it."

"Will you not return, Miss Brotherton, while it is made ready?" said the clergyman.

"Not if you will walk on with us, dear sir. The evening is delightful, but already quite far enough advanced to make it prudent not to lose any time." And having given orders that the carriage was to follow, they strolled on towards the turnpike.

"There," said Mr Bell, pointing to the towering chimneys of a large

factory at some distance, "there, Miss Brotherton, is an establishment
where, though carding and spinning go on within the walls, and some
hundreds of children and young girls are employed in attending the
machinery that performs the process, the voice of misery is never heard,
for there the love of gold is chained and held captive by religion and
humanity."

"Thank God!" exclaimed Mary, as she looked at the sinless monster to
which he pointed. "It is not of necessity then, that this dangerous trade
is fatal to all employed in it."

"Certainly not. Were but its labours restricted both for young and
old, to ten hours a day, there is no reason on earth why it should not be
carried on with comfort and advantage to every individual concerned
in it, and with credit, honour, and prosperity to the country. But you
can hardly guess what up-hill work it is, when one good man has got
to stand alone, and breast the competition of a whole host of bad ones
his commercial enterprises. The high-minded owners of yonder factory
are losing thousands every year by their efforts to purity this traffic of
its enormities—and some thousand small still voices call down blessings
on them for it. But while it costs them ten shillings to produce what
their neighbours can bring into the market for nine, they will only
be pointed at as pitiably unwise in their generation by all the great
family of Mammon which surrounds them. Few, alas! will think of
following the example! All they can do therefore is in fact but to carry
on a system of private charity on an enormous scale—but till they
are supported by law, even their vast efforts, and most noble sacrifices
can do nothing towards the general redemption of our poor northern
people from the state of slavery into which they have fallen. And yet
I do believe, Miss Brotherton," he continued, after a pause, "I do most
truly believe that these greedy tyrants would fail more rarely than now
they do in their efforts to realize enormous wealth, if the system were
to undergo exactly the change we ask for. The plan of under-selling
may indeed in some few instances enable a very lucky man to run up a
blood-stained fortune; and blood-stained it must be, for whenever this
method of commanding a sale is pursued, and ruin does NOT ensue,
it is demonstrable that the bones and marrow of children, working

unlimited hours, must have been the main agent in the operation. But it is quite certain that the under-selling system must upon the long run be ruinous. If all the losses upon our production were fairly set against all the gains from the immoderate working of young hands, the slavery scheme would appear as little profitable as holy. But here is your carriage, my dear young lady! God bless you! and may we live to rejoice together over an effectual legislative remedy for the evils we have passed this our first interview in deploring!"

So saying, he extended his hand to assist her into the carriage which had already drawn up beside them—but Miss Brotherton stepped aside while he performed this office to her friend, and then laying her hand on his arm, drew him back a step or two to the spot from whence the factory chimneys he had pointed out to her were visible.

"Tell me, before we part," she said, "the names of those to whom that building belongs?"

"WOOD AND WALKER," replied the clergyman.

"Thank you!" she replied; "I shall never hear those names without breathing a blessing on them!"

Friendly farewells were once more exchanged, and the meditative heiress was driven back to Milford-park in silence so profound, that her old friend believed her to be asleep, and carefully abstained from any movement that might awaken her. But Mary Brotherton was not asleep.

XX

*Trade in a flourishing state—The benefits conferred
thereby to those employed in it—The natural logic
of religion—Its fallability when put to the test*

THE MOMENT AT WHICH MICHAEL Armstrong entered the cotton mill
at Deep Valley, was a critical one. The summer had been more than
commonly sultry, and a large order had kept all hands very sharply at
work. Even at dead of night the machinery was never stopped, and when
one set of fainting children were dragged from the mules another set
were dragged from the reeking beds they were about to occupy, in order
to take their places. The ventilation throughout the whole fabric was
exceedingly imperfect; the heat, particularly in the rooms immediately
beneath the roof, frightfully intense; cleanliness as to the beds, the floors,
and the walls, utterly neglected; and even the persons of the children
permitted to be filthy to excess, from having no soap allowed to assist their
ablutions—though from the greasy nature of their employment it was
peculiarly required, while the coarse meal occasionally given out to supply
its place was invariably swallowed, being far too precious in the eyes of the
hungry children to be applied to the purpose for which it was designed. In
addition to all this, the food was miserably scanty, and of a nature so totally
unfit to sustain the strength of growing children thus severely worked,
that within a fortnight after Michael's arrival, an epidemic fever of a very
alarming description began to shew itself. But it had made considerable
progress, before the presence of this new horror was revealed to him.

Notwithstanding all the hardships of Brookford factory, no infectious
disease had ever appeared there, which it is possible might have been

owing to the fact that the majority of the labourers in it lived at a considerable distance, thus insuring to them a walk morning and night, through the fresh air. This, though it added to their daily fatigue, probably lessened the danger of it, while the wretched hovels to which they returned for their short night's rest, miserable shelters as they were, reeked not with the congregated effluvia of fifty uncleansed sleepers in one chamber! Michael, therefore, had never before witnessed the hideous approach of contagion. The general appearance too of the Deep Valley troop was so far from healthy, that the sickly aspect of those first seized upon was less remarkable than it would have been elsewhere. Thus another week wore away, during which, though several of those who had been working when it began were withdrawn, and known to be in the sick-ward ere it closed, the fact that an infectious fever was among them had not yet got wing.

"Poor dear Betsy Price!" whispered Fanny Fletcher to her friend Michael, as they sat side by side at their miserable dinner one day.

"I heard missis tell master that she was dead. But I am trying to be glad for it, Michael."

"Glad, Fanny?" replied the boy, "you told me once that you liked her more than any other girl in the mill, and now you are glad she is dead!"

"I am not so glad as I think I ought to be," returned Fanny gently. "She will not be hungry in Heaven, Michael, nor will she work till she is ready to fall: and surely God will give us green fields and sweet fresh air in Heaven, and there must be flowers, Michael. Oh! I am quite sure of that, and Betsy Price will have it all! Ought I not to be very, very, glad?"

Michael looked in her sweet, innocent face, as she said this, and tears filled his eyes.

"And if you die, Fanny, must I be glad too?"

"If you thought about Heaven as I do, and if you loved me very much indeed," replied the little girl, "I can't tell how you could help being glad."

"But I do love you very much indeed," said Michael, almost choked by his efforts not to cry, "and I do think of Heaven, too, Fanny, but I couldn't be glad if you was to die!"

"Not when you hear that, Michael!" said Fanny, starting up as the last of the governor's whip resounded through the room as a signal that their numbered moments of rest were over. "I suppose then I love you better than you love me, for I could not help being glad if I knew that you would never hear nor feel that lash again!"

When they met again at supper, Michael, though still unsuspicious of the cause, missed three more children from their places. He fancied, too, that there was something new and strange in the aspect of their hard-featured female tyrant; she was paler than usual, scolded not at all, and when she spoke to her husband, it was in a voice that hardly exceeded a whisper. Yet, notwithstanding this, some young ears again caught words that told of death. Yet still the mill worked on and nothing seemed to mark that any calamity more than usual had got among them.

By degrees, however, the growing pestilence burst forth, as it were, before the eyes of the terrified children, and they knew that the grave yawned before them all. Then it was that the ghastly countenances of each doomed victim struck dismay into the hearts of their companions even before they were permitted to leave their labour, and sink down to the rest that should be disturbed no more. But still the mill went on for Mr Elgood Sharpton had just received a glorious order from Russia, and it would have been perfect madness, as this gentlemen was heard to remark to his eldest son, if a death or two among the apprentice children was to check the mill at such a time as that.

So the mill went on, and death went on too. But as it is considered by all parties concerned to be extremely important that the cry of epidemic contagion should not be raised in the neighbourhood of a factory under these circumstances, it was deemed best by Mr Elgood Sharpton and his confidential managers, not to call in medical assistance.

"For first and foremost, Poulet," said the experienced proprietor to the governor of the apprentice house, "first and foremost, it is of no manner of use. I never knew any proper, regular contagious fever in my life, that could be stopped short by a doctor. You must take care of yourself and your wife, of course, and I will see that you have a hamper of good old port sent in, and mind that you both of you take two glasses a day each, Poulet—one before you go into the rooms in the morning, and the other, after you have seen them all down for the night, and we must order in a cask of vinegar to sprinkle the chambers. Trust me that this will do more good than all the doctors that ever were hatched. Besides the vinegar cask will never sing out you know, Poulet, and the doctor might."

To this reasoning, and to these arrangements, no objection whatever was made by the governor of the apprentice-house. Of athletic frame, and iron nerves, he grinned defiance at any danger that threatened his own person, rightly enough thinking, perhaps, that any disease to which his water-porridge-fed troop appeared peculiarly liable, would be little likely to attack himself.

It was, however, not the least part of his wisdom upon this occasion, that he systematically paid as little attention to what was going on round him as possible. Had he made it a habit to look into the haggard faces of the drooping children, as one after another they pined, languished, and sunk, first into the horrible abyss of wretchedness called the sick-ward, and then into the grave, it is possible that he too might in some degree have been shaken. As it was, however, he went on so cleverly supplying the missing hands by recommending to the management that one healthy child should do the work of two, and so cleverly, also, getting all that died by day buried by night, without making, as he said, any fuss or fidget about it whatever, that Mr Elgood Sharpton felt him to be eminently deserving of an especial reward, and when fifteen children had been noiselessly buried, in Tugswell churchyard, he presented him with a Bank of England note for ten pounds, as a testimony of his esteem and gratitude for his very exemplary and praiseworthy behaviour. It fared not quite so well, however, with his wife. Whether it were that the poco-curante system was less within reach of her position than of his; or that her frame was less stoutly proof against the malaria with which she was surrounded, a visible change came over her about three weeks after this visitation had been first felt at the Deep Valley mills. Strong in constitution, and athletic in form, it seemed, however, no easy matter for disease itself to conquer her. The large dark eye grew dim, and sunk back behind her high cheek-bones by degrees. Her coarse firm-set features appeared to relax, and her active limbs to languish, for two whole days before she yielded herself to the invincible power that had seized upon her.

"Do! you devils imps! I'll do ye! off to
your mules or by …"

It happened during this interval that Fanny Fletcher and Michael, in
their eagerness to communicate to each other their observations on the
rapidly-increasing sickness of their fellow-labourers, hung back together,
as the frightened train swept on before the lifted lash of the governor, and
permitted nearly all their companions to reach the mill ere they had left the
supper-room. They were perhaps themselves unconscious how much they
were emboldened to this hardy defiance of a standing law by the unwonted
stillness of tongue, and tameness of aspect observable in Mrs Poulet. But
if they fancied they were to escape entirely they were mistaken, for whilst
the little girl was telling Michael that they ought always, at work, or not
at work, to be thinking of God, who was perhaps thinking of them, and
meaning to take them both up together to his own happy Heaven, just as
she had laid her hand on his to enforce her words, and looking wistfully in
his face pronounced aloud, "Do Michael, do!" the sick dragon stepped back
on hearing them, from the passage that led into the kitchen, and turning
her ghastly face full upon them, exclaimed, while her languid fist strove in
vain to clench and raise itself, as in days of yore, to threaten castigation.

"Do! you devil's imps! I'll do ye! Off to your mules or by —". But ere she could finish the sentence, her fever-laden sinews relaxed, aud seizing upon the long table for support she sank almost insensible upon a bench.

Greatly terrified, both Michael and Fanny screamed together, but they screamed in vain. There was no longer any one within hearing save in the closely packed chamber above, where more than twenty sick children lay two and two together, in their miserable beds, but totally without nurses or attendants of any kind, so that their loud cries, though heard by many, brought assistance from none.

"Oh! Michael! Michael! she'll die too!" said Fanny shuddering. "I would make her live longer if I could. She is not fit to die. Go to the pump, Michael, and fetch water! Go, go, dear boy. We must not leave her this way!"

The little girl endeavoured to raise the woman's head, which had sunk upon the table, but the effort was beyond her strength, and feeling after a moment's reflection that the best manner of assisting her would be to call others, she cried, "No, no! don't go Michael! Don't go for the water. It is no use my trying to hold her up, and besides we don't know if it is good for her or not. Oh dear! How dreadful bad she looks. Let us run away to the mill, Michael, and tell the master."

The seizure of Mrs Poulet, unlike every other, became, within an hour, from the time it was known, the theme of every tongue throughout the whole establishment. Had it been Mr Elgood Sharpton himself it could not well have occasioned a greater sensation. The effect this produced throughout the sickly troop might have served as a proof of the wisdom of a government when it conceals the mischief it has brought upon an empire, from those who are likely to discuss it. The total silence which till now had been preserved among the managers and overlookers respecting the contagious nature of the malady which had got among the children, the absence of all medical attendance, and of all precautionary or medical measures in any way calculated to excite attention, had hitherto very successfully prevented rumour from doing her usual work on such occasions; and it is probable that this partial ignorance of their own danger considerably lessened its consequences; for it was passed without many fresh victims sinking under its influence, and it was no uncommon thing to see two or three wheelbarrows at a time, towards the evening of every day, conveying children from the factory to the apprentice-house who had fallen while following the machinery.

For a whole week after the death of Mrs Poulet, Michael and his friend Fanny, both continued as it seemed, unscathed, and many were the grave discussions between them, as to whether they ought to be sorry or glad that they were so—Fanny very steadily adhering to her first opinion, that if they had a great deal of love for each other, they would not let themselves be sorry, if one saw the other go away, and Michael as steadily persisting that right or wrong he must be so very sorry if Fanny went, as not to care at all how soon he followed after.

The disinterested reasonings of the little girl were soon put to the proof. Michael looked so very ill one morning at breakfast, that even the iron-hearted Poulet told him he had best mount to the sick-ward before it was needful to carry him; but Michael looked at poor Fanny, and saw such an expression of terror and misery in her countenance, that he could not help thinking she would change her mind about being glad, if he did not go into work along with her. So he told the governor that he wasn't bad at all, and had rather work than not; an assurance, which it could not, under any circumstances, be Mr Poulet's duty to combat; and accordingly Michael got to his place in the mill, and spoke cheeringly to Fanny as he went along. But before the hour of dinner he was on the floor, and when the overlooker called to a stretcher to have him wheelbarrowed back to the 'Prentice-house, Fanny Fletcher thought that she certainly did not love poor Michael Armstrong so much as she fancied she did, for that if the choice had been given her, she would a great deal rather have been taken ill herself. And spite of a strap that she saw coming towards her, and flourishing ready for duty in the air, she helped to drag the unresisting body of her poor companion from before the mules, and thoughtless and reckless of the consequences, sat down and held his head on her knee, till he was raised in the arms of the stretcher and carried off. It was then, and not till then, that her tears began to flow, and they flowed so fast, that she could no longer see the uplifted strap, nor was it till the blow had descended sharply on her arm that she was sufficiently mistress of her thoughts to remember, that there was at any rate a hope that it might be her turn next, and with this to comfort her, she yielded meekly to the arm that pushed her to her usual place, and resumed her occupation with more stedfast courage, than at that moment any other hope could have given her.

But even this sad hope proved vain. Fanny Fletcher still continued one of the very few upon who the contagion had no effect. For the first day or two after the removal of her friend, her mind was almost wholly occupied by the expectation of feeling the same symptoms that she had witnessed in him; and when these came not, her thoughts reverted to the possibility of his recovering and coming again to work near her.

It was an established custom among those who alone could give information on the subject, never to permit any questionings concerning the sick, or if they were boldly hazarded, to give no other reply than a rebuke. So that day after day, and week after week elapsed, without her being at all able to guess, whether Michael were dead or alive. By degrees, however, all hope of seeing him return faded from her mind, and then, poor little girl, she found out that people can't always wish truly and really for what they know to be best either for themselves or others. And day by day, though still the fever touched her not, she grew more pale, more thin, more melancholy. Now and then, indeed, it still occurred to her as possible that Michael might reappear again, as many had done after many days of sickness; but, alas! none had ever staid away so long as he had done! She had questioned many who had been ill concerning him, but none seemed to know or care any thing about who had shared the sick chamber with them; till at length, a boy to whom she had often addressed these questions, because she happened to know that he had been taken to the sick-ward on the same as Michael, replied as if by a sudden effort of recollection,

"Oh! that chap? Him what was one of the last as come? Ay, ay, I mind all about him. He was dead and buried before he had been down three days."

Fanny Fletcher asked no more questions, nor had she any longer hope of following where so many of her happier companions were gone. The fever was pronounced to be over, the Factory and Apprentice-house were whitewashed, and a number of new inmates arrived. All things in short at the Deep-Valley Mills appeared to be going on as prosperously as usual; a statement which could be hardly impeached by the fact that one little girl there was growing paler and more shadow-like every day.

XXI

*Miss Brotherton exerts her eloquence, and nurse Tremlett is
brought to reason thereby—The heiress hardens her heart, and speaks
harsh truths to Martha Dowling, but all in vain—She conceives a
project, and sets about putting it in execution with great spirit*

"WELL, MY DEAR MARY," SAID Mrs Tremlett, on sitting down *tête-
à-tête* with Miss Brotherton, after their return from Fairly,
"don't you think that you will come at last to confess that I was right
when I told you that you had better let things alone, and not attempt to
make any fuss or stir about these factory goings on?"

Mary looked sick at heart, and only shook her head in reply.

"Why, what have you gained, my dear child, by all your labour and
pains to get information, as you call it? You are looking as white as a
sheet—your eyes are sunk in your head—when I look at you, instead of
the smiles you used to give me, I get nothing but sighs, and all for what?
Can you in honesty and truth say that you have gained any thing worth
knowing by following your own opinion instead of mine? What good
in the world can you do, dear, by listening to all the shocking stories
that clergyman there told you? I dare say he is a very good man, and
he looks like it, but upon my word I think he is doing nothing but just
wasting his time, as well as yourself; for though I sat and said nothing, as
of course it was my place to do, I listened to every word, and it is just
because I believe every word was true, that common sense makes me see
there's no good to talk about it. Indeed, and indeed, my darling, I would
not make free to talk to you in this way, which looks for all the world
as if I was taking advantage of your goodness to me, if I did not see
that you was going the way to torment yourself for everlasting, without

doing one bit of good to any one. For how, my dear, can you, or that good clergyman either, hope to put down all the wicked doings he told about? And to be sure he said as much himself—didn't he, Miss Mary? Then do make up your mind to be quiet and happy, and let things that you can't mend, alone. Put as many children to school as you like, my dear, and you may give them a pretty neat uniform, you know, and that will be a pleasure for you to think about, and to look at; but for pity's sake my dear, dear, child! give up at once, and for ever, this bothering yourself for everlasting about the factories, which you can no more stop, Mary, than you can stop the sun from rising in the morning, and setting at night."

Here the good woman ceased, and looked with some anxiety in the thoughtful eyes of her young mistress. She felt that she did not understand their expression, and no wonder, for Mary Brotherton herself sat silently doubting how she should answer her. A languid feeling, proceeding partly from fatigue and indisposition, and partly from the discouraging conviction that she had no very satisfactory arguments by which to rebut her old friend's charge of useless devotion to a hopeless cause, made her for some minutes unwilling to speak at all. Then came a somewhat peevish wish to interdict for ever the discussion of the subject between them; but as she raised her eyes to utter it, she encountered a look of such humble love, deprecating her displeasure, yet fondly clinging to the freedom which risked the incuring it, that her purpose suddenly changed, and instead of the chilling command she was meditating, she threw her arms round the old woman's neck, exclaiming,

"Oh! my dear nurse! How much, how very much you must love me! since care for my already too-much-cared-for peace and quiet, can harden such a heart as yours towards all the sufferings we have this day heard recounted!"

"Thank God! you are not angry," cried the affectionate old woman kissing her, and then arranging the neglected ringlets of her pretty charge, and looking cheerily in her face, she said. "Now then, Mary I won't teaze you any more about it. You are so sweet and so gentle to me that I am quite sure you will not long think my heart is hard; and that by degrees you will find out that I am right; and then all will go well again, and I shall see my dear girl look like herself once more."

"Nurse Tremlett! the time is already come when the impossibility of my efforts being of any avail to stem the torrent with which avarice and cruelty are overwhelming the land, is made evident to me. So much, dear nurse, I concede to you, and therefore on that point we will argue no more. But, my dear old woman, have patience with me if I tell you that there are some points on which my reading may have given me, young as I am, as much, or even more information than your experience has given you. You have heard of the slave trade, nurse Tremlett—you have heard more than one excellent charity sermon preached in aid of the funds that were to assist in freeing these poor helpless black people from the tyranny of their masters, and I suppose you let that it is now unlawful to buy and sell these poor creatures. And how do you think this happy change in their favour has been brought about?"

"By the king and the parliament, Miss Mary, making that most good and righteous law," replied nurse Tremlett.

"And how were they persuaded to make that law, think you?" demanded Mary.

"I can't tell how that was brought about, my dear. I suppose it was because they saw that it was right and fit."

"It was brought about, nurse Tremlett, by the voices of the people of England, which were for years raised quietly, and with no breach of law or order, but with patient and unshrinking perseverance against this great sin, till the lengthened cry could be no longer resisted, and the law they perseveringly asked for, was granted to them. Do you think, nurse Tremlett, that if during these years of orderly, but steady remonstrance, every Englishman and woman had acted upon the principle you recommend, and had turned their thoughts and their conversation from the subject of negro slavery, because each one knew that he or she individually possessed no power to stop it. Do you think that if such had been the system acted upon, England would now have to boast of having abolished this most wicked traffic?"

"Perhaps not, my dear. I think I understand you now," replied the honest-hearted old woman, eagerly.

"Then now my dear old friend we shall, I think, never have any more disputes upon this subject. You—I—every servant in my house—every acquaintance I have in the world, may aid and assist in putting an end to this most atrocious factory system, WHICH OUGHT TO WEIGH HEAVIER UPON EVERY CHRISTIAN ENGLISH HEART THAN EVER THE SLAVE-TRADE DID. If the whole British empire, nurse, did but know what we are about here—if the facts we heard from Mr Bell to-day were but impressed upon the minds of all my fellow as they are on mine, the horrors he detailed would cease before another year was come and gone."

"God forbid then, my sweet child, that I should ever more raise my sinful voice to drown your righteous one. I have been a vain self-sufficient old woman, my dear Mary, and clearly have been talking a great deal about of which I know nothing. Only don't think I am cruel and hard-hearted for though I do—as you truly say—though I do love you very very much indeed, I am not such a wretch as to hear all we were told to-day without wishing to mend it."

This was the last time Mary Brotherton had to do battle with her nurse on the subject of the factory system. Once awakened to a sense of its tyranny and injustice, and made to feel that the only hope of remedy lay in the possibilty of universally raising British feeling against it, there was no danger that the right-hearted old woman would ever again turn with indifference, weariness, or displeasure, from the theme. Her young mistress felt that she had touched the right string, and that she should never again have to fear discord where it was so essential to her comfort to find harmony. This change was really a comfort, and she felt it to be so, removing as it did one irksome feature from her situation, and for a few minutes it cheered her, and she said so, cordially, but the next, a pang shot to her heart, as she remembembered that this assurance of accordant counsel with her venerable nurse, could avail her nothing in the most painful of all her difficulties, for it promised no help either in obtaining light upon the mystery of poor Michael's abode, or in the still more pressing embarrassment of confessing to his unhappy mother and brother the impossibility of obtaining it. Yet this painful task must be performed, and that without delay, for well she knew that every hour that passed without their seeing her, would be rendered dreadful, both by the agony of fear, and the sickening hot and cold fits of uncertainty. But never had she felt herself so very a coward as while meditating this visit of the morrow. She saw in imagination the eager questioning of Edward's speaking eyes, and the heavy glance of his mother, anticipating the worst she had to tell.

Sometimes she thought she would await the coming of the boy to take his place in the school, and let him report the failure of all her inquiries to the poor widow. But there was a selfish cowardice in this which instantly struck her, and she seemed to hate herself for the suggestion. For above an hour after she had laid her head upon her pillow these thoughts kept her painfully awake, and it was only after deciding that she would once more see Martha Dowling, and try the effect of repeating to her, but without quoting her authority, the dark hints she had listened to, respecting Sir Matthew's possible motives. It was only when her restless thoughts had fixed themselves on this, that she at length closed her aching eyes in sleep.

Above an hour before the usual hour of rising, Mary Brotherton was already at her writing desk. The idea of going to Dowling-lodge, and encountering the knight and his family, was intolerable, and she had therefore recourse to her pen as the means of obtaining the interview she wished for, without paying for it the penalty of such a visit. She wrote a follows:

"My dear Miss Martha,

"I trust you are too good-natured to be angry with me even if you should think that I am taking a great liberty with you. But the truth is, that I much wish for the pleasure of seeing you, and yet am too idle this morning to venture upon a drive. Will you then have the great kindness to pass the morning with me here? I send my carrriage, lest Lady Dowling should not have one at leisure to send with you.

"Believe me, my dear Miss Martha,
"Yours very sincerely,
"MARY BROTHERTON"

Having written, folded, and sealed this epistle, Mary recollected that it would be impossible to send it for at least four hours, and she smiled first, and then sighed, as she thought of the restless but useless activity which had caused her so needlessly to forestall her usual hour of rising. It would, in truth, have been better for her, poor girl, could she have slept through the time, for her waking thoughts had little that was pleasant to rest upon. Even the commencement of Edward's studies, to which she had before looked forward with great delight, now recurred to her only to bring the recollection that if she saw him, his thoughts would be neither his new clothes nor his new books, but of Michael, and of her promise to get tidings of him. For his sake; and her own too, she determined at least to escape this interview, feeling that it would be better for all parties that no tidings should be delivered to both mother and son at once, which could be done after his school hours by her driving to Hoxley-lane, after she had taken Martha home.

In pursuance of this resolution, she walked to the school-house, renewed her orders that the greatest attention should be paid to the new scholar, Edward Armstrong, and care taken that if he were found backward for his age, he should neither be laughed at nor chid. She then left a message for him, stating that she should be engaged all the morning, but would see him at his mother's house, after he left school.

At eleven o'clock Miss Brotherton's equipage set off for Dowling-lodge, bearing her letter to Martha, and the interval till its return was an anxious one. First she felt doubtful if her unusual invitation would be accepted; and if it were, she felt more doubtful still as to the nature of the scene which must follow. Nothing short of her earnest wish to redeem her promise to Mrs Armstrong could have given Mary courage to do what she now meditated.

She entertained not the slightest doubt of the intrinsic excellence of Martha Dowling. All she had ever seen of her, and still more, all she had heard from the Armstrongs, convinced her of this; and to pain her therefore particularly in that most tender point, the exposure of her father, the tremendous effect of which upon her, Mary had already witnessed, was one of the very last measures she could have been led to adopt. But a strong and stern feeling of justice, urged her not to shrink from this. It was evident from the statement of Mrs Armstrong that Martha had been actively instrumental in sending Michael to his present destination, let it be where it might; and painful or not painful, it was unquestionably right to make her understand the doubts that existed as to the boy's well-being, in order that she might avail herself, as she was bound to do, of her access to the only person who could explain the transaction.

Having screwed her courage, therefore, to the strictness of examination necessary to her most righteous purpose, Mary left her boudoir in the possession of Mrs Tremlett, and repaired to the library to await her guest. Nor did she wait long. Almost before the time arrived at which she had calculated that the carriage might return, the great house-bell gave signal of a visiter, and the next moment Martha Dowling stood before her.

The two young girls shook hands, and each observed that the other looked paler than she was wont to do. The heart of Mary sank within her as she marked the expression of Martha's countenance. Not only was it pale, but most speakingly anxious, and in addition to her usual shy and reserved manner there was an appearance of uneasiness, and almost of fear, as she thought, which seemed to tell that her object was suspected. Nor was she wrong. In pursuance of a promise given to Michael, Martha had visited the widow Armstrong, and the intense anxiety under which she found her suffering respecting the destination of her boy, awakened for the first time in her own mind a shadowy suspicion that all might not be right concerning him. The pang this cost her was terrible. Good and kind-hearted as she was, there was no strength of fibre in Martha's character which might enable her to brave every thing rather than remain in doubt. She loved her father fondly, but she feared him more, and the stronger her suspicions grew (and unhappily the more she meditated the more they strengthened), the less power she felt either to refute or confirm them.

The note of Miss Brotherton was delivered to her at the family breakfast table, and the instant she read it, the truth suggested itself to her mind. Had she been a free agent, the wounded shrinking spirit of the poor girl would have certainly led her to invent some excuse for refusing an invitation so full of terror; but she was not.

"What's that about, Martha?" said Sir Matthew, holding out his hand for the note.

"It is from Miss Brotherton," muttered Martha, as she resigned it to him.

"Mercy on me!" exclaimed her eldest sister, "what a wonderful fancy Miss Brotherton seems to have taken for Martha! I do think it is the very oddest thing I ever heard of."

"What a goose you are, my dear, not to understand it!" observed Miss Harriet, the second sister, giving at the same time a very significant glance towards her brother Augustus.

"But good gracious!" retorted Miss Arabella, "why might not any other of us do as well? It would seem so much more natural in such an elegant and fashionable girl as she is."

"She is afraid of us, Bella," replied Miss Harriet, tittering.

Sir Matthew, who had not only read the note, but contrived to hear all that his two eldest daughters said concerning it, here burst into a laugh.

"Set a thief to catch a thief—hey! Harriet? Come Martha! start away! You have finished your breakfast long ago. I won't have the carriage kept waiting."

"Must I go, papa?" said poor Martha, turning very pale.

"Must you go? and with that die-away look too? Why, Martha! are you jealous because some folks fancy that the young lady wants to make friends with you, for more reasons than one?"

"I would a great deal rather not go, papa!" replied Martha in a beseeching accent.

"Martha! I shall be in a downright passion with you in half a minute. Upon my honour, I never heard any thing so cross-grained and unsisterly in my life. Go this moment, and get on your bonnet, and remember if you please, from first to last, to speak of your brother as a sister ought to speak. And if she hints any thing about his having flirted a little with Carry Thompson, be sure to say that he only did it to laugh at her."

As he spoke these words, Sir Matthew rose from the table, as if to accelerate the movement which was to send her off.

Martha listened to him with the habitual reverence which she ever bestowed on all he uttered; but shook her head, as it seemed, involuntarily, as he concluded.

"Why, you don't mean to say he was in earnest, you good-for-nothing spiteful girl!" cried Lady Dowling, suddenly rousing herself from the dignified apathy in which she usually indulged.

"What a shame!" cried one sister.

"That's too bad!" cried the other.

"Just like her, though!" sneered Mr Augustus.

"Hold you tongues, all of you," said Sir Matthew, "I know Martha better any of ye, trust me for that, and what I bid her do, that she will do, and nothing else. Run away Martha. Don't mind any of 'em."

Thus urged, thus goaded to the interview she dreaded, Martha hastened to leave the room; but ere she passed the door, something at her heart told her that her best course would be to take her father apart, and tell him all. She turned back to look at him, but met a frown so strongly indicative of growing impatience at her delay, that yielding to the sort of slavish feeling in which she had been nurtured, she hurried forward to obey him. Had she possessed greater moral courage, many subsequent events would have been different.

After the first salutation was over, Miss Brotherton, making a strong mental effort to subdue her agitation—of which she was infinitely more capable than her companion—begged her to sit down; and then, placing herself where she could have as a commentary on what she might induce her to say, the advantage of watching her countenance, she pronounced in a voice that she in vain laboured to render steady, "My dear Miss Martha, I have suffered a great deal of uneasiness since I last saw you respecting the little boy for whom—concerning whom—I mean Michael Armstrong, Martha! His mother is very wretched because she cannot discover to what place he has been sent; and I, nothing doubting that it would be perfectly easy to learn this from you, rashly promised that I would obtain this information. Can you, dear girl! tell me more upon this subject now, than you could when last we met?"

"I cannot, Miss Brotherton!" replied Martha Dowling, in a voice so low and husky, as hardly to be audible, but with a complexion and features that spoke so plainly what was passing in her heart, that Mary felt ashamed of having placed herself where she could so distinctly read all she suffered, and leaving her chair to share the sofa on which the poor girl was seated, she took her hand and said,

"My poor dear Martha! It would be better for us both that I should speak sincerely. I have become acquainted with an individual, Martha, who knows more, much more, than either you or I can do, my dear girl, respecting the factories—those great magazines of human life and labour by which your father, and mine also, have grown from poverty to wealth. This person, Martha, on my questioning him respecting the probable destination of a child so circumstanced, did not scruple to reply, that if his master were displeased, and wished to be rid of him, there were places—factories, mills, dear Martha, where the business was so managed as to render labour very heavy punishment, and where it was easy to keep children, ay, hundreds of them, unseen and unknown for years. Do not tremble thus, dear Martha! Do not draw your hand away from me! Most sure I am that your heart and my heart must beat in sympathy on such a subject as this. Let us be mutually sincere, and we may help each other to undo whatever wrong may have been done. We know, we both well know, that your father *was* displeased with this poor widow's son. We know, too, that he is a person of great power and influence. The boy is gone—he will not tell us where. What is the inference? Turn not from it, Martha Dowling, turn not from it, my poor friend, but boldly and honestly seek out the truth, and let me know enough of it to save this helpless child from further suffering."

"I have no means, Miss Brotherton," faltered poor Martha. "If all your dreadful thoughts were true, which you have no right to think they are—and still less have I—but if they were true, all true, I have no means to know it."

"If we have ANY reason to believe them true," said Mary, solemnly, "means MUST be taken, Martha Dowling, to stop further wrong; and this can only be by learning where Michael Armstrong has been sent. I apply to you for this with great reluctance, because I know the subject cannot be brought before you without causing you pain. But I feel it my duty not to shrink from this, and it is yours, my dear girl, to obtain the information I require."

"But if I agreed with you in this, Miss Brotherton, what are my means of obtaining it beyond your own?" said Martha, rousing herself, and

feeling renewed courage from remembering that there was no proof yet
of the boy's being otherwise than well and happy.

"Nay, Martha," returned the heiress gravely, "amongst those engaged
up your father's service, you can hardly be at a loss to find some one
who must have been employed in removing him."

"And would you have me," replied the poor girl, indignantly, "would
you have me tamper with my father's servants, in order to obtain a
knowledge of what it may be his will to keep secret? Miss Brotherton,
I would rather die than do so."

"I honour your filial feelings, Martha, and grieve to think that you
are placed in circumstances which must compel you to make them
secondary," said Mary, gently.

"Nothing can make them secondary," retorted Mattha, warmly, "I
love my father, and I hold my duty to him the first and the highest I
have to perform on earth."

"Save only what you owe to your own soul, Martha Dowling," replied
Mary. "Had you been yourself for nothing in this matter, I might think
as you do, that your duty as a child must prevent your interfering in
it, though even that, I suspect, would be but doubtful morality. But,
Martha! the case is otherwise. It was by your influence that this helpless
widow was induced to send her child away. She did *not* trust your father,
but she trusted you. Do you not know, Martha, that I speak the truth?
And if I do, can you for an instant doubt that your first duty is to redeem
the pledge you gave to this poor trusting creature, who hazarded all that
was dearest to her in life, upon your assurance?"

A passionate burst of tears, that seemed rather to convulse than relieve
the bosom on which they fell, was the only answer Mary received to
her cogent reasonings, and so evident was the suffering of the innocent
culprit who appeared writhing under the discipline she inflicted, that
nothing less deeply impressed on her heart than was the remembrance
of Edward and his mother, and the grief that threatened to destroy them
both, could have given her courage to persevere.

"Martha! my dear Martha! Be reasonable!" cried Mary, throwing her
arms round her. "If you knew what I suffered in making you suffer, you
would pity me! But I have no choice left me. I am not a free agent,

Martha, any more than you are; we are both bound in honour, honesty, Christian faith, and Christian mercy, not to let any feeling stop us till we have restored Michael Armstrong to his mother."

"Restore him!" sobbed Martha. "Alas! Miss Brotherton, the poor woman herself has prevented the possibility of that! Do you not know that he is apprenticed?"

"Let us but know *where* he is, Martha, and if the situation be one that his mother can reasonably disapprove, there can be little doubt but means may be taken to release him. Teach us but where to find him, dearest Martha," cried Mary fervently, "and we will all pray for blessings on your head!"

"I cannot do it," replied Martha, with a sigh that very nearly approached a groan.

"How know you that you cannot, Martha? Will you not try to learn this cruel, this nefarious secret?"

"No, I will not, Miss Brotherton," replied the unhappy girl with sudden firmness. "If any wrong has been done to this boy, I know that it must rest upon my head. So let it. The remembrance of it may bring me to the grave, and there I shall find mercy and forgiveness. But it shall not place me in rebellion to my father, nor force me to reveal any secrets which it may be his pleasure to keep. Now let me go, Miss Brotherton. I doubt not you have acted according to your sense of duty, and so have I. In this at least we are equal. Pray let me go; I am not well, and greatly wish to be at home."

Mary looked at her with surprise, and almost with terror; she was as pale as death, and shook, as she stood up before her, as if she had been seized with an ague-fit.

"Alas, Martha!" she exclaimed, "I have made you very miserable, and very ill, yet have gained nothing by it! You shall go, my poor girl, you shall go instantly, but ere we part, let me implore you to examine in silence, and alone, the question of right and wrong in this case. Paint to yourself the misery of the wretched mother, and remember that yourself—I must say it, though I wring both our hearts as I do it—yourself, Martha Dowling, are the cause of it."

"You have said enough, Miss Brotherton, to destroy my peace for ever," replied the miserable girl, "but not enough to make me act as a spy upon my father. Farewell! Do not let us meet again! It is too painful."

Without waiting for an answer, Martha Dowling wrapped her shawl about her and hurried to the door.

"The carriage is not waiting, Miss Dowling," said the vexed and disappointed Mary, who had gained nothing from this painful interview, but the conviction that the well-intentioned, but erring Martha, was as much persuaded of the boy's having been unfairly dealt with, as herself. "Let me order the carriage for you."

"No, no, I cannot wait. I can walk. I know the way. Indeed I can stay no longer!" replied Martha, hurrying on, and closing the door of the room after her, and before Miss Brotherton could reopen it, she had already passed through the hall, and was almost running from the house.

Mary lost not a moment in summoning a servant, and ordering the carriage to follow her with all speed, an order which was so well obeyed, that the unhappy Martha was overtaken ere she had walked a mile, and gladly did she then avail herself of it; for by that time every other painful feeling was merged in the terror of having to explain to her father the cause of her having so parted with Miss Brotherton, as to return unattended and on foot. "Perfect love casteth out fear," and perfect fear may perhaps petrify the heart into a sort of unstruggling desperation; but a union of the two reduces the mind to a sort of slavery the most abject, leaving no strength whereby any healthful moral feeling can be sustained. Martha's whole care, on returning home, was to satisfy her father that *nothing* particular had passed in her interview with the heiress; and, unfortunately for all parties, she succeeded.

Miss Brotherton, meanwhile, mounted a little pony phaeton with Mrs Tremlett, and with a heavy heart proceeded to Hoxley-lane. But, painful as was her errand, her condition was a far happier one than that of Martha Dowling; for in her there was no mixture of motives to paralyze every word and act. Her kind heart sought and found counsel in her sound and upright judgment, and, sustained by it, she executed her task without shrinking. A little reflection on the subject convinced her that it was now become her duty to confess to her poor client, not only that her exertions to discover the abode of Michael had been unsuccessful, but that she began to fear that there must be some unpleasant reason for the difficulties thrown in the way of obtaining the information she had sought. It required some courage to utter this; but when it was done, Mary was surprised to perceive that its effect, both upon the mother and son, was very trifling. Having candidly stated her fears, she remained silent, the eyes of both being fixed upon her with a sort of quiet hopelessness that was perhaps more painful to contemplate than more vehement demonstrations of grief.

"Our thanks are not the less due to you, ma'am," said the widow gently, "and don't vex your kind heart by thinking that we are disappointed. Edward and I guessed true from almost the first; that is, from when he was taken off without bidding us good-bye. Sir Matthew known better by his mill people, ma'am, than by the great gentry that turns their eyes away from labour and sorrow, to revel and grow fat upon our graves. You would never be like to hear the truth from them, and I am told that even now, the country round rings with praise of Sir Matthew's goodness to Michael. 'Tis bitter to hear it. But it is God's will our portion should be bitter here. He has power to make it up to us hereafter, and it is there we must fix our hope."

"Most sure and most blessed is that hope!" replied Mary, fervently, "yet it should never check our efforts to put to profit the means of happiness he has granted to us here. I have now told you the very worst, Mrs Armstrong, for I have told you not only all I know but all I fear—nor will I again pledge myself to do more than I am quite sure it is in my power to perform. I think you will believe, without my talking about it, that I shall not give up the search I have undertaken. But till some new light reaches us, we should but waste our time, and wear our spirits by speaking on the subject. Let us rather think and speak of the welfare of the dear boy that is left you; this will be no hindrance to our restoring his brother, if it be God's will that we should have the power. Tell me, Edward, how did you get on at school to-day?"

"Every body was kind to me," answered the boy.

"That's well, dear boy, and every body will be kind to you. He looks nicely in his new clothes, does he not, Mrs Armstrong?"

"He does indeed, ma'am! and I could almost fancy that he looked better in health already, for having left the mill," replied the widow.

"And I feel better," said Edward, looking at his mother with his soft thoughtful eyes, "and I don't think that it would be impossible for me to grow well again."

"My boy! my boy!" cried the poor cripple, raising herself in her bed, and throwing her arms around him. "Should I dare to complain of any thing if that were possible! But oh! Teddy! wouldn't he have given one of his little hands to see it?"

This appeal, which in truth only echoed the thoughts of his own heart, overthrew all the courage of Edward, and his tears again flowed as fast as those of his poor mother; a renewal of weakness of which they might both have been still more ashamed than they were, had they not perceived that neither Miss Brotherton nor her old friend had dry eyes.

Mary, however, was too wise to let this last.

"This dear boy," said she, "has said that which ought to give us all courage. I can hardly tell you the delightful feeling which the hope of his restoration to health would give me. It would repay me a thousand fold for all the pain I have suffered. Let us fix our thoughts on this hope, and trust me it shall be realized, if medical skill and kind treatment can do it."

It was with this assurance she left them, and if any earthly promise could have healed the anguish of the mother's heart, it would have been this. But her two children were so twined and twisted together in her thoughts, that meditating upon her hopes for Edward inevitably brought her terrors for Michael before her, and it was but with a fitful sort of satisfaction that the boy dwelt upon his anticipations of being useful to her, or that she listened to him.

Two days after this, while Miss Brotherton and Mrs Tremlett were pursuing their usual morning occupations in the boudoir, a servant announced that a lady and gentleman were in the drawing-room.

Had the announcement been of a gentleman alone, Mary's thoughts would have instantly suggested Mr Bell, for they had been fixed upon him, and the hope of his coming, through both the preceding days. But the mention of the lady puzzled her. Nevertheless the gentleman was Mr Bell, and no other, and the frank and simple kindness with which he said, as he led the lady forward to meet her, "Miss Brotherton! I wanted my wife to know you too," rendered the introduction as agreeable as it was unexpected.

"If you and I, my dear young lady," said he, "take to consulting together concerning what we may hope, and what we may do in aid of the suffering people by whom we are surrounded, we shall do well to take this good little woman into the committee, for she has probably more practical knowledge of the subject we were discussing when last we met, than any other lady you could meet with."

Equally cordial and sincere was the welcome Mary gave to her new friend; and if sympathy of feeling, and a community of interest, on a subject of deep importance to them all, could have sufficed to make them happy, the long morning they passed together would have been one of great enjoyment; but they were all too much in earnest to be called happy while dwelling upon the frightful subject to which their thoughts were turned. The longer Mary listened to those whose lives were past in struggling to assuage the misery around them, and in battle with the horrid principles which produced it, the more deeply did she feel that she, too, was called upon to labour in the same thorny vineyard. Yet terrible as were the subjects they discussed, and sad as was the conviction that no power less mighty than that of the law could redress the evils they deplored, there was still something inexpressibly soothing to her feelings, in finding herself thus in intimate relation with persons who comprehended and shared in the sentiments which had become so essentially a part of herself. Though her conscience had told her, from the first moment her attention had been called to the subject, that it was her duty not to turn away from it, she had hitherto met little but opposition from those around her, and though steadfast and firm in purpose, she had often felt heavy in spirit from herself to be alone, when she so much wanted assistance and support. This oppressive loneliness she could never suffer from again as long as Mr Bell and his excellent wife were within her reach, and fervently did she bless the courage which had led her to their dwelling. Tidings of poor Michael, however, there were none. Mr Bell had sought information concerning him wherever he thought it possible to obtain them, but he had learnt nothing. Nevertheless he declared himself by no means satisfied that the boy might not be at some one of the Bastille-like establishments to which he had applied. "I know them, and they know me too well," he said, "for me to place implicit confidence in any answer they may be pleased to make, to any question I may venture to ask. If I knew where to find a trustworthy stranger, who could not by possibility be recognised by any one as a friend of mine, I still think the chances would be greatly in favour of our finding the boy at some of the noted apprenticing establishments which I have named. But, in truth, I know not where to look for such a person."

"Am I not such a one?" cried Mary, eagerly. "Hardly a creature in the world, beyond the town of Ashleigh and its neighbourhood, know me personally, and in all such places as those you have named, the Emperor of all the Russias would not be less likely to be recognised."

"But how, my dear young lady, could you represent yourself with any face of probability as interested in the inquiries you would have to make?" demanded Mr Bell.

"A serious gentleman as owns a factory"

"Methinks, Mr Bell," replied Mary, colouring with her own enthusiasm,—"methinks I could carry through an enterprise which had the recovery of little Michael for its object, with a degree of diplomatic skill that would surprise you. It should not be by downright and direct inquiry that I should proceed. Where such inquiry would be likely to excite suspicion, I would only contrive to insinuate myself and my eyes, and would ask no questions save what they should answer."

"Many strangers, travelling, desire to see the factories, certainly," replied Mr Bell, musingly. "But you are so young to undertake a wandering expedition. And then, how could you be accompanied? Your servants would unquestionably announce you every where."

"I am older, I think, than you suppose," replied Mary; "and if I undertake this, I will be accompanied by Mrs Tremlett with whom I have no reserves, and by no one else."

"You cannot travel without attendants, Miss Brotherton?" said the clergyman, looking at her kindly, but as if doubting that she was quite in earnest.

"Do not either of you judge me harshly," replied the heiress, with great earnestness; "do not set me down in your judgments as a hot-headed girl, indifferent to the opinions of society, and anxious only to follow the whim of the moment. Did I belong to any one, I think I should willingly yield to their guidance. But I am alone in the world; I have no responsibilities but to God and my own conscience, and the only way I know of, by which I can make this desolate sort of freedom endurable, is by fearlessly, and without respect to any prejudices or opinions whatever, employing my preposterous wealth in assisting the miserable race from whose labours it has been extracted. If you can aid me in doing this, you will do me good; but you will do me none, Mr Bell, by pointing out to me the etiquettes by which the movements of other young ladies are regulated. I cannot think that I have any right to a place among them; and I therefore feel that to check any possible usefulness by a constant reference to the usages of persons with whom I have little or nothing in common, would be putting on very heavy harness, neither effective for use, nor for ornament. But 'something too much of this.' I must not talk of myself," she added, cheerfully. "Let us examine the possibility of my setting off with Mrs Tremlett on a little home tour, without announcing the important event to the neighbourhood, or taking any servants with me to enact the part of Fame behind my chariot."

"By what conveyance would you propose to travel, Miss Brotherton?" inquired Mr Bell, still looking, as an American would say, "as if he could not realize the scheme."

Mary meditated for a moment, and then replied—"In the first instance, if you and Mrs Bell will permit it, we shall go to your house in the same manner a before, only carrying with us a small travelling-trunk or so, such as would be necessary if we were going to pass a week with you. On the following morning we would set off by the —— coach, in which you will secure places for us. At —— we will order dinner and beds, like any other travellers, and inquire of the waiter what will be the best way of getting a sight of the factories."

"And he will tell you that such and such factories—naming precisely those in which there would not be the slightest chance of finding the boy—may be seen by application made to Mr So-and-so," said Mr Bell.

Mary coloured, and seemed about to answer him; but, either from consciosness that she had nothing very satisfactory to reply, or because she had some notion in her head not sufficiently digested to communicate, she changed her purpose, and instead of combating an objective which seemed almost fatal, drew from her pocket a set of little ivory tablets, on which she had written the names of all the establishmehts within a distance of twenty miles, notorious for taking apprentices and of retaining them by means that converted the scene of their labour into a most strict and wretched prison-house. She read their names aloud. "These, I think, were all you mentioned to me," said she. "I think they were," replied Mr Bell. "But to these, believe me, you will get no admission as a visiter."

"Will *you* admit me as a visiter, if I come to you the day after to morrow Mrs Bell?" said the heiress, playfully, and apparently wishing to wave any further discussion of her projects.

"Most joyfully!" was the kind and hospitable reply.

"Then, for the rest we must trust to chance. And now, if you will let me, I will show you my pretty garden," said Miss Brotherton, rising, and taking from a chair by the open window the ever-ready shawl and parasol, which made her lawns and shrubberies essentially a part of her dwelling-place. "Of all the fine things I possess, I believe I am only truly thankful for this," she continued, "I hardly know how I should pass my life if I had not a garden."

The garden was indeed one that spoke of its owner's love, by a multitude of enjoyable nooks that seemed all courting her approach, and by that perfection of elegant neatness which is never found in an equal degree where the mistress is indifferent respecting it. To her new friends' praises of all this she listened with pleasure, and sketched many pleasant plans for future meetings, when they should not, as they declared unavoidable now, remain only while their horse was resting. But Mary said not a word more on the subject of her purposed expedition till the very moment of their departure, and then it was only to remind them that they would see her come with her friend to claim their promised hospitality on the next day but one. This was received with renewed promises of a joyful welcome, and so they parted.

The next day was a busy one for Mary. In the first place she was closeted for at least two hours after breakfast with Mrs Tremlett, and, whatever might be the subject of their conversation, it appeared to end satisfactorily, for when it was over Mary embraced her old friend very cordially, saying, "I feel more grateful, much more grateful, than I have words to express, nurse Tremlett, and never shall I forget your kindness to me!"

After this they drove to the entrance of Hoxley-lane, and walked thence to pay a farewell visit to Mrs Armstrong; and here it was evident that, however wild the projects might be which the heiress had conceived, she knew how to be discreetly silent concerning them, for after bestowing upon the widow a gratuity sufficient to supply all her wants for a longer time than she purposed to be absent, she took leave of her, saying, "You will not see me again Mrs Armstrong for a week or more; I am engaged to go from home for that time; but I shall take care that Edward shall receive as much attention at the school as if I were at home. Be sure also, that my absence will not make me the less mindful of Michael. Neither at home or abroad shall I cease to employ every means in my power to obtain intelligence concerning him."

To Edward, whom she visited at the school, she gave the same
assurance, adding an earnest injunction that he should keep in mind the
necessity of exerting himself, both for the industrious prosecution of his
studies, and the not less important regulation of his mind on the subject
of his brother's absence, the welfare of his mother greatly depending
upon both. Weakness of every kind seemed to vanish before the
powerful stimulant thus offered, and she left her little *protégé* comforted
and invigorated by the belief that he had a great duty to perform, and
that his mother was the object of it.

The preparations for her own and her friends' convenience during
the journey were very simple, but they puzzled her maid considerably.
First, it was so very odd that she should be going out upon a visit and
take absolutely no dinner dresses at all with her; and secondly, it was, if
possible, odder still, that she should not take her. But Mary listened to
all the hints and innuendoes to which these feelings gave rise with a
sort of gentle indifference, which was doubtless very provoking, till at
length she was induced to damp the curiosity, which she feared might
prove inconveniently active during her absence, by saying, "I am going
to visit the family of a clergyman, Morgan, and, as much dress will not
be necessary, I shall not want you."

This was perfectly satisfactory. "A clergyman's family, where much
dress would not be necessary, was where the lady's maid never did nor
never could want to go."

Nothing could have been more judicious than these explanatory
words. They accorded perfectly with the report of the servants who
attended the carriage, and so completely satisfied the household, that,
though it was the first absence of so long duration that she had made
from her home since she became mistress of it, it fortunately led to no
gossipings whatever.

We must not pause to describe the pleasant sociable evening passed
by our travellers at the house of Mr Bell, nor even relate all that was
said in the course of it, concerning the expedition they were about to
undertake. Every instruction, every hint which Mr Bell believed might
be useful, he gave clearly and succinctly, and not a word of it was lost
upon Mary.

XXII

*Miss Brotherton sets off on her travels, and feels frightened at
her own temerity—But speedily recovers her courage, and plays
the heroine—She visits some factories, and is introduced to a
Sunday-school—She approaches the precincts of the Deep Valley*

IT WAS ABOUT NINE O'CLOCK on a bright autumn morning that Miss
Brotherton and her faithful nurse mounted into a lumbering six-
inside vehicle, bound for ——. Their two small trunks, with "*Mrs
Tremlett, passenger*," modestly written on both, were safely lodged on the
top; Mr Bell gave them a silent blessing and a silent nod; the horse-boy
vociferated "all right," and the richest young lady in Lancashire rolled
off, very literally in search of adventures.

The novelty of her situation, and of her sensations of every kind, the
unceremonious examination bestowed upon her by a smart young clerk
who sat opposite, the anxious look of Mrs Tremlett's usually tranquil
face, and the consciousness that the enterprise she was upon must even
by herself be characterized as wildly extravagant, if not carried through
with much steady courage and discretion, altogether produced a feeling
of oppression on her heart that very nearly overcame her. "Am I acting
rightly in thus exposing myself?" was the question that her startled
nerves uggested: and had her conscience been unable to answer it boldly
and promptly, her condition would have been really pitiable. Happily,
however, this was not the case. There was some feminine timidity about
Mary Brotherton, but not an atom of false shame or affectation of any
kind. "Yes!—I am right!" was the answer recorded on her heart of hearts,
"and shame to me if I shrink at the first step, for no better reason than
because the dust flies, and a vulgar young man stares me in the face."

From that moment Mary recoiled no more; and a little resolute meditation on her object, and of the strength demanded to obtain it, so effectually restored her usual self-possession, that she looked round upon her fellow-travellers with as little embarrassment as if she had been used to travel in public all her life, nodded to Mrs Tremlett with an encouraging smile, and thought how very silly people were who fancied that every thing unusual, must of necessity be terrible.

"Are you going all the way to ———, miss?" said a good-natured looking woman who sat *bodkin* between the smart clerk and Mrs Tremlett.

"Yes, ma'am I am," replied Mary, civilly.

The good-natured woman twisted herself round to reconnoitre Mrs Tremlett.

"Your mamma, I suppose, my dear?"

"No, ma'am—the lady is a friend!"

"Oh! I ask your pardon; you are so very much alike made me say it." Mary bowed—Mrs Tremlett smiled.

The good-natured-looking woman persevered in the same train of pertinent observation, sometimes addressed to one passenger, and sometimes to another, so as to prevent the party from sinking into total silence, which might otherwise, perhaps, have happened. But Mary bore her share in this trifling annoyance with perfect good-humour; and when at length they arrived at ———, and Mrs Tremlett asked her in rather piteous accents, the moment they were alone together, whether she did not feel dreadfully worn out, she cheerfully replied,

"Not the least in the world, my dear friend."

"Thank God!" replied the old woman, fervently, "I know you do so hate to be bothered, Mary, that I was afraid that old fool would put you out of all patience."

"Times are altered with me now, nurse Tremlett," replied Mary "I have left off living for myself, and I feel my temper improving already by it. Now, then, ring the bell, and give your orders; remember, nurse, you are the great lady, and must order every thing."

Encouraged by this cheerful submission to circumstances, which was in truth somewhat more than she expected, Mrs Tremlett began to think that Mary might indeed prove capable of carrying through the scheme, the first sketch of which had appeared so wild, that nothing short of a devotion to her will, which knew no bounds, could have surmounted her averseness to it.

"My darling child!" cried the old woman, looking at her with equal admiration and delight, "your mind is as strong as your heart is tender, and never will I again oppose my silly ignorance to any thing you wish to do."

It was not difficult in this first stage of their expedition to follow exactly the plan that had been laid down. The two ladies professed themselves to be travellers, anxious to see all objects of curiosity, and particularly the factories, which were, as they observed, so famous throughout all the world. The master of the hotel where they lodged exerted himself with the utmost civility to gratify so natural a desire, and Mrs Tremlett and Mary were accordingly promenaded, on the following morning, through one of the largest establishments of the town. It is probable, from the drowsiness of the public mind on the subject, that many travelling strangers who are in like manner led by a skilful official through the various floors of a factory, retire from the spectacle they present without having any feeling of sympathy excited by the cursory glance they have thrown over the silent unobtrusive little beings, one moment of whose unchanging existence they have been permitted to witness. It is the vast, the beautiful, the elaborate machinery by which they were surrounded that called forth all their attention, and all their wonder. The uniform ceaseless movement, sublime in its sturdy strength and unrelenting activity, drew every eye, and rapt the observer's mind in boundless admiration of the marvellous power of science! No wonder that along every line a score of noiseless children toiled, unthought of, after the admirable machine. Strangers do not visit factories to look at them; it is the triumphant perfection of British mechanism which they come to see, it is of that they speak, of that they think, of that they boast when they leave the life-consuming process behind them. The more delicate, and (alas!) living springs by which the GREAT ARTIFICER has given movement to the beings made in his own image, are not worth a thought the while. The scientific speculator sees nothing to excite his intellectual acumen in them; he hardly knows that they are there, but gazes with enthusiasm and almost reverence on the myriads of whirling spindles amidst which they brethe their groans, unheeded, and unheard.

But it was not thus that Mary won her way through the whirling hissing world of machinery into which she now entered for the first time in her life. The hot and tainted atmosphere seemed to weigh upon her spirits, as well as upon her lungs, and the weary aspect of the Drakes, and the failing joints of Edward Armstrong became fearfully intelligible as she watched the children (and she watched nothing else) who dragged their attenuated limbs along. Then it was that Mr Bell's tremendous statemeut of the number of suffering beings thus employed came with full force upon her mind. She would have given years of existence at that moment, could she have believed it false. Two hundred thousand little creatures, created by the abounding mercy of God, with faculties for enjoyment so perfect, that no poverty short of actual starvation can check their joy so long as innocence and liberty be left them! Two hundred thousand little creatures, for whose freedom from toil during their tender years the awful voice of nature has gone forth, to be snatched away, living and feeling, from the pure air of heaven while the beautiful process is going on by which their delicate fabric gradually strengthens into maturity,—taken for ever from all with which their Maker has surrounded them for the purpose of completing his own noblest work—taken and lodged amidst stench and stunning, terrifying tumult,—driven to and fro, till their little limbs bend under them—hour after hour, day after day—the repose of a moment to be purchased only by yielding their tender bodies to the fist, the heel, or the strap of the overlooker! All this rushed together upon poor Mary's heart and soul, and, turning deadly pale, she seized the arm of her friend to save herself from falling.

"Terrible hot day!" roared their conductor, in the hideous scream by which some human voices can battle successfully with the din of machinery.

Fortnnately, they were near the door of the room, and Mrs Tremlett, urging her steps forward, now brought her to an open window outside it. The fresh air, so carefully excluded within,★ soon revived her: the colour returned to her lips, and having remained silently inhaling the breeze for another minute or two, she signified her wish to proceed.

"Not now, Mary! Pray, not now!" said the frightened Mrs Tremlett. "Indeed, indeed, you have not strength for it!"

Mary gave her one steady look, and the opposition ceased; for it said as plainly as look could speak—"Is it thus that I shall find Michael Armstrong?"

"For moment I felt the heat oppressive," said Miss Brotherton, in a voice of very steady composure. "But I am quite sure the sensation will not return. I came to —— on purpose to see the factories, my dear friend, and, indeed, you must not disappoint me."

"The young lady's right," replied their conductor. "She'll never see the like of our mills, you may depend upon that. Why all the machinery in the known world put all together won't equal one of our spinning-mill's. There is nothing in creation to compare to it; and I don't question but the young lady heard as much before she come. So it would be altogether wrong to disappoint her of the sight of 'em."

"Thank you," said Mary. "Are we to go up stairs now?"

"Yes, if you please, miss. We have got seven stories here, and, thank God, all is busy just now, one as the other, from the bottom to the top."

On entering the second room Mary felt, as she expected, that her bodily strength was quite sufficient to sustain her. She had not habituated herself to "seek the sun upon the upland lawn," for nothing. Few girls so lapped in luxury could boast of equal vigour and activity. The first aspect of the system (the horrors of which had been so clearly explained to her) in action, was for a moment overwhelming—but it was past—the terrible "*premier pas*" could not come again, and far from shrinking from the task she had imposed upon herself, she left the enormous fabric, after having perseveringly mounted to its summit, with the satisfactory

---

★ Except in the mills of Messrs Wood and Walker, at Bradford, it is difficult to find any factory properly ventilated—free admission of air being injurious to many of the processes carried on in them.

conviction that she should not fail in her enterprise either from want of strength, or from want of will.

Good Mrs. Tremlett, however, still felt less confident upon the subject, and no sooner found herself *tête-à-tête* with her young mistress within the shelter of their drawing-room, than she said, "You will never stand it, Miss Mary!—feeling about it all as you do—the sight of those poor ragged sickly little souls will be the death of you."

"Then so let me die, dear nurse!" replied Mary. "If I have not vigour enough both of mind and body to be in some degree useful, I should hardly think it worth while to live; but I know myself better, nurse Tremlett. I turned sick and giddy, I confess, on entering that first room, but it is my friend, Mr Bell, who has to answer for it. The impressions received at that moment by my senses served as a specimen of all the horrors he had described to me. The account I had heard enabled me at a glance to comprehend the scene before me, while that scene itself acted back again, as it were, upon my memory, making me understand, a thousand times more clearly than before, all the frightful details he had given me. The effect of this was overpowering, but it cannot return upon me again in the same manner; I am already hardened. Think therefore no more of me, dear friend, but let us cogitate together upon the likeliest way of turning all such visits to account."

This cogitation led them both to the conclusion that it might, for the sake of appearances, be as well to take the landlord's recommendation to another of the establishments, usually pointed out to the attention of strangers, and then to consult the ivory tablets, and venture upon a visit to the only one near —— named therein, as notorious for the reception of apprentices.

In pursuance of this plan, the waiter was again interrogated when he attended the ladies at their luncheon, and again he brought a written address his master, accompanied by a message intimating that the following morning being Sunday, the ladies might have the advantage of visiting the Sunday-school attached to the factory, for which he had given the address, to a sight of which they would be admitted without difficulty, if they would make known their wishes for such admission to the person who would show them the factory.

"There is a Sunday-school attached to the establishment?" said Mary in an accent of great satisfaction. "Yes, miss," replied the man, "Messrs Robert and Joseph Tomlins, the serious gentlemen as owns the factory, has built a school-room altogether at their own expense, and attends their ownselves in person every Sunday morning to see that both master and children puts the time to profit. Their factory is about mile or so out of the town, but master says as he can let you have a carriage very reasonable."

"I should wish to go there by all means," replied Mary, "desire the carriage may be got ready for us directly."

The man left the room to obey her.

"Thank Heaven!" exclaimed Mary, as the door closed behind him, "there is, then, some Christian feeling still left among them here, as well as at Bradford. We shall not here, at least, be shocked by witnessing such degrading ignorance as that of the poor Drakes.—They are treated like Christian children, at any rate."

"Most surely it is a pleasure to hear of it, my dear," replied Mrs Tremlett, "and it is quite as well, Mary, that we have got to ride to it—at least if you feel like me, my dear."

Less than half an hour's drive brought the travellers to a large factory, which, whatever it might be within, was on the outside, though in itself as grim as coal-smoke could make it, surrounded by a fine expanse of rural scenery. In answer to their application at the gates they were civilly desired to walk in, and presently found that the routine of exhibition as precisely similar to that of the morning. It struck them both, however, that if possible, the children looked more worn and weary, more miserably lean, and more frightfully pallid, than those they had seen before; nevertheless Mary failed not, when taking leave of their conductor, to request permission to attend the Sunday-school on the morrow.

"Certainly!" was the reply, pronounced in a tone as clearly announcing the speaker's connexion with the party self-styled evangelical, as the broadest Irish brogue does the birthright of the speaker to call himself a son of the Emerald Isle. "Certainly! the Lord forbid that Christian women should ask to be present at the doings of the godly and be refused!"

On inquiring the hour at which they should be there, the man replied, "As the clock in the tower of the Lord's house strikes seven, Mr Joseph Tomlins, by the blessing of God, will begin to speak the exhortation. The prayer will follow from the lips of Mr Robert, and then the schooling will begin."

"We must be here, then, exactly at seven?" said Mary.

"Ten minutes earlier, would be more decent time," replied the man, with a gravity of aspect that approached a frown, "our gentlemen are very strict as to their hours in all things."

They civilly promised to be very punctual, and departed. The factory was built on the side of a hill, so steep, that the back part of it, to which the shed used as a school-room was attached, could not be safely approached by a carriage; Miss Brotherton, therefore, and her old friend, on arriving at the bottom of the hill on the following morning, got out, and, desiring the vehicle to await their return, proceeded on foot by the path pointed out to them as " the way to Master Tomlin's school." The ladies were more than punctual, for it still wanted a quarter to seven, they therefore seated themselves on a fallen tree by the road side, and watched the arrival of one or two miserable-looking children who were laggingly approaching the spot.

"You look half asleep my poor child!" said Mary, laying her hand on the shoulder of a little girl, who ragged, pale, half-washed, and with eyes half-closed, was being dragged onward by an older child, a boy, apparently about ten years old.

"She be so hard asleep by times," said the boy," that l can't get her on."

"But why is that, my dear? surely seven o'clock is not so very early!" said Mary.

"We were all to the mill till five minutes afore twelve," said the boy, making another effort to pull his sister onward.

"How!—do you mean to tell me that you were working at midnight?" demanded Mary.

"Five minutes afore twelve we stopped—'cause it was Sunday," replied the boy.   "Come along Peggy!" he added with another stout tug, "I shall catch it to-morrow from the looker if I'se too late for the 'sortation."

The little girl who had fallen fairly asleep, during this short delay, being thus roused again, stumbled onwards, leaving Mrs Tremlett and Mary alike undeceived as to the humanity of instituting a school to be carried on under such regulations. They determined, however, to witness with their own eyes the operation of teaching children to read, who were fast asleep, and walking on came within sight of the schoolroom door just as Mr Joseph Tomlins showed himself on the step before it, with his watch in one haud and a bible in the other.

"Wicked and ungrateful children!" he began, "Is this the way you obey your earthly master, who leaves his comfortable bed, and his breakfast untouched, to lead you to the feet of your heavenly one? Wicked, idle, and ungrateful——" But at this moment Miss Brotherton and Mrs Tremlett appeared in sight, and in a voice suddenly chunged from reprobation into drawling softness, he went on, "Come unto Him little children——I forbid you not, but urge you with tender Christian love, early and late, late and early, to hear His word, and sing His praise."

Here he stopped, and bowing to the ladies offered to lead them to a place where they might be well accommodated for the exhortation and and prayer, and for hearing the children also, if they wished it.

As soon as they had entered the sort of pew to which Mr Tomlins led them, the twenty or thirty miserable-looking children who were assembled n the room were called upon by a loud word of command to "KNEEL!" and down they tumbled, the elder ones in several instances taking the little creatures already asleep beside them and placing them on the floor as nearly as they could in the attitude commanded. The sonorous voice of Mr Joseph Tomlins was then heard pronouncing an exhortation, intended to show that obedience to their earthly masters was the only way of saving children from the eternal burning, prepared for those who were disobedient, in the world to come.

Mary, as she looked earnestly round upon every child present, greatly doubted if there was one sufficiently awake to listen to this; and in her heart she blessed the heaviness which saved them from hearing the mercy of their Maker blasphemed. A prayer followed this exhortation, as little like what a prayer ought to be, as was the preparation of the little congregation who listened to it for bearing part in a religious ceremony.

Still Mary Brotherton waited to the end, nor left her station till the
nominal business of instruction had proceeded sufficiently to convince
her that poor Sophy Drake's account was strictly true when she said
"keeping our eyes open Sundays wasn't possible, 'cause they didn't strap
us." The children were *not* strapped, and consequently they were, with
very few exceptions, literally fast asleep during the hour and half that
this ostentatious form of instruction was going on.

Unwilling to attract more notice than was necessary, Miss Brotherton
and her companion remained till the drowsy tribe were roused,
awakened, and dismissed by the loud voice of Mr Joseph Tomlins, and
then they also slipped away, regained the carriage that waited for them,
and returned to ——.

"Now then," said Mary, as their one horse dragged them deliberately
along, "now then, dear Tremlett, our search must really begin. As soon
as we have breakfasted we will set off in this same equipage for ——
Mill, that being the first on my list where apprentices are taken, and,
moreover, within a morning's drive of ——."

"And how shall you endeavour to gain admittance my dear?"
demanded her friend.

"As we did yesterday—merely stating that we are strangers, travelling,
who are desirous of seeing the factories," replied Mary.

"But you don't expect to get in, my dear, do you ?—after all Mr Bell
told you about apprentices!" exclaimed Mrs Tremlett.

"Probably not," was the answer, "and in that case, my dear woman you
know what is to happen."

"You are really in earnest then, Miss Mary?" rejoined her friend in
an accent which betrayed some nervousness. "You really mean to do all
you said when we were shut up together?"

"Most certainly I do," replied Miss Brotherton, gravely. "Did you
suppose I was jesting, nurse Tremlett, in what I then said to you?"

"Not jesting, Miss Mary.—No, certainly, not jesting. Only I thought that
may be after a little more thinking about it you might change your mind."

"You do not yet understand me, nurse!" said Mary, with vexation.
"You do not yet comprehend how determined I am to persevere in the
business I have undertaken."

"Do not say so, dearest Miss Mary!" replied the old woman with emotion, "I do understand you,—I do know that you will leave no stone unturned to obtain your object,—and indeed, indeed, I love you a thousand times better than ever I did, and that is just because I do understand you; only I did not feel quite sure that you would have courage."

"We shall see, nurse Tremlett. Courage, I believe, often depends more upon the earnestness of the will than the strength of the nerves," said Mary.

Their attempt to get admittance to the apprentice factory was, as they both expected, abortive; they were told that no persons were admitted there except on business, and having nothing such to plead, they retreated as they had advanced, somewhat fearful lest their having taken so much trouble for nothing, might excite the alarming observation, "It is very odd," on the part of their driver or some of his gossips.

The distance was considerably greater than they had expected, and they had little more time on their return to ——, than sufficed for securing places in a cross-country coach for the morrow, which would convey them to a small town named by Mr Bell, within a morning's drive of which were two establishments known to receive apprentices, howsoever and wheresoever they could get them.

Having again booked their places in the name of Tremlett, prepared their travelling luggage for a further progress, and taken a meal that served for dinner and tea in one, they went to rest. But it was long ere the excited mind of Mary permitted her to sleep; nor did she, in fact, close her eyes till, after repeated consideration, she had decided totally to change the plan of operations she had fixed upon for the morrow.

Mrs Tremlett had not yet left her bed, when her young mistress appeared at the foot of it, on the following morning, with her ivory tablets in her hand. "Nurse Tremlett," she said, "do you remember which, among all the places mentioned here, was the one Mr Bell declared that he considered as the *most* likely for Sir Matthew to have selected, if his purpose was to keep the abode of Michael Armstrong unknown?"

"Dear me! My dear Miss Mary! Only think of your being up already and me lying abed so!" was the reply she received.

"Never mind that, dear nurse. It is not getting-up time yet—only I am restless. Do you remember the name of the mills Mr Bell particularly dwelt upon?"

"I dare say I might, Miss Mary, if I was to hear it spoken again," said the old woman, sitting up in bed, and endeavouring to feel awake.

"Now then listen, dear soul, and stop me when you think I name the right." Mary then turned to her tablets, and read the names, with the descriptions of the localities inscribed there. It was not till she had reached the last in the list that Mrs Tremlett again spoke, and then she exclaimed promptly, "That is it, Mary! I am quite sure that is the place! 'I will bet ten to one,' he said, 'that if Sir Matthew has been for putting the boy out of sight, Deep Valley Mill is where he will have lodged him.' Those were his words, Miss Mary— I could quite swear it."

"I was pretty sure of it before, nurse Tremlett, but now no doubt can possiblly remain. Hear me, then, my dear kind friend, and tell me truly if I am right or wrong. I settled last night, nurse, to set off and visit all these factories exactly in the order in which they are here set down. But, after I went to bed, it struck me that it would be surely better to begin with the place pointed out by our good friend as the most likely to afford success. I like the business quite as little as you do, nurse, and would gladly shorten it, if possible."

"But, my dear, won't the stage we are going in take us the wrong way?"

"A little round about—but I see no objection in that; we have no particular wish, you know, to have our course traced, and this setting off in one direction, when our purpose is to take another, must go far towards preventing it. So that you see we have no immediate change to make, and you have only to get up, and eat your breakfast in time to be ready for the coach, that is to stop for us here."

"God bless your dear heart!" said the old woman. "You think ten times more of me than you do of yourself, darling! Little sleep last night, Mary, and getting up before any body else in the morning, is not the way to be quite strong and composed by-and-by."

"Fear nothing—I feel perfectly well, and greatly pleased by our changed plans. I have great faith in this visit to Deep Valley, and long to have the experiment made and over."

Mary Brotherton was quite correct in her geography; the place to which the coach conveyed them was at about the same distance from Deep Valley as from ———; and, without making any further inquiries concerning that mysterious spot, which indeed the memoranda received from Mr Bell rendered quite unnecessary, she ordered a chaise, on quitting the stage-coach, to convey them to the nearest town at which he had stated that it would be likely they should find decent accommodation for the night.

Both the young and the old lady were rather surprised, on reaching this place, to find every house in it that offered public accommodation so poor and miserable looking, as to make them almost afraid to enter. Their driver, however, soon drew up to one which, upon Mrs Tremlett's inquiring if it were the best, he assured them, was not only the best, but the only one that ladies could find comfortable. "Here then we will get out," said Mary, courageously, and giving her friend an encouraging smile, she preceded her into a room that smelt strongly of tobacco-smoke, ale, and gin.

"Can we have an up-stairs room that might be more open and airy like?" said Mrs Tremlett, looking anxiously at her young mistress.

"To sleep in?" demanded the woman who had received them.

"A sitting-room, good woman, I mean," responded the meek-spirited Mrs Tremlett, half frightened by the woman's look and accent.

"What, this is not good enough, I suppose? Then you may trudge—it is good enough for your betters," replied the woman, looking most alarmingly sulky. Had the last been addressed to herself, Mary Brotherton would have thought it one of the duties imposed by her pilgrimage to endure it; but, as it was, she slipped out of the dungeon-parlour with great celerity, and reached the house-door before the postboy had succeeded in his attempts to untie the cord which fastened their trunks behind the chaise. Apparently hands were scarce at this unpromising hostelry, for he was performing the business alone, at which Mary greatly rejoiced, as it enabled her to address him unobserved. "This does not seem a comfortable house, my lad, that you have brought us to. Don't you think we might do better if we tried another?"

"It be the best in the town," was the reply.

Miss Brotherton held half a sovereign between her finger and her thumb,—"I will give you this" she said—

"Then could you not drive us a mile or two out of it?" said Mary, in a very coaxing voice. "We should like to sleep at any little country inn by the roadside a great deal better than this."

"And how would my master's horses like it I wonder?" said the postboy. By this time Mary's purse was visible in her hand. The youth's countenance softened as he gazed upon it, and he presently gave an unequivocal symptom of relenting, by scratching his head. Miss Brotherton held half-a-sovereign between her finger and thumb—"I will give you this," she said, "beyond the sum you are to receive for the horses if you will drive us on to some clean country inn at which we could sleep."

"Where is the old lady?" demanded the boy in something like a whisper.

"I will bring her out this moment," said she; and, without waiting further parley, Mary flitted back again through the vapour of tobacco and spirits to rescue her old friend,—a deed of daring that found its reward in the look of gentle satisfaction with which her signal to quit the parlour was obeyed; for Mrs Tremlett was one who could not bandy words, and she had therefore endured, without intermission or resistance, as much insolence as could be compressed into the period of her abode in the apartment.

"Why did you not follow me at once, dear nurse?" said Mary, as soon as the postboy had closed the carriage-door upon them.

"Bless you, my dear, I never thought of getting away again till tomorrow morning, and I staid with her to prevent her following you. How very glad I am we are got away safe and sound from that terrible woman! How could you have the courage and cleverness to think of it, Mary? Sure enough, dear, it is you that take care of me—and that's a shame, isn't it?"

"It is but fair, nurse, that we should divide the labours of the road between us. It is you who always take care that we are not starved, and it is not too much in return that I should be watchful for your preservation from all the wild cats and tigresses we may chance to encounter."

The postboy earned his golden gratuity, greatly to the contentment of its donor, by drawing up at a small but perfectly neat little mansion, where milk-pans set on end to dry before the door offered a delightful contrast to all that had been visible at the sign of the Three Crowns. The clean-coifed landlady looked a little surprised at being asked for sleeping-rooms by ladies entitled to so splendid a mode of travelling, but the demand being satisfactorily answered, they were quickly installed in a parlour smelling of geraniums instead of gin, and giving orders for their evening meal to the bustling good woman of the house with an air of old acquaintanceship, that looked as if they had been her guests for a month.

"Nothing was ever so fortunate as this, nurse Tremlett," said Mary, as soon as they were left alone; "our stage-playing, as you are pleased to call it, must begin here. There is no danger that this kind simple-hearted creature should misdoubt a word we say, and if you will only perform your allotted pat with your usual quiet good sense, I have no doubt but we shall reach her heart sufficiently to make her very useful. I do not ask you to say any thing—only look sufficiently interested to support the character I assign you."

"Oh! dear Miss Mary!" exclaimed Mrs Tremlett, colouring,—"is it to be already?"

The countenance of Miss Brotherton fell from an expression of great animation into that of deep despondency and disappointment, she found that at all her difficulties with the old woman were about to be renewed. "Oh! why, Mrs Tremlett, if you are unequal to this, did you not honestly tell me so when I explained my purpose to you before we set out?" said she, with more of severity than she had ever used in addressing her during her whole life before, "I could then have taken measures to carry on this business without you. You know how deeply my heart is in it—I did not expect this weakness—I thought it was over!"

"You are wrong, Miss Mary—you are mistaken altogether," replied Mrs Tremlett, eagerly. "I am neither weak nor silly, and so you shall see if you won't be so very rash and hasty with me."

By no means displeased at the energy with which the good woman defended herself, Mary replied, "Let me see this, Tremlett, and my love and value for you will increase a hundred fold."

"Be then, as soon as you like, my dear, I am quite ready." And, in saying this, the good old woman assumed an aspect as full of confidence and courage as her own.

In a few minutes their repast, which a good dairy made luxurious, was before them, the landlady remaining in attendance to replenish the tea-pot, and so forth.

Miss Brotherton's manners, though by no means remarkable to those in her own station for that perfect polish which guards every thing without, and every thing within, from disagreeable impressions, were always conciliatory and kind to all below her, and seldom was she waited upon by any one who would not have gladly retained that office near her. So it was with Mrs Prescot of the King's Head; the good woman lingered in the room, evidently because she liked being there, and taking advantage of this, Mary addressed her, venturing to give her the name she had read upon the sign.

"We are in Derbyshire, are we not, Mrs Prescot?"

"Yes, miss; this is Derbyshire, sure enough."

"What distance is it from hence to Deep Valley?"

"What, the factory, miss, that is called Deep Valley Mill?"

"Yes; how far is it to that factory?"

"Why it is not over easy to say rightly, seeing that there is no direct road to it. It is a lonesome out-of-the-way place as ever human beings thought of taking to, and I can't say as much is knowed about it by any of the neighbours round. There is a cart-road, I believe, as goes right down to the mill, but the nearest way would be over them hills there, of course, because the factory is built down amongst the very middle most of 'em," replied Mrs Prescot.

"Would the walk over the hills be too far for my aunt and me?" inquired Mary.

"Oh dear yes, miss! I should think so! Besides, 'tis no place whatever for ladies to go to. The poor little creturs as bides there bean't no sight for them to look at; and, besides, nobody of any sort is ever let to look at 'em."

"We must get there, somehow or other, Mrs Prescot," said Mary; "and I trust in God that we shall not be refused admittance, for our business is no common one."

"You have got business at Deep Valley Mill?" demanded Mrs Prescot, abruptly.

"Indeed we have," replied Mary, "and, by some means or other, we must get in, and, what is more, we must see every apprentice they have."

The woman shook her head.

"I have had more than one lodging here for a night," said she, "who for some reason or other was curious to get inside of Deep Valley Mill. But I never knowed one of 'em that ever did more than get a look down upon it

350

from the top of one of them mountainous hills out yonder; and it's no easy matter, they say, to get to the right place even for that; for, by what folks say, them as built the mills seem to think that they could puzzle the wicked on himself to find 'em out. But there's one eye as sees 'em, if no other do."

These last words were added in a mutter that might, or might not, be noticed according to the pleasure of the parties within hearing. Mary did not notice them.

"Could you have the kindness to tell us to whom we should apply for permission to go through the factory?" said she.

"Indeed, miss, I am happy to say I knows nothing about 'em, and if all's true as I've heard said over the ale-pot by the kitchen fire, the more people ask for leave, the less they are likely to get it. But may I make so bold, miss, as to ask the reason why such ladies as you wants to get in there? It would only break your hearts; and what's more, they've been having a horrid fever there, and that I know for certain, though they sent the poor little creturs off by night to be buried, some to one churchyard, and some to another, to stop people's tongues. It bean't no place, ladies, for you to go."

"When I tell you *why* we wish to enter there you will not say so," replied Mary. "The mill is worked by apprentice children, is it not?"

"Yes, miss, the more's the pity—for that's what makes the poor wretches slaves for life—for not many of 'em, by all accounts, lives till their time is up."

"Hear me then, Mrs Prescot—among those miserable apprentices we hope and expect to find a dear child who belongs to us."

"Lack-a-day! what a story-book that would make!" exclaimed Mrs Prescot. "How long is it since you lost him?"

"It is a long time," replied Mary, evading the question, "and it is a long story, to tell how it happened. He is my own brother—and this lady who is come with me is our aunt."

"Are you quite sure, miss, that you shall find him there?"

"How can I say that, Mrs Prescot, when you tell me so many of the children are dead?" replied Mary. "But so much do I think I shall, that I will give five sovereigns to any one who will only put me in the way to get admittance to the mill."

Mrs Prescot again shook her head. "There be a many and a many poor souls round about that would do amost any thing honest for such a reward but if any body told you they could do as much, they would only deceive you. I don't believe there is any body in the parish, not even the parson, could make 'em open their doors to let strangers in."

"Do you think that the person who has the power to open them would do it for a hundred pounds?" demanded Miss Brotherton.

"I can't take upon me to say, miss; it sounds like a fortune to me—but they are all rich at Deep Valley, as folks say, managers, overlookers, and all—so, maybe they mayn't think so much of it."

"Mrs Prescot, I would give five hundred pounds, rather than not look over the children at Deep Valley Mill."

The woman stared at her with a very natural mixture of curiosity and astonishment; but there was a friendly interest in her eye, also. "It's late to-night, ma'am to do any thing," said she, "and if you'll be pleased to say nothing to nobody till my husband comes home, I don't know but what he may be as likely to think upon what would be the best way to set about it as any body; not that he ever meddles or makes with the people of the mill in any way, but he's a good schollard, and a quick-witted man too, as ever I knowed, though I say it as shouldn't."

This proposal was readily agreed to, and the interval till their host's return employed in a ramble of a mile or two along the road, where a recent shower had laid the dust, while every woodbine in the hedges which skirted it, seat forth a delicious perfume. The outline of the hills around them, though hardly deserving Mrs Prescot's epithet of mountainous, was bold and picturesque, and the foreground, with its hanging levels and rich copses, altogether formed a scene of considerable beauty

"All this is very pretty, my good Tremlett," said Mary, offering her arm to her old friend to assist her ascent of a steep hill, "and I should enjoy it greatly did I not fancy that could we look over yonder hilltops we should see a hateful roof, excluding the sweet breath of evening from the helpless creatures it encloses."

"God grant that you may snatch one of them from it, my dear child," replied the old woman; "let that thought comfort you."

"Should I succeed!" cried Mary, "should I indeed carry home that little fellow to his poor mother and my pretty Edward, I should certainly feel something approaching to perfect happiness! But if I fail how shall I bear to meet them?"

"Think not of it, dear! see how that last bit of sunshine comes full upon your face as you talk about it; that is a sign my dear that you will have your wish."

It *was* the last bit of sunshine, for the next moment the golden disk was hid behind a ridge of hills; yet they walked on for nearly a mile further, and, when they returned to the King's Head, they found the good man of the house already returned, and his supper, as his wife assured them, very nearly finished. "He shall come to you in half a minute, ladies, if you'll please to be seated, while I bring in the candles;—I have told him all you said to me, and he don't seem so much put out about it, by much, as me,—but he's uncommon 'cute, as you'll find when you comes to talk to him."

In about a quarter of an hour Mr Prescot knocked at the parlour door, and being properly introduced to the ladies by his wife, was left standing before them, while she retreated to pursue her various avocations.

"Your wife has told you, Mr Prescot, our reason for coming here?" said Miss Brotherton, glad to escape the repetition of her fictitious tale.

"She has, ma'am," was the succinct reply.

"And do you think it possible for us to obtain admission to Deep Valley Mill, and to go over it in such a manner as to give us an opportunity of seeing all the children?"

"If I had heard that much, as to your purpose, ladies, and nothing more, I should have said NO, you could no more get into Deep Valley factory than into the moon. But my missis added something to the back of it as makes a difference." This was said with a look and accent which fully justified Mrs Prescot's assurances of her good man's "'cuteness."

"I think, Mr Prescot, that she said no more than I am willing to make good," replied Mary. "I do not wish to expend money wantonly, but, if less will not serve, I am ready to give five hundred pounds to any person who could enable me to see all the children in Deep Valley Mill."

"It is a long sum, miss," replied the man thoughtfully, "and I can't but fancy that less might serve. The people as is in authority there is bad people, I don't scruple to say it, and sooner than open their doors for pity towards any Christian soul, man, woman, or child, they would see 'em all in the bottomless pit. But 'tis just because they do all the wickedness we hears of, that I sees hope they may be bought to break their own laws; for if they does one thing for the love of gold, they may do another. 'Tis plain enough to see, to be sure, that they knows it is for their interest to keep all eyes off their cruel goings on—and what's for their interest they won't easily give up.—So it may be that squire Elgood Sharpton himself would turn away from five hundred pounds, rather than show off his poor miserable apprentices.—But that mayn't hold good for his agent, and I believe in my heart that, if we could quietly get to offer Woodcomb the manager a hundred pounds, you would not have long to wait for a sight of the children."

"And how is this to be done, Mr Prescot?" said Miss Brotherton, "if you can undertake to manage it, you may put what price you like on your services, I feel certain that you would not name a higher sum than I should be willing to pay."

"Why, as for me, miss, I must not be known to meddle or make in the matter. Squire Sharpton would have my licence away before I could say Jack Robinson. Any advice I can give is at your service, and I may be able to put you up, perhaps to doing the thing in the likeliest way; but as to my going to the mill, it won't do. One reason is, that I never was there before, and it's like enough that, seeing a stranger, to set the dogs at me before I had time to say my errand. No!—that won't answer. The only man I can think of as would give us a chance is one Smith, the miller as serves 'em with oatmeal, and pretty stuff 'tis, as I've been told, which don't speak over-well for his honesty, you'll say, though, 'tis likely the price is in proportion. Howsomever, whether he be good or bad, I don't know another as comes and goes to Deep Valley as he does, and that's what makes me fix upon him as a messenger."

"And when could I see this man?" demanded Mary.

"Why, betimes to-morrow, miss, there's no doubt, if I goes and gives him notice."

"Then, do so Mr Prescot, and be assured your trouble shall not be forgotten."

"There is no fear of it miss," replied the acute landlord with very honest sincerity, "and I'll go to the mill outright. But I think—you'll be pleased to excuse me for speaking my mind—that you two ladies must settle between yourselves what you'd be willing to give Timothy Smith himself for the job—seeing that he's not one to work for nothing;—and another thing I'd make so free as to mention is, that you'd do well to make him understand that you don't want to get inside their wicked den, but only to see the children, one and all of 'em—and then you know, miss, they may trim 'em and scour 'em up a little for shame's sake, afore they brings 'em out."

Miss Brotherton, after this conversation, felt as folly convinced as the good wife herself could desire of the value of the landlord's head, and determined to be guided by his advice. After a little further conversation between them, it was settled that she should write a note to Mr Woodcomb, the manager, in readiness to give into the hands of Mr Timothy Smith on the following morning, if she could prevail upon him to deliver it.

Mr Prescot performed his part of the business ably, for the portly miller was waiting for the ladies in the parlour when they returned from their early walk.

Miss Brotherton possessed a sort of instinctive skill in reading the human countenance, which rarely deceived her, and it took her not long to discover that the man she had now to deal with was one upon whom it would be folly to waste any arguments which did not affect his own interest. She, therefore, briefly stated the fact that it was of great importance to her to obtain sight of all the apprentices at Deep Valley Mill, having great reason to hope that she should find a young relative there, for whose release from all engagements she was willing to pay handsomely.

"It is not the custom, ma'am, to admit visiters at that factory. It have been found to hinder the work," replied the miller solemnly.

"So I understand, sir. But, hearing that you are in the habit of visiting the mill on business, I have taken the liberty to send for you in order to say, thaf if you would undertake to deliver this note to Mr Woodcomb, the manager, I would willingly give you five pounds for your trouble."

"That is hardly enough, ma'am, for the risk of offending so good a customer," replied the miller.

"Will double that sum induce you to do it for me?" said Mary.

"On what day do you wish it to reach Mr Woodcomb's hands?" demanded Mr Timothy Smith, endeavouring to retain a doubtful expression of countenance.

"To-day, sir; as early as possible."

"Then, ma'am, I'll be fair and open with you, and not go about to mince the matter, or deceive you in any way. If you will pay me down twenty pounds in gold, or Bank of England notes, I will consent to give up all the important business I had fixed to do this morning, and undertake, not only to give your letter to Mr Woodcomb, but to use my influence with him—which is greater than you may guess for—to make him do what you wish, provided that you treat him with the liberality which a gentleman like him has a right to expect."

Miss Brotherton drew forth her pocket-book.

"I will give you the twenty pounds you demand, Mr Smith," she said in a tone as business-like and decided as his own, "if you perform my errand successfully. I will give you this ten-pound note now, as payment for conveying the letter, and another of the same value when you return to me with the manager's permission to see the children who are apprenticed at the mill."

Mr Timothy Smith looked at Miss Brotherton's pocket-book and he looked at her. His glance at the first inspired a strong inclination to increase his demands; but the miller had studied the human countenance as well as the lady, and when he looked at her he felt certain that though young, rich, and very eager in pursuit of her object, she was not a fool, and that if he pushed her to a more preposterous payment than he had already proposed, she would be likely enough to turn about and look for another agent. He therefore demurely replied,

"It is all fair, ma'am; I agree to the terms."

And without wasting any further time, the man of the mill received the note, put on his hat, and departed.

Not all Mary's self-command, and, considering all things, she had a great deal, could enable her to await the return of her costly messenger with composure. All that she heard of this mysterious mill tended to prove that it was precisely such a place as Sir Matthew Dowling would be likely to fix upon as the abode of Michael. The more she meditated the more she became convinced that the boy was there, and she was hot and cold, pale and red, a dozen times in an hour.

She had kept a copy of her letter to the manager, that she might show it to Mr Bell, from whom she hoped to receive absolution for the innocent fraud she had practised. To read and re-read this letter, and to speculate with Mrs Tremlett upon its probable and possible effects, occupied some portion of the tedious time; slowly dragging her steps up and down Mrs Prescot's little garden, and occasionally sitting for a fidgety five minutes in a bower of scarlet-runners, employed the rest. But the morning seemed endless, and more than once she suspected that her watch stood still.

The important letter to Mr Woodcomb was as follows:

> "Sir,—A wealthy and respectable family have recently had reason to believe that a dear child, long considered as lost, has been sent as an apprentice to Mr Elgood Sharpton's factory at Deep Valley. Fully aware that the examination necessary to prove whether this hope be well founded, must be attended with considerable trouble to you— inasmuch as the children must be brought out from their work for me to see, I beg to say that, if, without giving me further trouble, you will permit this, I will pay the sum of one hundred pounds for the accommodation. Should it be refused, I must have recourse to other means for the purpose of ascertaining what it is so important for me to know.
>
> > "I am, Sir,
> > "Your obedient servant,
> > "Dorcas Tremlett."

It was not till five o'clock in the afternoon, by which time Mary was fully persuaded that her commission had failed, that Mr Timothy Smith, in his white hat and well-powdered blue coat, was again seen approaching the King's Head. The heiress, who was sitting near the window, started up, and would certainly have stepped forward to meet him, had not Mrs Tremlett whispered, "Sit down, Miss Mary, sit down, there's a darling, and look like a great lady as you did this morning; and that's what you are and always should be."

Mary reseated herself, and, after a short interval, the miller knocked at the parlour-door, and was desired to enter. Miss Brotherton pointed to a chair, and he rested himself. "The weather is warm, ladies,' said he, drawing forth a cotton handkerchief, and wiping his head and face, "and I have not loitered in my errand, as you may see by the state I'm in; but my horse is getting in years, like his master, and it's no easy work to drive him by such a road as that I have comed by."

"Have you succeeded, sir?" said Miss Brotherton, looking as grand as Mrs Tremlett could desire,

"I am happy to say, ma'am," he replied, with dignity, "that the second ten pounds is fairly won."

"I rejoice to hear it," cried Mary, brightly colouring; "and I shall have great pleasure in paying it. When, sir, may I see these children?" she added, pulling out her pocket-book as she spoke.

"Here, ma'am, is Mr Woodcomb's reply to your note, and on the roading of that, I look to hear you say that the ten pounds is mine."

Miss Brotherton took the dirty epistle offered her, and read:—

"Madam,—My employer is strict in his orders not to let the hands be interrupted, as they too often are in some mills, to gratify the idle curiosity of strangers. But in consideration of your handsome proposal, and hoping that you won't scruple to follow it with a like sum in case of your finding and carrying away the child, which will be no more than just, seeing that if I part with a hand I must get another in the place of it, on this condition I am willing that all the children on the premises shall be placed in the feeding-room for your inspection at twelve o'clock to-morrow.

> "I am, Madam,
> "Your humble servant,
> "JAMES WOODCOMB."

The miller kept his eye fixed upon her as she read, and the result he
looked for followed the perusal of the despatch he had brought. Miss
Brotherton handed the letter to her friend, and then drew the promised
bank-note from her pocket-book. The jolly miller rose, and received it
from her hands. "I thank you, madam," said he, folding it carefully, "and I
beg to say, in return, that you would have been troubled to find another
man who could have done your errand as well."

"I am quite satisfied, sir," she replied, "and will only ask in addition to
what you have already done for me, that you would be obliging enough
to tell me by what conveyance it will be best for us to get to the factory
to-morrow? Mr Woodcomb, as you probably know, has named twelve
o'clock. I suppose the distance is too great for us to walk?"

"Quite impossible, ma'am—altogether out of the question. But I shall
have no objection to hire out my chay-cart for the day, if so be you
would think that suitable," said the obliging miller.

"I have no doubt it would do perfectly well, provided you have a
horse that can draw it—I should be sorry to lose time in going, and
should not choose to be later than the hour appointed," replied Mary.

"I'll look to having a fitting horse, ma'am, and one as is used to the road,
and that is what but few are. The road is no very good one in parts, that's
the truth, and I'm not over sure that there's another man besides myself
that would like to undertake the job; but I've no objection to driving you
myself, ladies, provided you think it worth while to pay a tradesman for
the loss of his time—of course I can't charge my labour like a postboy."

"If you take means, sir, to get us to Deep Valley Mill, by the hour
appointed, and drive us back again safely to this house, we shall not
dispute about the price. But remember, if you please, that the carriage,
or cart, or whatever it is, must have accommodation for the child I hope
to bring away with me."

"I will take care of that, ma'am. I will put a little stool in on
purpose—and I think if I say two guineas, ma'am, for the job, which is
no easy one, that you can't complain of the price."

"I certainly shall not complain of it," said Miss Brotherton.

Nine o'clock was then fixed as the hour of setting out, and Mr
Timothy Smith departed.

Mrs Prescot's roast chicken and French beans were treated very differently from her previous breakfast and luncheon. Mary Brotherton was in higher spirits than she had enjoyed for many weeks—she felt confident of success, and for the first time in her life, perhaps, fully enjoyed the possession of the wealth which gave her such power of surmounting difficulties. The kind-hearted Mrs Tremlett was at length as sanguine, and almost as happy as herself; and very freely confessed, again and again, that her dear young lady knew ten times better how to manage things than she did, old as she was.

The evening was again spent in a long late ramble, and though they did not forget that over a certain towering height, pointed out by Mrs Prescot, lay the dismal spot called the Deep Valley, the exceeding happiness which was anticipated for one who dwelt there, made them almost forget the misery of the rest.

XXIII

Miss Brotherton and her friend arrived at the Deep Valley—
A review—Disappointment—"A sudden thought strikes"
the heiress—She concludes a bargain, though not the one
for which she meditated—She sets out upon a walk

Mᴿ Tɪᴍᴏᴛʜʏ Sᴍɪᴛʜ ᴡᴀs ᴘᴜɴᴄᴛᴜᴀʟ to his appointment, and at a very few minutes past nine, Mrs Tremlett and Mary were jogging along in the miller's jockey-cart, on a seat whereon cushions, that looked very like pillows, had been carefully strapped, and with a little stool placed before them, the sight of which conjured up so delightful a picture of the manner in which they should return, and the joy it would be her lot to confer, and to witness, that the pretty eyes of the heiress sparkled through tears of pleasure, and she would not have exchanged her present expedition for the best party of pleasure that ever was devised by man.

A considerable part of the way was the same as that followed by Mr Parsons when he conveyed Michael to the factory, and need not be again described. The tranquil loneliness of that portion of the road which ran along the stream, before it made the turn which brought the hideous prison-house in sight, lulled her spirits into a state that but ill prepared her for the aspect of the grim, desolate-looking dwelling into whose recesses she was about to penetrate and when it suddenly became visible, something like a groan escaped her.

"I hope that jolt didn't hurt you, ma'am?" said the miller, turning towards her. "Here we are, safe and sound, and that's half my bargain, at any rate."

The vehicle drew up to a small door in the exterior wall of the extensive enclosure in which the buildings stood; Mr Smith threw the reins upon the neck of his horse, and bringing his stout person cautiously to the ground, offered his services to assist the two ladies in doing the same.

Miss Brotherton trembled as she stood waiting till the miller's summons at the door should be answered. Now that the moment was come which was to decide the question of her success or failure, she no longer felt the same confidence which had cheered her while the trial was still distant, and her heart sunk with anticipated disappointment. Several minutes of irksome delay gave her time to dwell on these oppressive forebodings; and when the door was at length slowly and cautiously opened by Mr Woodcomb himself, her pale face spoke such painful anxiety, that the suspicious guardian of the unholy spot was comforted from the satisfactory conviction that her tale was true, and that she came not under any false pretences to look at that which he considered it to be the first duty of his life to conceal.

"Good morning, Smith—all's right, and all's ready for you. Walk in, ladies, if you please," said the stern manager, relaxing his habitual frown, and intending to be extremely gracious.

Mary and her friend stepped forward, and heard the stout lock and two heavy boots secured behind them.

"This way, ladies, this way, if you please; there is no need to trouble you to enter the factory, which, do what we will to keep it nice, can never be quite free from dust. You are a trifle after your time, Mr Smith, but it's no matter; dinner time is over, but if the ladies will walk into this room they shall have all satisfaction. Howsomever, as the young 'uns is again at work, I can't well stop the mills to march 'em in all together. Nevertheless, I don't see but it may be quite as agreeable, or may be more, for the ladies to look at 'em one or two at a time."

Miss Brotherton did not attempt to speak, but placed herself in a chair near the open door, and bent her head to indicate that she was satisfied vith the proposed arrangement.

"You had best walk this way with me, Mr Smith," said the amiable Woodcomb, "the ladies look quite agitated, as is but natural, and would sooner be without strangers I don't doubt." A proposal which truly was a welcome one to all parties—for Mrs Tremlett and Mary longed to be at liberty to speak without restraint—Mr Smith was thirsting for his accustomed mug of ale, and the manager himself bursting to make a few inquiries respecting his mysterious visiters.

"Have you seen the colour of their money yet, friend Smith?"—were the first words uttered as they crossed the court.

"Twenty odd pounds," replied the miller, expressively patting the pocket where the treasure lay, "and given as freely as if it had been twenty pence of a full pocket-book, too, Mr Woodcomb, I can tell you that—and I can tell you besides, that your money's as sure as the bank, and your customer one as is thinking of her own concerns and not of yours."

"That's what I'm judging too, Mr Smith. One can see in a minute if folks eyes are roving here and there, up and down, to take account of all they can see. God grant that those poor whey-faced females may find what they want, and we shall both of us have made a good day's work of it. I sha'n't wish the thing talked of, that's a fact, not but what I shall be ready with an answer, if I'm troubled with questions. People as have money to throw about, like these folks, are not to be off with a short word, and a lock turned in their faces. It mayn't chance once in a century that any such should trouble themselves concerning the cart-loads of live lumber as we takes off to relieve the overstocked parishes. But now it *is* come to pass, in course we must manage to get through it quietly—so I'm not without my answer, Mr Smith, if the squire should hear of it, and make a riot."

"No, to be sure you arn't—besides there's no need to say nothing," replied the miller.

Mr Woodcomb, in answer to this, gave an assenting nod, and an approving smile. "Now then, my man," said he more gaily than he often uttered any thing, "sit you down here, and you shall presently have a snack and a mug to keep you company. I'll see myself to the turning in a few of the hands at a time, to be looked at. For I have been thinking the matter over, Master Miller, and I judge it will make ten times less talk and tumult that way, than if they were all turned out at once. I'll have out a few boys and girls together, chance-like, just as they come—and ten to one nobody but Poulet will find out that there's any thing more going on than some job, as I wants to get done."

Mr Woodcomb accordingly proceeded to the different parts of the large establishment, and contrived, without stopping the work any where, to perform the task he had undertaken. As the selected children came forth from the various rooms, he told them to cross the court to the 'prentice-house, where they would find one as wanted to look at them, adding an order to come back again as quick as light, "if they didn't wish to be strapped dead."

Whenever such promises were made, Mr Woodcomb was known to be strictly a man of his word; and Mary and her friend had soon gazed with anxious eyes and shuddering hearts upon a greater number of half-starved trembling little wretches, than could possibly have been made to pass before them in an equally short space of time, by any other mode or process whatever.

They came so quickly in succession, however, that no interval was left in which Miss Brotherton and her faithful attendant could exchange a word on the melancholy panorama of human misery that passed before them. Strange and unwonted as was the spectacle of "two ladies sitting in the 'prentice-house," the cowed and frightened children, for the most part did little more than stand before her with eyes and mouth wide open for a single minute, and then start off again, while Mary herself aided the celerity of the process by a shake of the head, and a wave of the hand, which indicated plainly enough that they were not to stay, but go.

"What a multitude, nurse Tremlett!" she exclaimed at length, her spirits worn with repeated disappointments, and the contemplation of the wretched creatures for whom she knew she brought no help. "The train seems endless!"

The old woman returned her a speaking look, and whispered in her ear—"Could you not question them, Mary? Might not this dismal work be shortened by your asking them if the boy is here? They can't have any reason to hide him. They can't be agents of Sir Matthew."

Mary took the hint, and said to the next young skeleton that presented itself—"Can you tell me if there is a boy here named Michael Armstrong?"

The result was a stupid and silent stare, and, without answering, the child darted off like the rest. Thrice she repeated the question, but with no better success, for two out of the three were among those newly arrived to supply vacancies caused by the late mortality, and the third from working and sleeping in another chamber, had never heard poor Michael's name; "No!" was pronounced by this one, "No, ma'am," by the two new comers, and Mary's heart almost failing her, she resumed her silent examination. In truth there was in most of the unhappy faces that thus presented themselves, such a look of blighted intellect, and dogged apathy, that she clung to the ever-lessening hope of seeing the boy appear, in preference to any further questioning. And thus the coming and going lasted for another half-hour without a word being spoken.

At length the sad monotony of the spectacle was broken, at least to the eyes of Mary, by the appearance of a little girl, who though pale and lamentably thin, had not yet lost thereby the sweet expression of her delicate features, neither had the soul within yielded to the paralyzing influence of the hopeless, helpless, unvarying misery by which she was surrounded. Her soft gray eyes still retained their eloquent power of speak and the look of surprise, mixed with something that was almost approaching to pleasure, with which she fixed them upon Mary's face caused her to make a sudden movement to detain her, as the child, following the example of the rest, was turning away. At first this movement was caused entirely by the interest which the little creature herself inspired—but it almost immediately occurred to her, that here, at length, there was a chance of receiving a rational and intelligent answer to any question she might ask; and such strength did this idea gain as she continued to look at the child, that she told Mrs Tremlett to stop the approach of those who were coming on, aud by keeping them waiting in the court for a minute or two, to give her time to see if she could not learn something from this most interesting-looking little creature. Mrs Tremlett showed that she too thought something might now be hoped for, and with great alacrity stepped out into the court to meet the fresh arrivals, shutting, to Mary's extreme satisfaction, the door of the room behind her.

"My dear little girl!" said Miss Brotherton, taking the child's pale and slender hand in hers, "How came you in this sad place? You do not look as if you were used to it."

"Not for very long, ma'am," was the reply.

"But you have been here during the few last weeks?"

"I have hem here for several months," answered the little girl.

"Can you tell me"—and Mary almost gasped as she asked the question—"Can you tell me, if there be a boy here called Michael Armstrong?"

The look of modest and well-pleased curiosity with which the soft eyes were fixed on Mary's face, was instantly changed for an expression of deep anguish—for a few moments no reply was uttered, and large tears were already chasing each other down her cheeks before the trembling child found voice to speak; at last she uttered, almost in a whisper, and still looking through her tears in Mary's face—"Michael Armstrong is dead!"

"Dead!—Oh, do not say so!" cried Mary, in a voice so shrill as to reach the ears of Mrs Tremlett, who immediately opening the door, close to which she had been stationed, entered in dismay, exclaiming,

"What is the matter, Mary? For Heaven's sake, tell me, was it you who cried out in such a piercing voice?"

Several of the children, who were by this time assembled in the court, followed at her heels, thrusting open the door, and staring at the scene before them.

"Shut the door, Nurse Tremlett!—Send them away—send them all away—I have no further need to see them!" said poor Mary, weeping from sorrow, disappointment, and complete prostration of spirits. Before she spoke another word, Mrs Tremlett obeyed her instructions, and gently pushing back the curious throng, closed and bolted the door.

"Now tell me then, my poor dear child, what new sorrow has come upon you? Sure nothing dreadful has happened to the poor little fellow?"

"Nurse Tremlett, he is dead!" replied Mary, weeping afresh, as if the boy had indeed been her brother.

"Lack-a-day for his poor mother!" cried Mrs Tremlett, "these are bad tidings to take home with us, after all our trouble and pains. Oh, Mary, dear, I wish you had never left your home!"

"Say not so, Mrs Tremlett," said Mary, recovering herself, "certainty is ever better than doubt—and here, here is one I may still save from misery. What is your name, my dear child, and who was it sent you to this dreadful place?"

"My name is Fanny Fletcher," said the little girl, " and it was mother's parish that sent me here as soon as she was dead."

"Have you no other friends?—no relations any where who could take care of you?" demanded Miss Brotherton, with quickness.

"No, ma'am, nobody," replied Fanny; but, in saying this, the child ceased to weep, and, young as she was, an expression of such hopeless, yet enduring composure took possession of her beautiful features, that Mary's memory instantly applied to her Byron's thrilling words—

"My thoughts their dungeon know too well;
  Back to my breast the wanderers shrink,
  And bleed within their secret cell."

"Tell me, Fanny," she said, "tell me quickly, should you not like to come away from this place? I came here to take away poor Michael Armstrong. I was to pay money for taking him, and I will pay it now for *you*, if you will tell me that you wish to come, and will be a good girl to me."

"Poor Michael!" said Fanny, while her tears again began to flow.

"Speak, Fanny! shall I take you with me?" cried Mary, impatiently, for she heard without the door the sound of a heavy step approaching. Fanny Fletcher heard it too, and an almost ghastly paleness spread itself over her face and lips, she seemed choking, and perfectly unable to articulate, but clasping her hands together, and dropping on her knees before Miss Brotherton, raised her eloquent eyes to her face with a look which required no commentary.

"Open door, Mrs Tremlett!" said Mary. "Don't you hear the knocking? This is the child I shall take away with me," she added in a whisper, and with a look that her friend perfectly understood.

Mrs Tremlett opened the door, and the well-pleased Mr Woodcomb stood before them.

"That's well," he said, looking at the kneeling child, and at Mary, whose arm encircled her neck, with an air of great complacency. "I thought by what those said, as you sent back without looking at 'em, that you had found what you wanted. And now, ladies, I hope you remember the conditions."

"Do not doubt it, sir," replied Miss Brotherton, instantly drawing forth her pocket-book. "Here is a note of one hundred pounds to repay the trouble I have given you, and here, a second of the same value to atone for the loss of Fanny's labour."

"All right, ma'am," said Mr Woodcomb, very graciously, "and if you had but told me that it was a little girl, with a very pretty face, and that her name was Fanny, I could have saved you all your trouble, for we don't happen to have another that would answer to that description."

"I have taken no trouble, sir, that I at all regret," replied Miss Brotherton, "but I am anxious to set off on my return without any further loss of time. Will you have the kindness to inquire if Mr Smith is ready?"

"I don't doubt, ma'am, but he will be ready to obey orders, though the horse have hardly been baited well yet. Howsomever, those as pay well generally looks to have things done in a little less time than other folk; and it's very right and fair that so it should be. If a horse can stand, he ought to go, if his owner is well paid—there is no doubt of it."

"I should be sorry to distress the horse," said Mary, "and if he be not sufficiently rested, we must wait."

"At your pleasure, ladies, at your pleasure. Pray sit down and make yourselves comfortable. And of course your ladyship would like to have this pretty little girl here made as decent as we can manage; the dirtiest part of her clothes can be changed easy, though the missis of the 'prentice-house being lately dead, puts us out a little in our management. However, if little Miss Fanny, as we must call her now, will please to come up stairs with me, I can make her look a deal better, I will answer for it."

Fanny Fletcher having been raised from her kneeling position by the hand of Miss Brotherton, still continued to hold that hand tightly, and the young lady now felt so strong a compression of her fingers, and was at the same time conscious of so tremulous a movement in the person of the child, as she nestled closely to her, that she felt persuaded the proposal of Mr Woodcomb had frightened her.

"You are very kind," she replied, drawing the child, sordid as its wretched garments were, still closer to her, "you are very kind, sir. But I shall prefer taking her away, exactly as I first looked upon her."

"Dear me! only to think of that now! That's the beauty of what's called natural affection! Then if you will please to keep seated I'll go tell Miller Smith as you're ready, and all the business done, so as he may set off as soon as he is able."

Mary again thanked him for his civility, but felt disposed to think that he might have executed his mission more satisfactorily, when he returned in about three minutes, with the assurance that Master Smith would be ready to start in little less than an hour.

An hour at that moment seemed to Miss Brotherton an almost interminable space of time; she felt painfully conscious of being, "confined and pent up" with sin and suffering. Heated, agitated, and impatient—panting for the fresh air, and longing to question her little purchased *protégée*, concerning poor Michael, she determined to walk forward on the road they had that morning traversed, and letting Mr Smith and his cart overtake them.

"Should you dislike walking on, Mrs Tremlett?" she said. "My head aches, and I am sure nothing will relieve me but a walk."

"I should like it too, my dear," replied her observant companion, looking anxiously in her face, and perfectly understanding her feelings.

"Walk, ladies!" exclaimed Mr Woodcomb, looking exceedingly shocked, "ladies such as you to walk out upon our wild moors? Oh dear no! That is quite impossible!"

This was said to prove at once his tender care of personages possessing the power of dispensing hundreds, and to show that he was not unacquainted with the refinements of polite society; but this civilly-intended opposition to their exit produced on his hearers an effect very different from what he intended.

That Fanny Fletcher should tremble at the mention of delay was not extraordinary, but that Mary should hear again, in fancy, the grating sound of the locks and bars, which had closed behind her as she entered, and feel a sick qualm at her heart, as if she were betrayed, and doomed to remain in that hateful spot against her will, showed that her nerves had indeed been severely shaken, and that her heroism had more of zeal than strength in it.

Mrs Tremlett, too, looked exceedingly annoyed, though certainly without the same lively recollection of the bolts and bars; but she was so accustomed to consult the wishes of her young companion, and to feel at ease herself only when she saw her so, that she too coloured with impatience, and sustaining admirably her character of aunt, said,

"I beg pardon, sir, but I know my niece's constitution so well, that I am quite sure the jolting of that rough cart would not do for her just at present. She is a great walker, and a mile or so, creeping along in the fresh air, will do her a deal of good."

"In course you know best, ladies, and I can't, for certain, take the liberty to oppose. But, by your leave, I'll just mention your plan to Mr Smith before you start, and then, maybe he'll be for pushing on his horse a little."

So saying Mr Woodcomb left them; when Mary, turning to the little girl, said, "Have you any bonnet and shawl to put on, Fanny?"

"I don't know," replied the child.

"Not know? How can that be, Fanny?"

"Because I have never been out of the doors since I first came into them," said Fanny.

"Poor dear! I wish they would not keep you here any longer—this is quite intolerable!" said Mary, again opening the door, and looking impatientiy across the dismal court.

"Keep me here?" murmured the little girl, in a voice of the most evident terror. "Do you think they will keep me here?"

"No, no, my poor child, they shall not keep you here," said Mrs Tremlett, "Here come the two men together."

Fanny did not venture to look at them, but Mary did; and again, in spite of her reason, she felt terrified at the idea that she was in their power. Mr Woodcomb, indeed, looked smiling and obsequious as before, but in the countenance of the burly miller there was something of opposition and displeasure that she could not understand

"Setting off walking, miss, is very like bilking your driver," said he, with considerably more bluntness than civility.

"What does he mean, Mrs Tremlett?" said Mary, turning pale.

"You had better pay the gentleman before you set out, my dear. That's what you mean to say, isn't it, sir?"

"Why surely, ma'am, it would be more like doing business," replied the man, looking a little ashamed of himself.

"Is that all?" said Mary, inexpressibly relieved, and drawing out her ready purse with such cheerful alacrity, that could the hearts of the two men before whom she stood have been read, there might have been found in both a strong inclination to profit by it a little further.

"That, I think, sir, is the sum you named for the hire of your vehicle?" said Mary, extending her hand with two sovereigns towards him.

Mr Timothy Smith took the money, but certainly thought that if that sharp-eyed rogue Woodcomb had been further he might have hit upon some excuse for demanding more. As it was, however, he could not venture it, and with a rather surly inclination of the head, pocketed the gold, and left the room.

"Now then, sir, if you please," said the still frightened Mary, "we will wish you good morning."

"Yes, ma'am, surely, you can go if you please. Only perhaps you might like, for the honour of your young relation here, to leave some little gratuity to be divided as a little treat among her late companions?"

Mary looked in his face, and the sort of half-ashamed glance with which the extortioner watched the effect of his words, appeared to her so sinister, that with a sudden feeling of something like rational alarm, she remembered that she had only a few shillings left in her purse, and that again to open in his presence her still well-filled pocket-book, might be dangerous.

"Aunt Tremlett, have you any money to lend me?" she said, at the same time drawing out again her almost empty purse. "I am very sorry I have only these few shillings left; but I will willingly send you five pounds, sir, for the purpose you mention, if the miller will take the trouble of bringing it to you."

"Oh! It's no matter, ladies. Pray do not trouble yourselves any more about it," replied Woodcomb, keeping his eyes however, furtively directed towards Mrs Tremlett, who was still engaged in seeking for money in the recesses of a very large pocket.

"I have two pounds and a few shillings, my dear," said the old lady, at length placing her little leathern purse in Mary's hand.

"That will do, that will do perfectly," said the worshipper of Mammon, with an air and tone of the most amiable liberality, but at the same time stretching out his hand, in which he received the entire contents, uncounted, of Mrs Tremlett's purse, which Miss Brotherton unclasped, and emptied into it.

Had she studied the man's character for years, she could not have devised any manœuvre so likely to hasten the unlocking the door which enclosed them as thus emptying their two purses before his eyes. He now moved forward of his own accord, drew forth from the pocket of his coat the massive key, applied it with a large, strong, and effective hand, to the enormous lock, drew back the heavy bolts, and finally threw wide the hateful door.

The three females passed through it with no lingering steps, and heard it close heavily behind them, with feelings assuredly very different in degree, but in so far the same, that each one as she stepped over the threshold, breathed a prayer that she might never repass it again.

XXIV

*The walk proves too fatiguing to one of the party, but not
to Miss Brotherton—She wanders further, and meets with
an adventure, but at last returns in safety to her inn—
A journey homeward, and a fact related without ornament*

IT IS BUT A DREARY and desolate landscape which greets the eye
immediately without the walls of the Deep Valley factory; but to all
who are happy enough to feel that they are quitting those hideous walls
for ever, it can hardly fail to convey a sense of beauty, freshness, and
freedom, sufficient to expand the heart with admiration and delight.
Mary felt disposed to bound along the grassy path beside the stream
with the joyous playfulness of a child, and rather than have re-entered
that creaking door again, would have been tempted, like another
Undine, to plunge into the water, and take her chance of finding
quarters less hateful beneath its rippling wave. Mrs Tremlett breathed
more freely, and seemed to have recovered the elastic step of youth, as
she moved briskly on. But compared with what was passing in the breast
of the ragged, dirty little creature that walked beside them, their feelings
wer most earthly cold and dull. Her small hand was still clasped in that
of Miss Brotherton, who felt that the child was urging her onward, even
faster than she was inclined to go, while her head upturned towards the
towering heights which hemmed them in, seemed eagerly seeking an
outlet from the region that her soul abhorred.

"You are glad, dear Fanny, are you not, to know that you have left that
frightful place?" said Mary, kindly pressing the little emaciated hand she
held in hers. The child stopped short in her hurried walk, and looking
up in her deliverer's face, with a doubting anxious look that it was

painful to see, murmured very softly, and as if fearing to be overheard from within the walls,

"Shall I never, never go back again?"

"No, never Fanny! Do you think I would be so cruel as to take you back?" said Mary.

"I do not know if it is not all a dream," replied the child. "I have dreamed that I saw green grass, and felt the air upon my face, before."

"Do not be afraid, Fanny! You are not dreaming now," returned Mary. "Run on, and gather that fine large stalk of foxglove. You never saw such a gay flower as that in your dreams, did you?"

The little girl sprang forward, and falling upon her knees on the grass, plucked the tall flower, and pressed it to her lips, and to her heart. But though this was a childish action, it was not done childishly: there was an appearance of deep feeling, and even of devotion in her look and attitude which strongly awakened Mary's interest, and when the little creature rose again, and holding the flower in one hand, slid the other once more into that of her new friend, the heart of that friend yearned towards her with newly-awakened tenderness. But when she spoke to her, and endeavoured to lead her into conversation, the attempt entirely failed. There are many who might have felt disappointed and chilled by this; but Mary Brotherton had truer sympathy, and as, from time to time, she felt a loving contraction of Fanny's little fingers upon her own, and sometimes caught her looking up, as if by stealth into her face, she felt no misgivings as to the cause of her silence, but loved her the better from knowing that her heart was too full to speak.

They all, and as if moved by one common impulse, walked quickly forward as long as their road continued along the margin of the stream; but when it turned round the steep hill's base, and began to mount, their pace relaxed, Mary felt that her little companion dragged on her steps with labour, and perceived that Mrs Tremlett was out of breath.

"Let us sit down under this ash-tree, and wait for the jolly miller," said Miss Brotherton, "it cannot be very long, I think, before he overtakes us."

This proposal was the more amiable, because, in the first place, Mary could herself have run from the bottom of that steep hill to the top, almost without perceiving that it was any hill at all; and in the next, she so exceedingly disliked both the miller and his cart, that had she consulted her own inclinations alone, she would probably have preferred retracing the whole way on foot.

But very gladly was her proposal for rest accepted, by both her old and young companion, and long did they remain seated under their pleasant canopy before they any of them grew weary of it; till at length, after consulting her watch, Miss Brotherton expressed a doubt whether the fat miller and his lazy steed intended to overtake them at all.

"Good gracious, my dear! do you really think so?" said Mrs Tremlett, considerably alarmed. "Why, Mary, we shall never get back to Mrs Prescot's without him!"

"I hope I may be mistaken, my dear old woman," said her kind mistress, affectionately; "for I fear such a walk would be too much for you. But when I remember that he is paid, and remember, likewise, how very little he seemed actuated by any motive, save that of sordid interest, I confess that I do think it very probable he means to leave us in the lurch."

"Then let us walk on, Miss Mary, without saying a word more about it. The shadows are beginning to grow long already, and you shan't be kept out half the night by my laziness. Come along, little girl."

With these words, Mrs Tremlett raised herself from between two comfortable roots, which had made her an excellent arm-chair; but the little girt whom she summoned to do likewise, though she exerted herself to get on her feet, seemed hardly able to stand.

"My poor Fanny, you are quite knocked up!" exclaimed Miss Brotherton, looking at her with great anxiety. "How in the world shall we ever be able to get her on?"

"It is only because I have not been used to walk lately," said Fanny; "that is, not as we have been walking now. Our work keeps us always on our legs, and that makes them bend about so, when I try to walk; but I can walk though it hurts me, and I think it would be better to die outright in getting on, rather than rest so near the factory—so, please ma'am, I'm quite ready to go on."

And again the party set off, but the difficulty with which the little Fanny got along became more obvious at every step, and it soon became evident that to get as far as Mrs Prescot's would be impossible.

The dilemma was not a pleasant one. They were still in a part of the road so little frequented, that it was probable they might wait for hours without obtaining assistance from any passer by, nor did either Mrs Tremlett or Mary recollect to have seen any dwelling nearer than the high-road, from which they were still at a considerable distance.

The distress of the little girl was painful to witness. At the very moment when the dark cloud which had seemed to settle upon her was, and gradually and with difficulty, as to eyes long unaccustomed to its light, began to reach her; at that very moment her strength failed, and a sensation, like the sickness of death, rendered every attempt at further exertion impossible.

"I must stay here," she said; "it is the will of God."

"No, no, Fanny," said Miss Brotherton, seating herself beside her, and letting the languid little head drop upon her bosom; "you have no reason to think that, while I have a thousand to believe the contrary. It is a most strange chance which has brought me here, and placed you in my hands—this was by the will of God, and I will not believe it has so chanced, only that I may see you die."

"You must not stay here," said Fanny, feebly; "night will come presently and you must go fast to get home. Do not be sorry for me—but indeed, I think I am as bad as Michael was, when he fell sick, and was carried away to die."

"I see—" began Mary, eagerly; but suddenly stopping herself, she added, "Not now my poor Fanny, you must not tell me about it now—when I have got you strong and well at my own home, we will talk of poor Michael. Try now, to think how glad you will be when we have got you home, and all our difficulties are over. But something must be done, I know, my poor child, before this can be. How had we best act in this dilemma, Mrs Tremlett? Do you think you shall have courage to remain with this poor child while I run on, and endeavour to find some house where we may get assistance?"

"Alone, Miss Mary?" replied the good woman, looking terribly alarmed. "How can I let you set off in a strange, wild country like this, with nobody to take care of you? Let us go together, Mary; nothing can hurt this little girl, you know, while we are away."

"Think it over once more, dear Tremlett," said Mary, "and then I believe you will perceive that there is more chance of your being useful to her, than to me. I shall get on faster without you, good nurse, and with a lighter heart than if I took you for company, while this little creature was left with nothing but her own melancholy thoughts and childish terrors to comfort her."

"Then I will stay," said the poor woman, sighing heavily; "but just think, Miss Mary, how I shall feel till you come back again!"

"I will not loiter to amuse myself," replied her young mistress with a cheering smile; "and now take my place, and let this poor little head rest on your shoulder."

"She shall lie down on that bit of level turf yonder, with her head upon my lap," said the old nurse, tenderly assisting Mary to lift her up.

"God bless you, my dear good soul! I will be quickly back again," replied her grateful mistress. "How much more you show you love me now, than if you insisted upon walking after me. There! she lies as nicely as if she were in bed. If our faithless miller makes his appearance, keep him and his cart till I come back; tell him he shall have more gold, and he will stand waiting beside you, as gentle as a lamb."

Having said these comforting words, Mary hastened onward and was speedily out of sight. Having reached the top of the hill, she looked anxiously round in search of a human dwelling, but nothing met her eye, but barren moor-land, which at some distance showed symptoms of cultivation, being enclosed in patches by low stone walls, and here and there the fragment of a stunted hawthorn fence, which seemed to sustain a hungry life with difficulty. Making her way across the rude and imperfectly-formed sunk fence, which marked the boundary of the cart-road, along which they had travelled in the morning, Mary found herself on a level of some extent, but without the slightest track to direct her steps amidst the long parched grass, and frequent stones with which it was covered.

"This will never do! I may walk here till I have completely lamed myself, without a chance of meeting any living soul," thought Mary, stopping short; "I shall do better by making for the high-road at once."

And having so decided, she turned about to retrace her steps, and regain the road; but ere she reached it, a sort of hillock at a little distance caught her eye, and wishing to take advantage of its elevation, for the purpose of reconnoitring, she turned aside to reach it. Her approach to it was from the east, and a dazzling sunset was in her eyes, as she made her way up the rugged side of what looked like one of the tumuli which served as resting-places for human bones, ere churchyards yawned for them. Greatly was she startled on reaching the top of it, to perceive on the western side, crouching in a hollow that looked as if it had been excavated by the shelter-seeking sheep, a strange wild figure, whose dress, as she looked down upon it, left its sex doubtful. The fragment of a hat, and the remnant of a jacket were evidently intended, by their original construction, for the use of the nobler sex, while something resembling a petticoat enveloping the lower half of the figure, suggested the probability that the masculine portion of the attire was worn by sufferance, and not by right.

Mary's light step among the matted tufts of coarse vegetation which covered the thin soil, had not been heard, and she stood looking down upon her doubtful neighbour with the advantage of being herself unseen.

"There goes another day!" said a voice, which though harsh and aged, was unmistakably female; "and the silly soul has got to wait for another."

Glad to find that her unexpected companion in this most desolate spot, was of the safer, because the weaker portion of the human race, the wandering heiress determined to address her; but deemed it wisest to approach her visibly, instead of startling the poor soul by speaking to her unexpectedly from the spot where she stood. For this purpose, she gently descended from her elevation, and making a little circuit, presented herself before the eyes of the sun-gazer.

The old woman, for such she was, sat nose and knees together, in a sort of hole which completely sheltered her in every direction but the west; and from the earnest manner in which her dim eyes were fixed upon the last bright rays of the setting sun, it seemed as if her lair was chosen on purpose to look upon it.

The appearance of Mary seemed to startle her, but not much; for after

"I am the only old woman in
the world! All the rest get their
death in the Factories!"

looking at her for a minute as if she examined her person with difficulty,
because her eyes were dazzled by the object on which she had before
been gazing, she said, pointing a stick that she held towards the point
whence the bright orb had just disappeared,

"Who be you, coming to spy out old Sally at her devotions?"

"I want to find a house, my good woman, for I have left a poor child
very ill at a short distance from hence; I want to find people who can
help me to remove her."

"There are no people here," said the old woman, in a gentle but
melancholy voice, and turning her eyes round the desolate moor as if in
confirmation of the assertion.

"But perhaps you may be able to tell me where I can find some one?"

"O dear! O dear! there is no want of finding for such as you. Just go upon the high-road and turn yourself about, and say, 'Come to me,' and you'll be seeing 'em flock in, right and left, and north and south, all bowing and scraping as genteel as possible. 'Tis only me as lives in a hole, and prays to the sun every night to be so kind as not to wake me the next morning; 'tis only me that never sees any body. I am the only woman in all the world—all the rest have got their death in the factories."

There are many circumstances of more danger, that are infinitely less appalling than meeting, when out of sight of every other human being, a poor frail shattered remnant of humanity with a disordered wit. Mary shuddered as the wild speech of this poor creature confirmed the idea of insanity which her appearance suggested, and her first impression was to turn and run. But her steps were stayed by the shrill, trembling voice of the old woman, who in an accent, the most helples and forlorn, called after her,

"One minute—only stay one minute! Let me look at you one minute!"

Mary turned again, and all feeling of terror was lost in pity as she beheld the miserable little crippled figure which was hobbling towards her. Her height hardly reached that of an ordinary child of twelve years old, her gait showed that her legs were dreadfully deformed, her uncouth garments hung about her in tatters, and as she painfully rolled herself at every step round the stick by whose aid she was supported, it was hardly possible to conceive a more complete image of poverty and decrepitude, than her whole appearance offered.

"Do not hurry so!" cried Mary, every idea of alarm lost in contemplating her suffering helplessness. "I will not go yet, if you wish me to stay." They were now close together, and the shaking creature looked up in her face, with a soft, silly smile, that had all the woeful innocence of imbecility With a small, skinny hand that was delicately pale, and perfectly clean, she took the end of Mary's silk scarf and gazed upon it in a sort of ecstasy. "Oh, fine! oh, pretty, pretty, pretty!" she exclaimed, smoothing and patting it with her hand, as if it had been a tame and favourite bird. "I think," she added, with a sagacious nod, "that I know where you come from. This is just the things, I know, that they wear in heaven—I think I know where you come from." Then breaking into what sounded like a genuine laugh, she again repeated, "I think I know where you come from—that is what the overlooker man said to me," she added, lowering her voice to a whisper, "when he caught me running away from the factory. It is not so very long ago—I can tell you all about it, if you would like to hear—and it is not like the rest of the things you know," touching her forehead with her forefinger; "I don't tell that backwards and forwards, nonsense-fashion, like the other things I talk about—that was beat in upon my brain by the blacksmith, and nothing can ever take it out again, they say, till one of the angels does it in heaven. It used to pain me a good deal," she continued, taking off her hat, and laying her open palm on the top of her head, "but since I took to sitting on my throne there, as the folks call it, and gathered the dew morning and night to put upon it, the pain is a deal better."

"I cannot hear your story now," said Mary, gently, "because there is a poor sick girl on the side of the hill that wants me very bad—she comes from the factory too, and she is too ill to walk—can you tell me where I can find any body to help me carry her?"

"Come from the factory, is she? Dear, dear, dear, dear! She will be sure to die, you may depend upon it—they all do die, except me. Don't you fancy that you'll ever take her back alive, it was only I that could bear that, and I was burnt in the head for it, as I told you."

"I do not want to take her back," said Mary, "I want to help her. Where do you live? Are there any houses or people near this place? Now, be a good woman, and take me where I can find some body to help us."

"Yes, I will," replied the poor creature, in a tone which convinced Miss Brotherton that she understood her, and at the same time beginning to hobble on before her towards the road.

Nothing probably less pressing, and less hopeless than her present position could have tempted Mary to trust herself to such a guide; yet she felt a strange sort of confidence that the old woman knew what she was about, and though aware that the experiment was rather a desperate one, determined to follow wherever her feeble guide should lead, certain, at least, that the distance could not be very great.

There was, however, much more strength and power of locomotion in the old cripple than she gave her credit for. Having contrived to crawl to the grassy dyke that fenced the moor, she crossed the road obliquely, and making her way through a very imperfect hedge of furze and quickset, hobbled on across a bit of miserably arid stubble, which presently descended abruptly, and led to a tuft of stunted elder-bushes, beside which stood a small farm-house, with its cow-yard, barns, and ricks.

Surprised and delighted to find herself so near a human dwelling, Mary had hardly patience to restrain her steps to the pace of her poor guide, nevertheless she had not the heart to leave her, for there was an expression of pride and pleasure in the woman's eye as she turned round from time to time as they advanced, which she felt it would be most cruel to check by showing that she could do without her. So it was together that they reached the bottom of the steep descent, and together that they entered the kitchen of the farm-house, where a very decent middle-aged woman was engaged in preparing supper. She looked exceedingly surprised at the appearance of Miss Brotherton and for a moment turned her eyes from her to her companion and back again, with an air that was almost bewildered; but soon recovering herself she courtesied with much respect, and said, "I hope you haven't been scared, ma'am, by falling in with this poor cretur? She is as harmless as a baby."

"O no!" replied Mary, "she has been very kind to me, for she has brought me here, where I should never have been able to get without her, the house is so completely concealed—and I want help, ma'am, very much indeed."

"You haven't met no accident, I hope?" said the good woman, kindly and ceasing her notable operations, she drew forward a wooden chair for her guest to sit upon.

"Thank you very much," said the young lady, seating herself. "Yet it is not rest I most want. I have a little girl with me whom I have left by the side of the road that leads from the mills; she is too weak and ill to get on, and I hope you will be able to lend me some conveyance—a cart, a waggon, any thing to take her as far as the King's Head, three or four miles I suppose from hence, upon the turn pike-road: I would pay well for it."

"From the mills?" repeated the woman staring.

"Yes; from the place called Deep Valley Mill," replied Mary, "perhaps rather more than a mile from here."

"Oh! ma'am, I know the Deep Valley Mill well enough," was the answer. "All Mr Woodcomb's own butter and milk comes from here. That is not the difficulty. But we shan't like to have nothing to do with carrying away any child from there."

"You need fear nothing on that point," replied Miss Brotherton, eagerly, "I have paid for permission to bring this child away."

"That alters the case for certain. But—I ask your pardon, ma'am,— there is something very odd then, in such a lady as you walking away from the factory with one of the children."

"Indeed I do not wonder at your saying so. But believe me, I tell you nothing but the truth when I assure you that I have permission, and have paid largely for it, to bring this child away. Our unfortunately attempting to walk was merely accident, and occasioned entirely by my foolish impatience to get away from the place before Mr Smith, the miller, who took me there, thought his horse sufficiently rested to return."

"Mr Smith, the miller? Then for certain all's right—for they be known for the greatest of friends, M. Woodcomb and he—and I dare say my husband, ma'am, would be proud to help you when he comes home. It's coming dark fast, and he won't be long I dare say."

"But I must go back to this poor child; I have left her with an old lady, who will, I fear, be greatly alarmed at being left so long," said Mary.

"*Poor child!*" repeated her limping guide, who, from the moment they had entered, had been reposing herself, by sitting on the floor, and had not spoken till now. "*Poor child!*—think of that!—and she comes from the factory! Think of speaking in that way of a factory child!"

"Hold your tongue, Sally, or I'll give you no porridge for supper," said the woman, but by no means harshly; and as she spoke, she dropped into the maniac's lap a piece of bread that lay in a plate upon the table.

"Had your factory child got this now," said poor Sally, nodding her head with a sort of boastful exultation, "she would not be so terrible bad. But there's nobody but me as gets this. I am the only old woman in the world; all the rest die young—and most of 'em," she added, in a whisper, "before they get away."

"Was this poor creature at the Deep Valley factory when she was young?" demanded Miss Brotherton.

"She tells you quite true, ma'am," replied the farmer's wife, resuming her cookery, which consisted in chopping up bacon, cabbage, and potatoes, for the frying-pan. She talks nonsense about the moon sometimes, and is very wild when it comes to the full, but she never makes any blunder when she tells of her own troubles at the factory. She never varies the least bit in the world when she tells about her getting away, and being stopped, and taken back again, poor cretur. 'Tis only too true, that's the worst of it—she has never been in her right mind since."

"I would bear her tell it willingly, and should listen to it with great interest," said Miss Brotherton. "But at this moment I can think of nothing but those I have left,"

"Whereabouts be they, ma'am?" demanded the farmer's wife.

Mary described the spot very accurately. "Why, dear me! them surely must be the trees right against our gate," said the good woman, with great apparent satisfaction. "And if so be as I'm right, 'tis hardly more than a stone's throw from our back gate. I take it, ma'am, as you walked by the lane just round our farm, and them trees as you speak of, bean't not one quarter of the distance as you have come."

"In that case," replied Miss Brotherton, greatly comforted, "I have no doubt that we could get the poor little girl here, and then if you would give us leave to remain till your husband has contrived to procure some sort of conveyance for us, all our troubles would be over, and most gratefully will I repay you for your assistance."

"I will show you the way this moment, ma'am," said the woman, with great alacrity; and once more suspending her labours for the good man's supper, she prepared to attend the lady by taking off an external apron, and smoothing that which was below it.

Though not quite *within a stone's throw*, the spot to which Miss Brotherton was so anxious to return, was reached by a very short cut across the piece of meadow-ground on which the back part of the farm-house opened.

The joy of Mrs Tremlett at seeing her was great indeed and poor Fanny, refreshed by the interval of rest, declared herself quite able to walk "a good piece more.'

"Poor little creature!" exclaimed good Mrs Roberts, the farmer's wife; "she do look bad, sure enough! It is seldom or never that we gets a sight of the children at the mill, for they sends regular for what they wants, and bean't over fond of having any body go near 'em;—but she puts me strongly in mind of old Sally's stories to be sure!"

The little party reached the farm without difficulty, and then, indeed, as Mary had predicted, all their present troubles seemed over, for nothing could exceed the earnest kindness with which Mrs Roberts administered to all their wants. Mrs Tremlett's appearance and manner appeared to have entirely removed the sort of doubtful impression which poor Mary's hurried *entrée* had produced, and having been told that the little girl had been reclaimed by them as a relation, the whole adventure appeared to her as one of the deepest interest, and her sympathy and good-will were most fully excited.

Old Sally was sitting upon the floor exactly where they had left her. "Poor thing! exclaimed Mary, "she has not moved an inch."

"Not she, poor soul," replied Mrs Roberts, "I told her to bide still, and when we says that to her, she'd keep still, if we was to be away a whole day I believe. Get up, Sally!" she added, good-humouredly. "There's a brave woman! Look at that little girl, and tell the ladies what she puts you in mind of."

The expression of the poor withered, idiot face, that was turned upon Fanny Fletcher when this was uttered, was most touchingly sad and solemn. The gentle, silly look, which her countenance usually wore, was exchanged for one full of deep mysterious meaning. She drew herself towards the little girl with a sort of stealthy movement, as if afraid of being seen to approach her, and when quite close beside her, said,

"You then have done as I did—you have run away? Poor, poor little thing! Can't you guess what will come next? Poor little thing They will catch you! hide where you will, they will catch you."

"I have not run away," said Fanny, gently.

The maniac shook her head. "Don't you scream as I did, my poor lamb, for it's no good; they care no more for screams and groans than for the whirring of the spindles. But the screams went into my own ears, and I have never got rid of them since. I still hear them, all night long when it is moon-time. Poor, poor little girl!"

"Come, come Sally—let her alone now, she is going to eat something."

And Mrs Roberts completed the arrangements upon which she had been occupied since they entered, by placing chairs at the table on which bread, butter, and cheese, were placed.

Not even did the Deep Valley apprentice feel more disposed to do justice to these preparations than did Miss Brotherton and her old servant. They had tasted nothing since breakfast, and when a bowl of fresh milk was added to the bread-and-butter, Mary gratefully assured her entertainer that she considered it as the most delicious supper she had ever eaten.

"Now that's different," said poor Sally, who had perched herself on a low stool close to Fanny Fletcher. "I never had any pretty creature like that, all clothed in heavenly trappings, giving *me* milk; but it will make no difference in the end—you must be dragged back again, poor little thing!"

"No, no—she won't be dragged back again," said Mrs Roberts; "and there's a cup of milk for you—so now let the ladies eat in peace, Sally. You know it's time for you to be crawling home—the master will be here in no time, and maybe he will be after asking how many stones you have picked up to-day, so you had better be off."

The docile creature immediately shuffled off her stool, and prepared to depart.

"I should like to hear her describe her own adventures, which you say she does so faithfully," said Miss Brotherton. "Do you think you could persuade her to repeat her story to us?"

"Yes, yes, ma'am; she will do that quick enough; it is just what she likes best," replied Mrs Roberts; "except now and then when she is moody. Now, Sally, if you will behave yourself like a sensible woman, you may sit down again, and tell the ladies how you ran away from the mill, and was caught and brought back again, and all the rest of it."

The little cripple's eyes twinkled, and a gleam of intelligence flashed across her countenance with a sort of Will-o'-the-wisp brightness, as she took the fragment of a hat from her closely-shorn gray head, and reseated herself.

"'Twas my knees as was the first of it," she began; "I couldn't bear it. The pain growed worse and worse, and my legs dipped down, and they strapped me harder and harder, and that was the reason that I couldn't bear it. So one day," she continued, in a deep, clear whisper, "one day when the 'prentices, and overlookers, and managers and all was off for dinner, I stopped behind 'em, and no body seed me—no, not one of 'em. And while they were at dinner, I slipped into the yard where the pigs bide, and then away again, all upon the sly, to the door where they takes the dirt out. I thought maybe, I might have the bolts to pull, but not a bit of it—there it stood wide open, with a barrow full of rubbish between the posts—that was fun!"

And here the poor creature laughed that dreadful laugh which none but maniacs utter.

"But the fun lasted longer than that," she went on, "it lasted while I creeped along for a mile or more among the bushes as grows so rank t'other side the mill; and there I laid down at last in the midst of 'em, 'cause I heard a noise, and what d'ye think it was? What d'ye think the poor cretur heard with her heart galloping just at the bottom of her throat, for all the world like the flap—flap—flap of a fly-wheel?"

"Perhaps 'twas a dog barking, Sally," said Mrs Roberts, humouring the maniac as she made a pause.

"No! 'twas not a dog barking, nor it wasn't a wolf, nor it wasn't a tiger; but it was something ten million of times worser than either—It—was—the—'printice-master!" replied Sally, in a slow deep whisper. "It was the divilish 'printice-master with his eyes of fire, and his breath of flame. Oh-h! I feel him at my throat now!" and she clasped her withered neck with her pale thin hands, shuddering violently from head to foot.

"Speak soberly, Sally, and like a sensible body, or you must not go on, you know that," said Mrs Roberts, interposing in a warning tone, which poor Sally seemed to understand, for though her breast still heaved with a panting movement, like one who had run a race, and was out

of breath, she assumed an affected air of composure, putting her hands
before her primly, and shutting her eyes.

"Yes, mississ, I know that," she replied, sedately, "I know that very well,
and we won't trouble Joe ploughman to help us home this time; but I
may go on, if I speak sensible, and like a wise woman, as I am?"

The farmer's wife nodded assent, and Sally continued more quietly.

"It was the 'printice-master, and none but he as dragged me forth,
head foremost, out of the bushes—very much like the butcher, you
know, my dears, when he takes the little lamb's head between his two
hard hands—I never sees that up at Tom Blake's shambles, without
thinking of it. So he dragged me back again—and then you may guess
how the strap went! But think of me! think what a spirit I must have
had in those days, my dears—will you believe that I made up my mind
to start again, though I hadn't a bit of unbruised skin upon my body?—I
did though, Oh, dear! oh, dear! how I used to hear the birds singing in
my ears o' nights, when I laid down, and made believe to sleep! But I
don't fancy it was sleep, not right wholesome sleep ever, as I got then;
for I can mind now, yes I can, with all my moonshine, I can mind now,
how I used to smell the grass, and see the dew shining, and hear the
pretty sweet cows a mooing, and I all the while shut up in a stone
prison-house—that was the divil tempting me, wasn't it? But I didn't
start again for two whole years though,—'cause why, I never found
no chance for it; and by that time my legs was shocking bad, and if it
was the divil as made me run, he ought to have sent me a stick to help
me—for, oh, dear! I crawled dreadful slow—and then—"

"Come, come, Sally," interrupted Mrs Roberts, "I won't have all that
at full length, or else we shall have you off again; make an end, there's
a fine woman. Tell the ladies about the shutting up, and then go home
and to bed, for 'tis time."

Miss Brotherton ceased to wonder, as she had first done, at the chartered
licence which the crazy cripple seemed to enjoy, when she observed the
perfect docility with which she obeyed every word and look of the farmer's
wife. She now resumed her story, exactly at the word commanded.

"Yes, I was shut up, my dears—I shall have soon done now, for I am
coming to the black gap, as call it, and I always stops there—but where

do you think they shut me up? In this room, or that room, or t'other room, perhaps? Not a bit of it. They shut me up in a little narrow place, not much bigger than a grave, and it was dark—dark—dark, all but one little narrow slip, and there was no light comed through that at first; but by and by, after I had been days and days locked in, I heard a horrid, horrid lumbering noise, and then I saw a flash of light through the narrow slip, for all the world like the light of a candle—and the light of a candle it was too, and what do you think it showed me? Crippled as I was, I managed to scramble high enough to peep—there was beams, on bricks or something, and what do you think I saw?"

The poor creature began shaking again, but on Mrs Roberts holding up her finger, she seemed to make a strong effort to control herself, and once more, slipping off her stool, she drew close to Miss Brotherton, and in a low rapid voice, hurried through the remainder of her narrative.

"I saw," said she, "the master's wife laid stone dead upon a truckle-bed, almost as close to me as I am to you—think of that! Stone dead! Stiffened, stark, and ghastly, and blue! There was a candle that flared full upon her dead face; but they as brought her was run away—they couldn't bear it, I'm sure they couldn't bear it, and I was left alone to look upon it, and I couldn't run away; but I could not bear it either! and then it was that I screamed—hush! I must not scream now, you know!"

Here she stopped, putting her hands before her eyes, and remaining perfectly still for a minute, and then added with more composure,

"After that came the black gap, and I don't know any thing more about it; only that I watch the sun go to bed every night, and I have been going on praying for years and years, all the time I have been growing into an old woman, that he would please not to wake me in the morning."

"Here's the master, Sally!" said Mrs Roberts; "so take yourself off, there's a good woman. Here's your mug of porridge; put on your hat steady, and wish the ladies a good night."

Again she was most docilely obeyed, and in another moment poor Sally was gone, and the hardworking master of the premises occupied her place. The situation and wants of his unexpected guests were speedily explained to him, and his best assistance as speedily promised. While he devoured a hasty supper, one of his farm-horses was put into the shafts of a jockey cart, and in less than an hour after his return, the comforted party set out by the light of a friendly moon, and were safely jolted to the King's Head, without having been over taken by the treacherous miller, who probably preferred sharing the jovial supper, in which his good friend Woodcomb indulged on this memorable evening, to forsaking it for the purpose of overtaking the ladies from whom it was derived—as there seemed but little chance of drawing thing more from the same source.

Great was the joy of Mrs Prescot at seeing her guests return; from their long absence, together with the nature of the business on which they were engaged had caused the good woman to torment herself with many dark forebodings. Nevertheless, she was well prepared to receive them, and nothing was wanting that she could furnish towards refreshing the adventurers after their fatigue.

But, alas! it was only then; it was only after the anxiety, and the agitation of the enterprise were over, that poor Mary fully remembered how abortive that enterprise had been; and then she wept, wept bitterly as she thought of the load of anguish she had to carry home to Michael's mother and brother. Yet as she listened to little Fanny's tearful narration of all that had passed between them, during the week they had worked together, she felt that when the first dreadful pang should be over, there would be something like consolation for them in listening to it also; and as she studied the delicate and expressive features of the pretty creature she had rescued, and watched the sort of timid, doubting hope, that by degrees took the place of the nervous, heart-struck look, that had been so painfully legible in her sweet face when first she saw her, it was impossible not to feel that while deploring the loss of one object of benevolence, she had to rejoice for having found another.

Luckily for the respectability of their appearance, in setting forth on their homeward travels the following morning, the active Mrs Prescot was enabled, by the aid of the heiress's magic pocket-book, to procure from a neighbour a suit of decent apparel for the little orphan. The same freely-flowing source supplied wherewithal to reward all the friendly offices performed by the host and hostess of the King's Head, and in addition, they were left in possession of a romance which was likely enough, from the frequency with which it was repeated, to furnish a legend to the little village to the end of time.

One single adventure occurred to Miss Brotherton on her way home, which though forming a very isolated episode in the history of her journey, shall be recounted, because the fact which it brought to her knowledge is one that well deserves publicity.

The heiress varied her road homewards, by driving through a village which, were it not infested by the plague-spot of a factory, might be considered as one of the most attractive in Derbyshire. At one point the road passes through a rocky defile of such wild beauty, that Mary, who was equally unacquainted with fine scenery, and capable of enjoying it, called to the postboy to stop, that she might get out and walk up the long ascent, in order the more thoroughly to enjoy the widely-spreading landscape it commanded. Neither of her companions accompanied her. Mrs Tremlett consenting, nothing loth, to remain in the post-chaise, upon the steepness of the road being pointed out to her, while little Fanny, though in her heart longing to spring after her benefactress, replied to the observation, that she was not yet strong enough to climb, by a look that spoke more of gratitude, than regret.

It was alone, therefore, that Mary Brotherton started forward, her active steps soon leaving the carriage behind; when cutting short the spiral ascent by making her way through the underwood which clothed the bank, she soon found herself high above the road, and on a spot of great beauty. After lingering here for a few minutes she proceeded, when hearing the ever attractive sound of rushing waters, she again stopped, and then, guided by her ear, followed where it led, till she reached an opening, not far from the high-road, but apart from it, where, instead of the mountain cascade she had expected, a spectacle greeted her that for an instant seemed to petrify every nerve, and the bounding elastic movement which had brought her within sight of it, was changed to the rigid stillness of marble. A man, almost ferocious in his aspect, from the squalid, unshorn, brutal negligence of decency which it betrayed, was supporting in his arms, and on his bosom, a boy of ten or eleven years old, whose ghastly countenance showed plainly that death was busy at his heart. Before the rock from whence flowed the gushing stream, whose sound had brought Miss Brotherton to the spot, stood what looked like the fragment of a rude pillar, and on this stone the father had rested the wasted form of his dying child. Before him stood a little girl gazing on the boy with a mixture of infant fear and sisterly love, as she tended a bowl, filled from the spring, to his lips.

"He is very ill!" said Mary, addressing the father, "can I go any where to get help for you?"

The man, who had the fragment of a pipe in his mouth, and who looked rather bewildered, and fiercely angry, than oppressed by sorrow, stared at her, but answered not a word.

"What is the matter with him?" said Miss Brotherton, addressing the little girl.

"He be worked down," replied the child, sobbing. "We have been at long hours for four weeks, and Dick couldn't stand it—father have carried him to and from mill for a week—but he couldn't stand it. Mother said, when we started, that he looked as if he'd never come back alive; but he'd have had to pay double fine if so be as father had left him to bide at home, so he carried him to mill; but though they strapped him, and strapped him, he couldn't stand to his work, and he have been lying in the mill-yard till father comed to take him."

This horrible statement was uttered amidst tears and sobs, but poor Mary lost not a word of it; and as her very soul sickened at the tale, she felt tempted to believe that she was doomed to witness every circumstance that could most painfully recall the source whence all her greatness flowed.

With clasped hands, and streaming eyes, she stood silently watching the gasping breath of this young victim of unnatural labour. The boy's eyes fixed themselves on the face of his little sister. He might be listening to her history of his early fate—or he might be consciously taking a last look at what he loved. In either case the effort demanded more strength than was left him—his eyes closed, a shivering movement passed through all his frame, and then he became still. The quick, short, unequal heaving of the breast was seen no more, and Mary hid her eyes as the mysterious change, which no human being can gaze upon unmoved, came upon the stiffening features. It was rather instinct than feeling, which prompted her even at that awful moment to proffer what she had learned to know would be felt as consolation, did one starving member of a family alone survive amidst the dying and the dead of a whole race. Without venturing again to look at the father and his son, she dropped into the bowl, which the little girl still held, what she hated to think would soon turn natural sorrow into unnatural forgetfulness of it: but she had no power to serve them more effectually, and hastily turning into the road, she awaited the slow arrival of the post-chaise in a state of mind which left no faculty at leisure to enjoy any longer the hills and valleys for whose sake she had left it.

Fron this time the journey homeward proceeded without accident or adventure of any kind, and Mary would probably have shared the pleasure so energetically expressed by Mrs Tremlett at being restored to the luxurious tranquillity of Millord Park, had not the heavy news she carried to the poor Armstrongs made her dread the day that would follow her reaching it.

But how she got through that painful day, and all that resulted from it—how little Fanny Fletcher fared in her new and most strange home, and whether her patroness had most reason to bless or deplore the sudden movement which had caused her to hazard the blending thus the destiny of one so utterly unknown, with her own, must all be reserved for future narration, as the adventures of Michael Armstrong, of necessity, draw the pen of his historian elsewhere.

XXV

The narrative returns to its hero—And relates why and wherefore
he was kept alive—The boy grows tall, and takes to thinking

THE ANSWER WHICH FANNY FLETCHER had received to her inquiries concerning Michael was as false as it was heedless. The little fellow who gave it had no intention of uttering what was untrue; he believed that the boy she inquired for was dead—so many had died, and been borne from the wretched garret where he had himself lain, battling with the fever, sometimes delirious, and sometimes asleep, that it was no great wonder he should blunder. But Michael Armstrong was not dead, though the state in which the malady left him was such, that for weeks the surly old woman, hired to supply the place of Mrs Poulet, muttered curses on him for not being in a state to be quietly buried out of the way, like the rest.

It was just five days after Fanny Fletcher left the Deep Valley Mills in company with Miss Brotherton, that Michael waked from that first sound healing sleep, which often announces the conquest of life over death, after a hard-fought struggle between them.

The little fellow raised himself upright on his straw pallet, and for a minute or two looked about him to make himself quite sure where he was; for so heavy had been his sleep that it was not immediately his senses could recover their usual powers of perception. But only too soon, alas, he made it all out. He was still in that foul den of misery and filth; and the first impulse of his fully recovered intellect was to utter a bitter expression of regret that his life had been spared for further suffering, while so many had been mercifully permitted to sink into their peaceful grasses. But even as he breathed the words, he repented of them. The image of his mother seemed to rise before him—he remembered that she had bade him ever to trust in God, and let no cause tempt him to take his name in vain. The quiet eye of his much-enduring brother rose to his memory, as he had seen it a thousand times fixed upon him, while he enjoined patience and submission for their dear mother's sake; and the more recently-heard precepts of little Fanny, all preaching the same righteous, but hard lesson, came in their soft, pleading, innocent tone to give him strength to bear. Michael crossed his emaciated hands upon his breast, and murmured, "God forgive me!"—then dropping again into a gentle sleep, awoke not, till the old woman shook him rudely, rather for the gratification of her curiosity, than in performance of her duty, in order to see whether the "wiry, hard-skinned little varment wasn't dead at last."

She started with a feeling very like terror, when the boy, opening his large eyes upon her, asked her to please to be so kind as to give him a drink of water.

"What, then!—you don't mean to die after all? If you bean't born to be hanged, it's a mystery. Water?—if you haven't got summut in it arter lying this fashion, the Lord knows how long, you'll balk the hangman at last!" And with these words the crabbed crone retreated, hastening, with the consciousness of having something wonderful to tell, in the presence of Mr Woodcomb.

"There's a boy, sir, as have been lying a dying amost ever since comed, as is actually coming to, now; not but what he must still be within an inch of the grave, seeing what he has gone through—and he looks for all the world as if he had been buried and dug up again. Howsomever I don't think but what he might come through, if so be as you thought it worth while to give him food. That sort of sleep as I wake him out of, shows plain enough as the fever is gone, and then you know, sir, as kitchen physic is all the cretur's wants, perhaps, for the sake of preventing the burying beginning again, your honour might think it was as well to give him a little broth, and meat, too, after a bit, for he won't do without it, that's certain."

"Last scene of all"

"I had clean forgot that there was one left up there, Molly," replied the superintendent. "But in Heaven's name, let him be fed, woman—I wouldn't have to bury any more of 'em just now, for ever so—he'll come round again, I suppose, before its very long? We are still very short of piecers, and it's as well to keep him alive, you know, as to go after another."

"As for that, sir," replied the old woman, "it won't be to-morrow, nor next day, either, as he'll pay for his salt; I'll tell you that beforehand. So you had best please to make up your mind at once about the keeping him alive. There's nothing will do it but giving him amost a bellyful every day, and maybe a little fresh air into the bargain, I'm thinking, seeing the time he's laid stewing up there, with such lots dying all round him."

"If it wasn't for the having to open ground for him again, I'd be hanged, drawn, and quartered, before I'd trouble myself about what sort of air a 'prentice had to breathe. Howsomever, I have got my own reasons for not choosing to trouble the parson again, nor yet for doing the job without him. So cram the brat as much as you like—I suppose my leavings is good enough for him?"

"Please master not to talk of my liking to cram 'prentice brats," retorted Molly. "Often and often, as I've been back and forward here, for one job or another, nobody ever saw me trying to pilfer any thing for the starving stomachs, the low creturs! I dispises 'em too much. But I knows what will save life, and what will lose it, better, maybe than most folks, and so now you may do just as you please, without putting it upon my likes or dislikes."

"Don't be so frumpish, Molly Bing," replied Mr Woodcomb, laughing, "there's nobody going to charge you with being such a fool as to make a pet of a factory 'prentice while there's a puppy-dog to be had for love or money. Don't you be scared at any such notion as that, for I knows ye a deal better, old woman, than to put any such affront upon ye. You just stop the creature from dying, if you can, for that will suit me a deal best just now."

The will of Mr Woodcomb, thus clearly expressed, was acted upon with very implicit obedience; the consequence of which was, that Michael Armstrong was not only saved from death, but his constitution greatly benefited. Molly Bing had pledged her judgment upon the result of his case, and in order to prove it correct, she contrived that he should swallow about ten times as much nourishment as fell to the share of any other child in the mill. He had grown surprisingly during the period of his confinement, and this gave so lengthy a look to his thin person, that Molly more than once fancied the audacious little villain would give her the lie at last; so she not only fed him, but got leave for him to clean out the pig-sties, scrape up the filth from the yard, and sundry other jobs of the same description, all of which, however unsavoury in their nature, bore, as the sharp-witted old woman well knew, the balm of health in every movement they enforced, compared to the monotonous and grinding slavery of the mill. But in the course of a month or two, another glorious proof of England's prosperity reached the Deep Valley, in the shape of a large order, and Mr Elgood Sharpton, in communicating the cheering intelligence to his manager, enforced the necessity of strenuous exertion in the execution of it, by telling him that, sick or well, the children must work long hours, and that it was far better that they should a little overwork the hands, than run any risk of disappointing so valuable a customer.

In consequence of these instructions, Michael was withdrawn from his out-door labours, and once more made to follow the mules. It was then, and then only, that he discovered the heavy loss he had sustained by the departure of Fanny. While employcd upon the out-of-door tasks assigned to him by the commands of Molly Bing, he had been strictly enjoined never to speak to any of the apprentices who might chance to pass while he was at work. His meals were eaten in Mr Woodcomb's kitchen, and the place assigned for his lodging by night, was a sort of closet that opened from it. No day, no hour had passed, unless in sleep, since he recovered his senses, without his thinking of her. At the risk, or rather with the certainty of cuffs and hard words, no foot-fall had ever passed within his hearing without causing him to turn his head to reconnoitre, and much as he preferred the labour on which he was now employed to that of the mill, he would willingly, nay joyfully, have exchanged it in the hope of again seeing his little friend. It was therefore with a feeling of gladness, instead of regret, that he received orders to turn into the factory.

"That is queer!" thought the little fellow, as he bounded to obey the command, with the double energy of recovered health, and awakened hope, "it is queer for me to feel glad that I am going back to the factory!"

As it happened, he was marshalled into the same room in which he had worked before his illness—but alas! when he turned his eyes to the spot which Fanny had formerly occupied near him, a singularly ill-favoured boy met his gaze, instead of the pretty creature he sought for.

This was a death-blow to the joy which a few minutes before had given him a gait and an expression of countenance so unwonted in a factory-boy returning to his well-known sufferings. Nevertheless, though a tear blinded the eyes which at length settled reluctantly on the broken threads which awaited his fingers, he remembered that the factory had seven floors, and cruel as it was to lose the pleasure of giving his little friend a look or a word as they each paced their weary walk, he still thought he might get a sight of her at their dismal meals, and fancied that he should not greatly regret exchanging scraps of wholesome meat, for musty oatmeal, provided Fanny Fletcher was by to tell him not to mind it. But the musty oatmeal came all too soon, for no word or look of Fanny's came with it; nor did any uncertainty long remain, on which to hang a lingering hope that some unfinished task detained her in the mill, and that he should see her soon. His first question, whispered to the girl who sat beside him, brought forth the history of Fanny's wonderful departure, at as full length as the time and place would permit. At first he listened to it with incredulity. It seemed, he thought, like a story made up to deceive him, for fun; and little as the blighted young spirits of that sad fraternity were given to jesting, Michael clung to the belief that such was the case, as long as the meal lasted. But, as usual, a few minutes followed, during which they were left alone—an indulgence which necessarily arose from the fact, that even the niggardly allowance of time awarded by the regulations of Mr Elgood Sharpton for their meals, was more than the famished children required for devouring the scanty portion set before them. No sooner had Mr Poulet withdrawn himself, after witnessing the orderly consumption by each, of the allotted morsel, than such of the miserable crew as had survived the pestilence, and remembered the close alliance between Michael and the heroine of the marvellous tale which was still in every mouth, all rushed together towards him for the purpose of recounting it. Notwithstanding the confusion of tongues, their noisy testimony was too consistent to admit of doubt, and Michael remained with the astounding belief that his little friend was taken away to be made a great lady of.

The heart of Michael Armstrong proved itself to be a very generous one on this occasion.

"Some natural tears he shed, but wiped them soon."

as he remembered that the more miserable the situation in which he was left, the more he ought to rejoice that Fanny had been taken from it. And he did rejoice; truly, sincerely, and at the very bottom of his heart did he rejoice. As day after day the hateful routine of unvarying suffering again laid its grasp upon his existence, with a power as irresistable as that of the vast engine which within those prison-walls seemed "lord of all," the generous heart of Michael felt thankful that Fanny Fletcher shared in it no longer. It had been quite in vain that he had laboured to persuade himself, while listening to the reasonings of his little friend, that they ought mutually to rejoice in the probability of each other's death. Though he had allowed that as far as he was himself concerned he might, easily be brought to think that it would be a comfort to die, he could never reach the pitch of sublimity necessary to form the wish that Fanny might die before him. But now it was evident that this weakness, which had more than once caused his little monitress to shake her head, and say that he did not love her as well as she loved him, it was now quite evident that it was no selfish motive which had caused it.

By degrees this truly noble feeling, this generous power of living, as it were, in the prosperity of another, so strengthened the character of the boy, as perfectly to save him from that worst result of youthful suffering a reckless, desperate despair, which by destroying hope, that beautiful mainspring of all our best actions, leaves the poor spiritless machine alive only to the wretched consciousness of its capacity for pain. It is, beyond all question, this bitter hopelessness which deteriorates in so remarkable a manner the moral character of operatives under the present factory system. In no other situation, excepting only that of slaves purchased and paid for like an ox, or an ass, is the destiny of a human being placed so wholly and completely beyond the reach of his own control. He is, as Wordsworth truly says,

"A slave to whom release comes not,
And cannot come."

In no other situation do labouring men, women, and children, feel and know that unless they submit in all things to the behests of their employer, they must die—and that too by a process ten thousand times worse than either the hangman's cord, or the headsman's axe—they must die the death of famine. If their lingering hours of labour be prolonged beyond the stipulated time for which they are paid, they cannot turn and say, "I will not, for it is not in the bond," for the ready answer is, "*Go*. We employ none who make conditions with us." And where are they to go? To the parish officers? As ready an answer meets them there: "*Go*. We relieve none who can get work, and refuse it." If they are fined, however unjustly, however arbitrarily, if the iniquitous *truck* system be resorted to for payment of wages, instead of money, if their women be insulted, or their children crippled, and remonstrance follow, the same death-dooming reply awaits them: "*Go*. We employ no grumblers here."

Then to what quarter can they look with hope? Where are they to find that only elixir by which human strength is mercifully made for ever equal to sustain human suffering? The sparkling draught is not for them! The factory operative alone, of all to whom God has given the power of thought, is denied the delicious privilege of hope. It is this which degrades their nature; it is this which from youth to age renders one ruinous hour of brutal debauchery more precious, than all that stedfast sober industry can promise or bestow.

It was long, very long, ere this intellectual blight, this smothering mildew of the soul fell upon Michael, for he seemed to possess a sort of twofold existence, "the worser half of it," being his poor self, while the better was found in the happy destiny of Fanny. Countless were the miles that he walked backwards and forwards before the mules, during which he cheered his fancy by painting her in the midst of liberty and green fields. Sometimes he thought that if she were rich, she would remember all he had told her about his mother and Edward—that she would find them out—would take compassion on their poverty—would talk of him—would sooth and comfort them.

All this may seem, to happier beings, but a frail support, under incessant labour, accompanied by every species of privation, yet it did

Michael service—it kept his faculties alive; for it gave a theme, and a pleasant one, on which to fix his thoughts, and half the tedium of his own sad life was forgotten, as he meditated on the probable happiness of hers.

Sometimes, it must be owned,—though he always told himself that such thoughts were nonsense,—ideas would suggest themselves less abstractedly disinterested; for it would now and then come into his hearing that Fanny Fletcher knew where Sir Matthew had sent him, if nobody else did; and that, perhaps, if she grew to be a great girl, with power to do what she liked, she might think of him, and try to do something to rescue him. Vague as was this notion, vague as he himself felt it to be, it was a blessing to him. When such thoughts arose, his bodily strength seemed to revive, his aching knees no longer bent under him, his gait was no longer that of an ordinary factory-child, the energy of his mind lent itself to his limbs, and wearily as he stretched himself upon his bed of straw, and long and lanky as his half-starved person grew, Michael Armstrong did not become a cripple.

But years wore away, and the stout-hearted young prisoner of the Deep Valley began again to think that he had better have died of the fever, than have lived so long, hoping for some happy chance to set him free, and hoping for ever and for ever in vain.

"I am a fool," argued Michael at fourteen,—"I am a fool for thinking so very much of one who it is quite plain has never thought of me—nor of mother—nor of my poor Edward either; she never gave a thought to either of us! I was a fool to dream it! The fine folks that carried her away, took her far enough from sight and sound of factory-people. And who can blame her if she never turned her head back again to inquire about any of them? Poor little Fanny! She was very kind to me once—and she was the very prettiest little girl that ever I happened to see. But other people may have found that out by this time, as well as I. Fanny Fletcher is a whole year older than me! I will try with all my might and main never to think of her any more!"

This resolution was not very steadily adhered to; but the struggle to do it, which was perfectly sincere, made the poor boy moody, and more miserable than ever. His dreams perpetually represented to him his mother and helpless brother, suffering from some unkindness from Fanny, whom he saw superlatively beautiful, and superlatively rich, but more superlatively hard-hearted still. These nervous and irritating visitations brought his mother and brother so vividly before him, that for weeks he could never, whether waking or sleeping, get them out of his head. He fancied himself again running at full speed from Dowling Lodge, with Martha's basket on his arm; his mother's little room, decent and orderly in spite of poverty, came back upon his mind as if he had left it but yesterday. He saw the soft expression of her faded countenance, and felt the welcome of her fond embrace.

"Oh, fool oh, proud and wicked fool!" he murmured to his tear-stained pillow, as these, and a thousand other tender recollections pressed upon him. "Why could I not endure the tyrant's cruelty? I might have kissed her now! I might have comforted poor Teddy!" The sound of his own voice as he pronounced this dear familiar name, though in a whisper too low to awaken the weary sleepers round him, wrung his very heart by the vivid recollections which it brought, and though he was now beyond fourteen years old, he cried himself to sleep.

Fitful and feverish were the transitions of his mind at this period. Sometimes he persuaded himself that his mother was no more, that the loss of him had broken her heart, and that she had died, believing him to have gone before her. At other times it was Edward whom he wept as dead. His shattered health, his feeble limbs were, as he thought, sure evidence that nature meant him not to struggle long against the misery of his lot, and there were moments in which this persuasion even soothed him.

"Sweet fellow!" thought he. "How calm and beautiful he must have looked in death! Even in suffering, even in agony, his countenance was lovely—so patient, and so heavenly mild! Better; far better he should die, than live a factory-boy like me!"

And then again his mood would change, and he had for ever before him images of the most fearful destitution—his mother starving, and Edward slowly perishing beside her, because *he* had been too proud and too impatient to endure sundry buffetings and other indignities, which, when put in competition with the thought of having injured them, dwindled into petty injuries, which he deserved eternal shame for shrinking from.

Dreadful were the hours he thus spent! and, fearful to think of, was the hopeless, helpless, joyless, comfortless existence by which he held to earth! His very soul sickened as he looked around him, and read in every withered melancholy face the history of blasted youth, and the prophecy of premature death.

But there are spirits which sorrow and suffering cannot quench, and Michael Armstrong's was one of them. Nature and accident together had been stronger than the tendency of his employment to cripple his limbs, and he was neither deformed nor stunted. This happy exemption from the common lot, was doubtless greatly owing to the pertinacity of Molly Bing, who, proving to Messrs Woodcomb and Poulet that she was no fool, and knew well enough what she was about. This steadfastness on her part, acting in unison with the superintendent's judicious objections to Michael's being buried at that particular time, had certainly given a very critical and efficient impulse to the vigour of a frame of great natural strength and comeliness. The energetic self-sustaining soul within it, had also much to do in defying the paralyzing influence of his miserable situation. It was rarely that Michael could be seen to drag his limbs along, even in the last hours of long-protracted labour, with the same crippled, dipping gait as his companions. A broken-spirited child, when his knees are aching, permits them to bend under him; and not one in fifty, perhaps, of the half-starved, over-worked apprentices of the Deep Valley, reached the term of their captivity, without carrying away with them some species of bodily weakness or deformity. But let the reason be what it might, Michael was saved from this, and though exhibiting a fabric, composed of little besides skin, bone, and sinew, he was, at the age of fourteen years and six months, both tall and straight.

But it seemed as if the inward strength of mental suffering kept pace with this vigour of frame; for day by day the bitter consciousness of his own wretched and degraded state increased upon him—and day by day his swelling heart grew more indignant as he looked around him, and watched the exercise of lawless power and coward tyranny upon his miserable companions.

It was after a peculiarly hateful display of this power, by an act of insult too disgusting to relate, upon the unresisting person of a little fellow who seemed crawling (only too slowly!) to the grave, that Michael, when every other sufferer in the chamber was fast asleep, set himself to meditate gravely and deliberately upon his own situation. He had that day been so near trying the power of his bony arms, by flying at the throat of the ruffian who had so revoltingly outraged his companion, that with more than boyish judgment he became conscious of the growing danger that beset him. Though he had felt almost to suffocation the boiling rage which nothing but injustice, and the pitiful abuse of adventitious power can generate, he was not such a Quixote as to hope that his arm could effectually redress the wrongs he witnessed, yet he thought with a sort of trembling exultation, that if he *had* seized the craven overlooker, as he kicked from him the helpless object of his tyranny, he might have held him with a grasp that would have stopped his breath for ever!

It was a horrid and a murderous thought! and poor Michael, once the gentlest, fondest little heart, that ever nestled to a mother's besom, did penance for it by a pang of self-condemnation, that made him grind his teeth in agony. Yet even then the goaded spirit seemed to rise in rebellion against its own remorse.

"I cannot bear it!" he exclaimed in smothered accents as he turned his face towards his bed of straw. "I know I cannot bear it long! I have seen two attempting to escape, who have been brought back to frightful tortures—to I know not what! A solitary cell? the whip? the knotted thong? What matters? Would they could slaughter me at once! All would be over then."

For a long still hour of that feverish night, the boy lay sleepless. A terrible conviction that there was something within him which might prove stronger than himself—stronger than all his mother's precepts, and the holy fear of God which they had left upon his mind—made him feel sick with horror, and shudder in abhorrence of his own wickedness. He prayed to God to give him power to turn his thoughts from this; and soothed to calmness by the healing act, he meditated without passion, and with great acuteness for his years, upon the probable result of attempting to escape.

The difficulties of the enterprise were greater than any can imagine who know not the locality, and the intricate network of security which surround the imprisoned apprentices of Deep Valley on all sides. Of this the elder children, and the few who lived to approach their majority, were by no means ignorant. Considerable pains were indeed taken to impress upon their minds the certainty of their being caught if they succeeded in clearing the walls; together with the important fact that, as apprentices, it was illegal to assist them in running away from their master, and that it was the duty of every justice of the peace to assist in securing and sending them back to complete the term fixed in their indentures.

All this Michael knew perfectly well; neither was he at all sanguine in his hope of avoiding the toils from which he had never heard that any had escaped. Yet he determined to make the attempt, assuring himself, that no change in the treatment he received could render him more miserable, and sincerely thinking that it would be better and safer for him, should the failure of this desperate attempt lead to such a degree of restraint as would render the yielding to such violence of emotion, as had that day seized upon him, impossible.

Having come to this conclusion, and firmly pledged his young spirit to the attempt, his feverish restlessness subsided, and he dropped asleep.

The waking of the next morning was unlike any he had ever known before. He no longer felt as one among a miserable crew, sharing in common with them starvation, labour, and indignity; he felt himself to be one alone, and apart from all. He was on the eve of doing that which would involve him in difficulties and dangers altogether new and strange to him, and the only termination he could be really said to expect was the being dragged back to his prison to suffer all that it was in the power of his tyrants to inflict. These were strange materials for meditation which was decidedly agreeable; yet such Michael felt it to be, in spite of reason. A sensation of active, dauntless courage swelled his breast, which, with all the danger it threatened, was well worth the heavy monotony of his ordinary existence. At times, too, a gleam of hope would dart across the stern and steady gloom of the prospect and during the moment that the flash lasted, he saw himself restored to his mother and Edward. He could hardly be said to hope this, yet the feeling that it was possible sufficed to sustain his spirits through the days and nights which preceded the attempt.

It was exactly by the same exit that poor crazy Sally had made use of some fifty years before, that Michael determined to leave the premise. The month or two during which he had been employed in cleaning the yard and its appurtenances, had made him thoroughly well acquainted with the outward door, and also with the region immediately beyond it, for it was thither that he was accustomed to convey all the rubbish which it was his office to remove—an office which might have been attended with some danger of the escape of him who performed it, had not those in authority taken care to inform him that no authority of step could avail against the watchfulness of certain eyes about the factory, which were always on the alert to reconnoitre that door, and never far distant from the commodious windows which gave them power to do so.

Poor Sally had found this but too surely in making her attempts, and Michael had more than once listened to the merry tradition, which was a favourite story with the overlookers; of how the silly girl had run in full sight of a dozen watchful eyes, till her strength failed, and she sank down among the bushes and was taken, like a bird that having been long confined, has no strength of wing left to bear him beyond reach of the first hand extended to recapture him.

Yet this open postern was the only one by which it was possible to pass; but the very extremity of the danger of passing it, made the attempt easy; for though it was always carefully locked at night, and the key placed, together with those of every external door on the premises under the pillow of Mr Woodcomb, the manager had more than once seen a miserable little head peeping through it when left open for the passage of the wheelbarrow, without testifying the least alarm.

The time chosen by Michael for passing this terrible door, was that during which the dirty herd were commanded to expose their faces and hands for a short moment to such cleansing as might be obtained in a huge trough, in company with a score or two of competitors. It was constantly a moment of great noise, bustle, and hustling; and it was in the midst of this that the young adventurer contrived, unobserved, to push pack the only bolt which secured the door during the day, leaving it in a position to yield noiselessly to a very slight touch. At the sound of a bell, which rang about ten minutes after the children were turned out into the court to wash themselves, the whole troop hurried back again to the apprentice-house for their breakfast. It was then that Michael, often the last to finish the too-short operation of washing, remained for a moment behind the rest, and in that moment, opening the door just wide enough for his slender figure to pass, he slipped through and closed it after him.

The interval which elapsed before his departure was suspected, certainly did not exceed two minutes; and before the expiration of ten, the fact was completely ascertained and known to nearly every inmate of the mill.

Mr Poulet's second wife, to whom he had then been married about three years, was in appearance the very reverse of the first, being as remarkably small, as the other was large. But what she wanted in muscle, was made up in watchfulness. Nothing escaped her restless and malignant little eyes, and either from the incessant danger of her spying sharpness, or the propensity of the human mind to think present suffering worse than every other, there were many who declared they would be glad to have her brutal predecessor back again. It was this woman who first descried the absence of Michael from the board.

"Hollo! where is No 57?" she cried.

No one could answer; and No 57 was sought for in vain from one end of the premises to the other.

"He is gone through the yard-door!" proclaimed the active and intelligent Mrs Poulet, after discovering that the bolt was with drawn. "Off with you, you stupid old fool!" she added, addressing her husband; "what d'ye stand staring there for? If you had the wit of a jackass, you might trace him by his feet on the dew—for there are the marks plain enough to any body, that has sense enough to look for 'em."

And so in truth there were. A continuous track of footmarks, were easily traced from the door to the steep bank behind the factory, where they were lost in the covert of bushes, which had of late years been coaxed to clothe its sides for the purpose of furnishing fagots. That some one had recently broken through these bushes was equally evident, from many boughs having been torn, and the soil beneath them trampled. This was enough to direct the pursuit, with so much certainty of being right, that Mr Woodcomb laughed as he gave the orders for it.

"The bushes last for about half a mile," said he, "and then he must take over the hills, of course. Fine fellow, isn't he? It will be mighty hard to take him again, won't it? There's only three justices of peace for him to be handed to, and only every man he meets ready to introduce him. The worst misfortune is, that I don't quite see where he is to get his dinner."

Two stout overlookers started accordingly upon the track thus easily hit upon, and Mr Woodcomb awaited the result of their exertions without the slightest anxiety, or any irritation of nerves whatever albeit he knew that, favourite as he was, he might run no small risk of losing his place, should one of the apprentices really escape—but the thing was impossible; no one could live without eating, not even one who had surved his apprenticeship to starving as well as piecing at the Deep Valley Mill. So Mr Woodcomb slept soundly, although in ignorance of the fact that Michael Armstrong was already within a few feet of his premises.

XXVI

A dismal enterprise, and its melancholy result—Martha Dowling punished more severely than she deserved—Very wild projects conceived by Miss Brotherton, and speedily put in execution

IT IS NOW NECESSARY THAT the narrative should briefly return to the period of Miss Brotherton's arrival at Milford Park, after her unsuccessful expedition in pursuit of Michael.

There was no needless delay between this return to her home, and the communication to Mrs Armstrong and Edward of the dismal news of which she was the bearer; nor was there any consultation on this occasion, concerning the mode of her reaching Hoxley-lane. Poor Mary had greatly advanced in independence of spirit within the last few months; and had she encountered all the military quartered within twenty miles, with the Dowling family marching in procession at their head; she would have quietly driven through them all, with the carriage-windows up, perhaps, but with no greater precaution—except, indeed, an order to the coachman to drive on without stopping, let them meet who they would.

The carriage was at the door the morning after their return, and Miss Brotherton had not yet named her intended expedition to Mrs Tremlett.

"You are going out without me, my dear?" said the old lady on hearing it announced.

"I am going to the widow Armstrong's, dear nurse," replied the heiress. "Your presence cannot help me through this dreaded visit. Then why should I make you share the pain of it?"

"Why? my dear! because I am of no earthly use, and had better die at once if I cannot be of some little comfort to you at such a time as this. Why, don't I know all about it, and how you must feel at this very moment, just as well as you do yourself, Mary? Sure it was a foolish notion to leave me here enjoying the arm-chair and the foot-stool, and the flowers, while you are having your heart broken by telling the poor pale body, that the child she loved so dearly is dead and gone for ever."

"If you could save either her or me a pang, nurse Tremlett, I would not thus have spared you," replied Miss Brotherton. "However, you shall go with me, dear friend. It is quite like yourself to wish it—and in truth, I might have guessed that you could not have remained easy and quiet at home while I was so engaged. And poor Fanny—I have left her very busy with Martin, assisting in arranging the little roon I have assigned her near my own. Shall we tell her where we are going, in case she should come in here to look for us?"

"My dear Mary! If you will take my advice, you will let her go too. If you do not, the whole of this terrible talk will have to begin all over again; for of course, when Mrs Armstrong hears that you have got with you the only person who can tell any thing about her boy, she will be restless and anxious to see her—and then won't it be all over again, Mary?"

"It will, indeed, dear nurse! You are very right, and very wise in this. She shall go with us, poor child. Though it will be a dreadful task for her!" replied Mary.

"And you would rather take it, dear, all on your own shoulders? I do not doubt that—only you don't know how to manage it," replied Mrs Tremlett. "But there is another thing, Mary, that I have been thinking of," continued the kind-hearted old woman, "and that is the other poor boy. I'll engage to say, he has never missed school for an hour, after what you said to him about exerting himself. I saw how he took it; and, therefore, you may depend upon it, that he is at the schoolhouse now. Then just think, my dear, what his going home will be after you have told all! Poor creatures! It makes one's heart sick to fancy it! If I were you, Mary, I would send for him, tell him every thing at once, and then take him home to his mother."

Miss Brotherton instantly rose and rang the bell.

"Do not say you are of no use, my dear good creature!" said she. "How infinitely better this will be than the hurried, thoughtless plan which I had sketched!"

A message was accordingly despatched to the schoolhouse to summon Edward Armstrong, and in a few minutes he stood before them.

Most true is it that there is something holy and imposing in the presence of sorrow. It would be difficult to imagine any *entrée* into the boudoir of Miss Brotherton, which would have inspired a feeling both in her and her friend so nearly approaching awe, as did that of Edward Armstrong.

"There is no need to tell him, poor fellow!" exclaimed Mrs Tremlett, mournfully shaking her head, as she saw the sudden and eloquent change in Edward's countenance the moment he looked in the face of Miss Brotherton. "There is no need to tell him! He knows it all, already!"

"He is dead, then!" said the boy, his pale lips parting, as it seemed, with difficulty, to pronounce the words, "Please, ma'am, let me go away."

He looked as if he were unable to sustain himself; and Mary, really fearing he might fall, started from her seat, and throwing her arms round him, almost carried him to the sofa.

"No, no, my poor Edward!" she said, "do not go away. Stay with those who love and pity you! Poor Michael is dead, Edward, and we must all try to support your mother under the dreadful news."

"How do you know he is dead?" cried Edward, starting up, and looking almost sternly at his benefactress. "How do you know that they have not hid him away where you cannot find him, that they may torture him, and work him to the bone, when there is nobody by to see?"

"I know that he is dead but too well, Edward," replied Mary, gently. "I have brought home with me a little girl who worked in the same factory, and who knew him well. He died of an infectious fever that killed many, many more. I am going to take this little girl with me to your mother, Edward, that she may question her, if she wishes it, about poor Michael, and I wish you to go with us, my dear boy; it is better that your poor mother should have you with her."

"You are going to tell mother?" said the boy with a shudder.

"Yes, Edward—it must be done, and the sooner it is over the better. Your mother is a good woman, and a pious Christian, my dear boy. She will know and feel that all that can befall her is the will of God and when she remembers this, she will rise above her sorrow, and thinking of the better world hereafter, will be able to say, 'His will be done!'"

"Yes, ma'am—if it does not kill her first," answered Edward.

"Indeed, I think a great deal will depend on you, dear Edward, as to her manner of bearing it. If she sees you sink, be sure she will sink too; but if you make her feel that she has still a beloved child to live for, to whom life may yet be a blessing, she will cease to repine for the loss of one child, for the sake of making the other happy."

Edward slowly and silently shook his head; but after the melancholy silence of a minute or two, he said, "I will do my best, ma'am."

The scene which followed beside the bed of the poor widow, was one of such deep, but patient sorrow, as left an impression never to be forgotten on the minds of those who witnessed it. Mary's counsel had not been thrown away upon Edward. The boy displayed both a delicacy and firmness of character beyond his years, and above his education. No ordinary topics of consolation were clumsily uttered to redeem his pledge to Mary, nor did he affect a stoical indifference which he could not feel; but with gentle endearments he drew the mourning mother to think of him, and there was healing, as well as agony, in the tears she shed upon his bosom.

Of all this Fanny was a silent, but deeply-moved spectator. The widow gave her one earnest look when Mary said, "This little girl was the last person who spoke to Michael before he was laid on the sick bed from whence he never rose, and she seems to have loved him dearly."

One long earnest look was turned upon her when this was said, but no word was spoken to her, for the time was not yet come when the bereaved mother could seek comfort in any thing. Nevertheless, when Miss Brotherton rose to go, and pressing the hand of the poor sufferer in her own, promised to pay her another visit soon, Mrs Armstrong murmured in her ear, "I should like to see that little girl again, when I can bear to name him." Mary nodded her assent, and left the mother and son to exchange thoughts and feelings, which, when deep and genuine, must ever be held sacred from every unkindred eye.

Most watchfully did Mary attend to this poor pensioner; and many were the hours during which she sat, reading the book of life beside her bed. By degrees, too, the bereaved mother did hear to name her lost darling to Fanny Fletcher; and having once listened to the sweet tones of her gentle voice, as she related all she had heard him say, all he had seemed to feel, and all he had seemed to think, the poor woman grew so enamoured of the uneventful tale, that she wearied not of making her repeat it. For days together Fanny would beg to be left beside her, while Edward resumed his place in the school; and Miss Brotherton often thought, when she drove to Hoxley-lane in the evenings, to bring back her little *protégée*, that she had never chanced to witness so pretty a specimen of female tenderness and pity, as this lovely little girl exhibited, while ministering to the poor crippled woman, whose only claim upon her love was, that she wanted it—a species of claim, by the by, that is very rarely made in vain upon any uncorrupted female heart.

With every want prevented, soothed by the most generous kindness, attended with the most watchful love, and cheered by a greater appearance of reviving health in the boy that she had thought crippled for life, than she had ever ventured to hope for, it might have been expected that the widow Armstrong would, in some degree, have forgotten passed sufferings, and have once more looked forward with hope. But no, it could not be! This last, this heaviest of all her sorrows came too late to be wrestled with, as others had been; and though her meek nature seemed so peacefully resigned, that there was more pleasure than pain in watching over her, she was, in truth, dying of a worn-out spirit and a broken heart.

By some means or other, the news that little Michael Armstrong was dead, reached Dowling Lodge. Sir Matthew knit his brows—wondered how the devil any body could have got tidings of him, but said nothing. To all the rest of the family, save one, the intelligence was too unimportant to be listened to at all; but to that one, to the already conscience-stricken and repentant Martha, it was a heavy blow! Most miserable, indeed, had been her state of mind for the last few months;

from the day of her painful, but useless visit to Miss Brotherton, her eyes
had been, in a great degree opened to the hard and avaricious nature of
her father's character. Like a person excluded from the light of the sun,
and seeing only by the delusive glare of an unsteady lamp, Martha had
passed her whole life in mistaking the nature and the value of almost
every object around her. The language of Mary Brotherton had shot
with a painful and unwelcome brightness upon the dim and uncertain
twilight of her moral perceptions; and the unhappy girl learned to know
that the only being who had ever seemed to love her, or whom she had
ever ventured to love, was one that her better reason shrunk from, and
her sober judgment condemned.

Yet still he was her father, and still she loved him, and gladly, joyfully,
would she have given her young life, could she thereby have changed his
love of gold, for love of mercy. Sometimes she thought that time and age
would teach him the hollowness of his present pursuits, and that if she
never left him but ever stood ready at his side to watch some favourable
moment, she might have the surpassing joy of seeing his heart open to
the truth, and in a state to permit her helping to lead him to efficient
repentance, and the all-merciful forgiveness of God. It was impossible
but that such thoughts and feelings must separate her, more than ever,
from the rest of her family, and she had already pretty generally received
the epithet of *methodistical,* from the whole neighbourhood; but she
hailed it as a blessing, and without a shadow of religious enthusiasm,
beyond what was almost inevitable under the circumstances, and with
no sectarian views or notions whatever, poor Martha gladly sheltered
herself under the imputation of both in order to avoid joining in scenes
of amusement for which she had no relish.

In such a state of mind it was natural enough that Martha should
deem a visit to the bereaved mother a penance which it was her duty
to perform (though it was more painful to her, perhaps, than almost any
other to which she could have been subjected), and she did perform it
accordingly. She found the poor sufferer, whose eye she dreaded to meet,
sinking fast into peace and rest, that never more could be disturbed. Miss
Brotherton and Fanny were both with her; a bible was in the hands of
the former, and Mrs Armstrong's countenance, though greatly more

pinched and pallid than she had ever before seen it, expressed a tranquil calmness which it was impossible to contemplate without pleasure.

But, alas! for poor Martha! she had the pang of seeing this consoled and consoling look suddenly changed to an expression of intense suffering, the moment her own person met the poor woman's eye. They had never seen each other since the fatal morning on which Martha had so innocently persuaded her to sign the articles of her boy apprenticeship, and the recollection of that scene, and all its consequences, could not so suddenly come upon one, reduced already to almost the last stage of weakness, without shaking her terribly. The distended eye, the open mouth, the heaving breast, all spoke a degree of agitation, which in her condition was frightfully alarming; and Mary, who dreaded lest the calmness of her last moments should be disturbed, hastily turned to the intruder, and said, "Go, go!—the sight of you will kill her!"

Though there was no more of harshness in this, than the urgent circumstances of the case seemed to call for, Mary Brotherton would have rather died than utter it, could she have guessed the pang it gave to the already wounded heart of poor Martha. She made no reply; but, fixing on the victim of her most innocent delusion, a look, just long enough to impress the terrible expression of her countenance upon her own heart for ever, she turned away, and reached her splendid home in a state of mind that seemed fearfully to verify the annunciation, "He will visit the sins of the fathers upon the children."

That day was the last of the widow's life, and it is probable it might have been so, even if Martha Dowling had not made her unfortunate visit; but the coincidence was fatal to the poor girl's peace, for the anxious inquiries she made respecting her, brought the intelligence of her death, and the time of it, with sufficient accuracy to leave no doubt on Martha's mind, that the event had been accelerated by her appearance.

Happily, however, for those who tenderly watched her last moments, the widow Armstrong's gentle nature permitted her not long to suffer from the irritation which the presence of Martha produced, and many hours before she closed her eyes for ever, she expressed her sorrow for having yielded so weakly to feelings which she had hoped were

altogether conquered; assuring Mary (who never left her) that she
acquitted the young lady of all intention to deceive her, and that
the shock she felt from seeing her, only proceeded from the vivid
recollections her appearance awakened.

Unhappily, however, it was long ere this healing assurance reached
poor Martha; for Miss Brotherton, who was far from guessing its
importance to her, had decided upon having no further intercourse
with the Dowling family, a resolution which would never have been
taken had her last interview with Martha at Milford Park ended more
pleasantly. But it had been already so long acted upon, that it would have
been equally awkward and disagreeable to break through it; and Martha
long continued in the terrible persuasion that she had been accessory
to the death of both mother and son.

The loss of the only relatives he had ever known, following as they did
so closely on each other, made Mary tremble for the health of Edward.
She had watched the affecting close of the poor widow's life with all the
tender feeling such a spectacle was calculated to excite in such a heart
as hers. She had mourned for Michael for many reasons, and mourned
sincerely; but she had hardly known the boy, and it was her sympathy
with the sorrow of others, rather than her own, which caused the event
to touch her so deeply. But to Edward she had become attached with
so much fondness, and he had inspired such a feeling of wondering
admiration in her mind by the extraordinary faculties he displayed, and
the justness and uprightness of every thought and feeling, that to watch
over his health and welfare had become nearly the first object of her
isolated existence. The few months which had elapsed since the whole
system of his life had been changed from all that was most injurious to
health, to a mode of living in every way conducive to its recovery, had
produced a more favourable and decisive effect in him, than could have
been reasonably hoped for in the time; and it was a remarkable evidence
of the powerful influence which such a change produces on the frame,
that not all the sorrow and suffering which Miss Brotherton's intelligence
brought, or the heart-wringing loss which followed it, could check the
active energy of benignant nature in restoring health, where all she
required for it was given, and all that had hitherto impeded her kindly

operations was removed. Yet Edward was still lame, though so much less so than he had been, that his benefactress could not help indulging a hope that time and judicious treatment might remove the infirmity altogether. For some reason or other Miss Brotherton entertained no very particular respect for the medical practitioners of her immediate neighbourhood, and for several months after her return she contented herself with following Mr Bell's prescriptions, for friction and moderate exercise, without calling in any medical assistance at all. But though the improvement that followed was very perceptible, it was not rapid, and the idea of London advice suggested itself, as the most satisfactory mode of ascertaining at once whether a perfect recovery might be hoped for; information which it was very desirable she should obtain, before she decided in what way she should bring him up. Since the death of his mother, Milford Park had been Edward's home, and the orphan boy's hold on Miss Brotherton's warm heart had been greatly increased by the opportunities this gave her of more frequent intercourse with him. In truth, though he still attended the school for an hour or two every morning, by far the more important portion of his education went on under her own eye, and, as well as that of his little companion Fanny, was beginning to take a form and extent totally different from what she had at first intended for either of them. Ideas respecting them both, began by degrees to arise in her mind, which she at first endeavoured to resist, as being too much out of the usual course to he safely indulged in; but "use lessens marvel," and the notion of making a man of learning of Edward, and a woman of fortune of Fanny, which once and again she had rejected, as too romantic and absurd, gradually grew into an habitual theme of meditation on which her fancy delighted to fix itself.

Mary Brotherton was at that time about twenty-two years old, extremely pretty, and moreover almost childishly young-looking for her age; and whatever she might have brought herself to think of it, most others would very naturally have deemed her adopting a boy of twelve, and a girl of eleven, a most outrageously preposterous and imprudent act. But her situation was one in most respects quite out of the common way, and she every day felt it more impossible that she could continue to endure the station of one of the magnates of a manufacturing neighbourhood, with all eyes fixed upon every thing she did, and her whole heart and soul recoiling from companionship with the only persons whom her neighbours and watchers would deem fit to be her particular friends.

The heart of this isolated girl was so clingingly affectionate that it is probable she would, under almost any other circumstances, have at least loved the beautiful mansion in which she had passed the greatest part of her life, and felt the trees and flowers that adorned it to be as companions, and familiar friends; but a thousand painful thoughts were mingled with the consciousness that she was mistress of that fair domain; and the very fact that the education she felt inclined to bestow upon the two orphans would bring down upon her the criticisms, and probably the reprobation, of the whole neighbourhood, making it very desirable that the extraordinary project should be carried into execution elsewhere, was in her estimation more in its favour, than against it. When, in addition to all this, she succeeded in persuading her from some of her miscellaneous reading, that there were German baths which might assist the restoration of Edward's limbs, and that it was her duty to consult the most approved authorities upon his case, the decision to leave Milford Park, and remove to London, was at no great distance.

Had her valued friend and counsellor, Mr Bell, led her to believe that all the wealth she had, if thrown back among the class from which it was drawn, could have sufficed to remedy the evils under which they groaned, she was quite capable of stripping herself to her last shilling for the purpose; but he knew better, and he taught her to know better too; and having convinced himself that her best chance of happiness, as well as her best opportunity of doing good, would be in yielding to the affection which "her boy and girl" had inspired, he promised to assist her projected removal, by seeing that the orders she left, respecting her property, were faithfully executed; and, about eight months after the death of Mrs Armstrong, the heiress left her parks and gardens, her splendid mansion and all its gorgeous appurtenances, to attend the orphan boy to London.

The consultation which, immediately after her arrival there, took place upon the case of Edward, was productive of, perhaps, the greatest pleasure Mary had ever known; for the sentence unanimously pronounced was, that the limbs of the boy were in a state of progress towards perfect recovery, the weakness and distortion brought on by his employment, not having lasted long enough to produce any deformity capable of resisting the tendency of nature to recover herself, if not impeded by any fresh unhealthy influence. That any such should arise to disappoint her hopes was not likely; all that was required for him being good air, regular and moderate exercise, wholesome food, and abstinence from all violent exertion for the next year or two. As to her question respecting German baths, the answer was less unanimous; two gentlemen being of opinion that they would do no good at all; two that it was doubtful whether the case would be affected by them or not; and one that great benefit might probably ensue. But as all were of opinion that change of air was desirable, and as a pretty strong inclination to try fresh fields and pastures new seconded this judgment, Miss Brotherton determined to start for the Rhine. Mrs Tremlett declared that she had not the slightest objection to foreign parts; Edward's heart swelled with an ecstasy made up of gratitude, hope, curiosity, and the delicious exhilaration attendant upon returning health; while Fanny looked around her, and listened to every one whose words referred to the expedition, with a very delightful consciousness of being wide awake, but not without some fear that she was dreaming, nevertheless.

Such was the party that filled the travelling-carriage of Miss Brotherton, while an English maid, a French footman, and a German courier, formed her suite.

Nothing, certainly, could be well more whimsical than the party with which she had thus surrounded herself; but this mattered little, since she was pleased with it—and we must leave her in the full enjoyment of a whole host of delightful feelings, while we return to follow the fortunes of poor Michael.

XXVII

Michael Armstrong sets out upon a dangerous expedition—
Its termination proves rather more than he can bear—He meets
a good man and takes service under him—He asks and obtains a
holiday, and meets several adventures in the course of it

WHILE THIS GAY AND HAPPY party, who would any of them have gladly exchanged pleasure for pain, could they thereby have purchased only the knowledge of his existence, were thus placing kingdoms between them, the unhappy Michael was still enduring all the miseries of an apprentice at the Deep Valley Mill.

It would be difficult to imagine a stronger contrast in the situation of two brothers than that which many subsequent years presented between him and Edward. Edward!—who had ever been to him as a dearer second self—who had never enjoyed a pleasure unshared by him and never known a sorrow that had not also been his—Edward was enjoying all that nature and fortune could give; while Michael still hopelessly dragged on a wretched existence amidst unceasing and unvarying suffering! At length the desperate resolution was formed which put the officials of the Deep Valley factory in the state of activity already described. And where was Michael the while?

Safely ensconced in a sort of rude drain, which he had himself assisted to construct, when he held the regretted office of scavenger to the court, and over the aperture of which he easily arranged sticks and rubbish sufficient to conceal him, Michael lay for many hours listening to the hubbub which his absence occasioned. He distinctly heard the expression of Mrs Poulet's anger and scorn, as messenger after messenger returned, without bringing tidings of him; and had, moreover, the advantage of knowing the track that he had purposely made on the grass which grew tall and rank immediately behind the field, had led them, and would continue to lead them, all one way, while he would of course take especial care to go another.

Having left his foot-marks on the grass in the manner described, Michael had scrambled through the bushes which covered the steep hillside, for the distance of a few hundred yards, and then, taking advantage of a layer of stones, by which a patch of marshy ground had been rendered firm, he again crossed from the hill towards the factory without leaving any trace behind. By this simple device his pursuers were completely thrown out, for when night came and he crawled out from his shelter, no eye was open to look for him close to his prison-walls, though very keen ones were busy elsewhere in search of him.

The same strength of frame which had enabled him to escape deformity in the mill, helped him well now, as without food, without sleep, and with every pulse throbbing between hope and fear, he strode rapidly onward on the road he had come with Parsons four years before, carefully avoiding its grassy margin, however, lest more footsteps might be traced. Then, revolving with great clearness of local recollection, the direction in which this road led, after mounting the hill, he firmly resolved, as long as his strength lasted, to pursue it, till it brought him to the door of his mother's home—provided always, that he was not stopped short by the grasp of an overlooker in the way.

The necessity of procuring food had not appeared to him any obstacle to the undertaking; for not only had he great faith in his own power of enduring abstinence, but he had faith too, in the impossibility of begging at a farm-house door for a morsel of bread, in vain—nor did either hope deceive him: he walked till nightfall with no other refreshment than water, caught in the hollow of his hand from a trickling road-side spring, and a few blackberries, snatched in terror, as he hurried on.

As the darkness thickened round him, he called a counsel with himself, as to whether it would be wisest to lay down under the shelter of a hay-rick, and let sleep serve him for supper, or to venture a petition for a morsel of food at a decent-looking mansion which he saw at some distance, and walk on through the night, if he succeeded, by help of the strength so recruited.

After many anxious reasonings, pro and con, he at last decided upon the latter, and so well did his handsome face and simple assurance that he was very hungry, plead for him, that he not only obtained scraps sufficient for a hearty supper, but a crust or two for the following morning; and with this treasure he trudged on, footsore indeed, and with a pretty strong inclination to lie down and sleep, but mental energy sufficed for many hours to conquer bodily fatigue, and it was not till past three o'clock the next morning, that he yielded, and at last laid himself down in a dry, and, as he thought it, most delightfully comfortable ditch, and slept the sleep of youth and weariness for three or four hours. The bright beams of an autumn sun shooting directly upon his eyes awakened him, and he started up, ready and able to walk forward, sufficiently thankful for the hoarded crusts in his pocket.

He was now not more than seven miles from Ashleigh; a fact which he joyfully ascertained by a milestone on a road which he had reached, he hardly knew how, but it must have been by missing, not hitting the way he had endeavoured to find; for Parsons had not followed the high-road from the town for more than a mile, and that was before Sir Matthew's carriage overtook him. Michael looked backwards and forwards along this wide unsheltered road, and trembled to think how easy it would be, to see and recognise a fugitive from any spot within sight of it; but there was a burning impatience at his heart when he thought of home, and remembered that he was within two hours walk of it, which left all caution far behind, and commending himself to God, he set off at the fleetest pace he could achieve, towards Ashleigh.

No symptom of pursuit, however, alarmed him. From the moment he quitted the mills, to that when he reached what had once been his own door, no terror of the kind had come near him; he had heard no whispering voices, nor seen shadowy figures stealing towards him from a distance. All he had most feared was got through with ease; but all he had most fondly hoped, turned out a fearful blank.

As Michael drew near the door, he remembered so well every object which met his eye, that he began to fear lest he himself might be remembered by others, and making a circuit to avoid Sir Matthew's mills, he reached Hoxley-lane without having met a single face he knew.

It was a tremendous moment for him, that in which he first caught sight of the lowly door through which he had passed a thousand times in eager anticipation of his mother's kiss! Some minutes followed before he could reach it, and the boy trembled so violently that he tottered as he hurried onward, like a drunken man.

At length his hand was on the latch; it yielded as in days of yore, and in an instant the door was wide open before him. Poor Michael! what death can have a pang so bitter as that he felt, when the almost impossible project of reaching his mother's home being performed, he found that home empty and desolate, and telling him as plainly as angels trumpet-tongued could do, that she was dead!

A dismal groan burst from him, and he sunk on the floor, just where he had last stood gaily talking to her of his bright fancies for the future a few hours before he was snatched away from her for ever.

The noise he made reached the ears of a woman in the front room,and she opened the door of communication to ascertain who it could be, rummaging in the empty room that was "to let."

"My gracious! I should like to know who you are? What do you want here, you ragamuffin? Is this the way you come to take lodgings, pray?"

This was said by a young and pretty woman who held a baby in her arms and who, being the wife of a confidential overlooker, had not only succeeded to the occupation of No 12, upon the death of Mrs Sykes and the dispersion of her family, but considered herself privileged to assume, on most occasions, an air of great importance.

"Mother lived here!" said Michael, with a look wretched enough to soften the heart of the saucy girl who had addressed him.

"Your mother, my poor boy? Are you the little orphan Armstrong, then?" was the reply.

"Is mother dead?" said the unhappy boy.

"Dead? to be sure she is. And where can you have been not to know that? Wasn't you with her, when she died?"

"No, no, no!" sobbed Michael; "I came here to find her."

"Poor fellow! that's dismal enough to be sure. I bean't Ashleigh born, but I have heard a deal since I comed here, about the widow Armstrong and the boy as died!"

"Died!" echoed Michael, looking wildly at her. "Is he dead too? Is my poor Teddy dead?"

"Sure he is," replied the unthinking young woman, who, in truth, knew nothing about either the widow Armstrong or her son, but remembered hearing that a little more than a year before she took possession of the premises, a widow Armstrong had died in the back room, for grief at having lost a boy. She was far from intending to be cruel to the poor lad, who looked himself so very nearly like a corpse, but was too indifferent upon all subjects which did not immediately concern herself to take the trouble of thinking before she spoke.

A few more questions might probably have obtained, if not the truth, at least some proof of his informer's ignorance of it, but Michael had heard enough; he rose to his feet, and without uttering another word, rushed out of the room.

The state in which he then found himself was certainly nearly approaching to delirium. His strength of body and mind completely exhausted by fatigue, fasting, and intense anxiety, the blow which had fallen upon him was heavier than his reason could bear, and he wandered forth into the fields without knowing where he was, or having any distinct idea of what had befallen him. His devious and unheeded path led him to a spot, at the distance of nearly a mile from his former home, at which several miniature rocks of sandstone give something of wildness and dignity to the little stream, which for the most part runs tamely enough, and looks little more than a wide and dirty ditch, as it passes through the town of Ashleigh. A multitude of cotton-factories, with their tall chimneys mocking the heavens, were visible in the distance, on the other side, and the boy stopped in his wild, hurried walk, to gaze upon them, with a feverish consciousness that there at least stood something he had seen before. A frightful flash of memory then shot across his brain—his mother dead—his darling Edward dead—himself a houseless, friendless, starving wretch, who soon would be caught and carried back to the prison-house he had ran from only to learn that he had no friend on earth! Such were the thoughts which racked him, as he stood upon the edge of the rocky little precipice, and fixed his eyes upon the quiet water that flowed some

twenty feet beneath him. It seemed to present an image of coolness and
repose; his burning lips longed to kiss the gentle ripple on its surface—
he drew nearer to the extremest verge.

"I should be safe there!" he murmured, looking downwards till his
sick head reeled. "God forgive me!" he added, raising his eyes to heaven.
"But if I drown, mother! I shall go to thee!" and as he spoke the words,
he sprang forward, and plunged into the stream!

The shock restored his wandering senses in a moment; he felt that
he was perishing, though unconscious that it was by his own act; and
forgetting how little reason he had to wish for life, struggled hard to
grasp a bush that protruded from the bank into the stream. But he could
not swim, and the efforts he made, though they served for a minute or
two to keep him afloat, only increased the distance between himself and
the object he endeavoured to reach. His heavy shoes filled with water,
and dragged him downwards—his strength failed, his arms ceased to
move, and in another moment the water rippled over his head.

But poor Michael's history was not finished yet. A heavy-looking
elderly man, who had as little as possible the air of one desirous of
seeking an adventure, was in the act of examining some sheep in a
field, the fence of which was not fifty yards from the rocky ledge from
whence the body had sprung. Having completed his survey, and directed
two men who were with him to select a score or two from the lot, the
old man reposed himself upon a style in the fence above mentioned,
and he chanced to turn his head from the sheep, towards the spot where
Michael stood, had watched for a minute or two the boy's agitated
movements and demeanour, but without the slightest suspicion of the
frightful catastrophe that was to ensue.

No sooner, however, did he hear the splash occasioned by the plunge,
than he sprang over the style with the activity of a younger man, and
calling to the others to follow him, made his way with little loss of time,
to a bit of pebbly ground on a level with the stream, and at no great
distance from the point at which Michael had sunk. But, short as the
time had been, the ripple had already disappeared from the surface of
the water, and no trace remained of the object of his search. The two
young men whom he had summoned to follow him, though they had

not seen the accident, had gathered from his words that something terrible had occurred, and clambering down the rocky cliff, were by his side in a moment.

"It is too late, lads!" exclaimed the old man, wringing his hands together. "I saw the poor distracted creature take the leap, but he was sunk before I got to the bank, and I take it he will never rise again. I shall never forgive myself for not going to him when I saw him throwing his arms about in that wild way. I might have guessed what was going to happen—and may Heaven forgive me for not preventing it!"

"'Tis a man who has thrown himself in?" inquired one of the men.

"Not a man, but a fine young lad as ever you see. Poor fellow! 'Twas early days for him to have found sorrow enough to throw himself out of life that way! If I had ran to him, as I ought to have done, and stopped the deed, who knows but we might have brought him round to a better manner of thinking?"

"'Tis ten to one but he'll come to the top again yet, if he hasn't done it already," said the man.

"But if he comes, he'll come dead, William!" replied the old man.

"I don't know that," rejoined the young shepherd. "The stream runs briskish round yon corner, and would carry him right away with it; but it's worth while having a look lower down. If he rises at all, 'twill be there."

And so saying, the young mnan set off at a swifter pace than his master could follow him; while the old man and the other shepherd-lad continued for a minute or two to watch the place where he had fallen.

"Halloo! Halloo! Halloo!" cried a voice at no great distance,

"That's William, by all that's good!" exclaimed the young shepherd, and without waiting for his companion's reply, he ran off at full speed, the old man following with no lagging step, and at the distance of a few yards, after turning the corner formed by another huge mass of sandstone rock, they perceived William, breast deep in the water, and grasping, at the utmost extent of his arm, a limb of the drowning boy. Before the old Westmorland statesman (for such he was) could overtake his young companions, the hero of our tale was lying high and dry upon the bank, but whether life was quite extinct, or still lingered in the cold, corpse-like form before them, was a question which, when the old man joined the group, the young ones were not able to answer. Luckily for Michael, the old statesman had seen a man saved from drowning some thirty years before, and he remembered enough of the process he had then witnessed, to enable him to give some very useful instructions on the present occasion. They managed to make their patient discharge from his mouth some portion of the superfluous draught he had swallowed, and after bestowing patient and assiduous friction on his breast and limbs, they had the great satisfaction of seeing the chest heave with returning respiration, and all other symptoms of revivification follow in their proper order, till the eyes of Michael were once more widely opened, and fixed with perplexity, and something like terror, on the faces which were bending over him.

"Thank Heaven!" ejaculated the old man earnestly, "he's safe now, at least from drowning, and I have not got that to answer for. But he isn't in a trim to be left, my lads. He would have been as well in the river, perhaps, as out of it, if we do no more for him."

Then causing Michael to sit, and examining his features, with a glance of very friendly curiosity, he said,

"You don't look like a bad boy, my poor fellow. What could have set you upon doing such a desperate action?"

The effort which the poor boy made to answer was ineffectual, and he only shook his head.

"I suppose it's oversoon as yet, to expect any information from him," resumed the old man, "so there's nothing to be done, as I see, but just to carry him up between us, if he cannot walk, to the Nag's Head, and have him laid upon my bed there, till he is in a condition to tell us something about himself. Can you feel your legs yet, my boy?" he continued, endeavouring, by the help of his man William, to make him stand up.

But Michael had no power to second their efforts; the two lads, therefore, raised him head and heels, and preceded by the gray-haired farmer, bore him between them above a mile, to the humble hostelry of the Nag's Head. The procession was too remarkable a one to escape notice, and before it reached the shelter of the little inn a miscellaneous crowd of men, women, and children had joined it. Many of these had been familiar with the features of poor Michael in days of yore, but not one of them recognised the widow Armstrong's boy, in the long-limbed, pallid figure, that they now gazed upon.

Muster Thornton, the Westmorland yeoman and farmer, was too substantial a customer to be refused any reasonable favour, and the ragged, dripping Michael was not only permitted to lie down on Muster Thornton's best of beds, but accommodated promptly with dry linen, and duly comforted with more hot brandy, water, sugar, and biscuits than he had any inclination to swallow. He took enough, however, to remove the faintness of inanition; and this, together with dry linen, and a bed, sufficed, in spite of the heavy sorrows upon which is mind had not yet dared to fix itself, to sooth him into a long and healing sleep.

When he awoke from it, he was capable of answering all the questions Mr Thornton put to him, and this he did with a simplicity of pathos that went straight to the good man's heart. That he had been working in a distant cotton-factory, where he had been very hardly treated, and having got away to see his mother and his brother, had found them both dead, was a tale, that if it could not excuse the desperate act which he had attempted, at least accounted for it, in a manner that left as much to pity as to blame.

"Poor boy! poor boy!" exclaimed the old man, with tears in his eyes. "It was wrong and wicked, very wrong and wicked!I but you must pray God to forgive you, my boy, and never think of any such desperate doings more."

"I did not know what I was about, if I remember rightly," said Michael. "My head seemed gone. I don't know how I got to the river, but I am sure I did not go there on purpose."

"So much the better—I am glad to hear it—and it's no great wonder, sure enough, if you did lose your head, coming to such a home as that. But what are you to do next, my poor fellow? I suppose there is no other home for you, is there?"

"I have no home, nor a single friend in the whole world," replied Michael.

"And the only work you have ever been used to, I suppose, is following wheels in the factories?" said the farmer.

"Except once for three months and a bit that I was kept to cleaning the outhouses and yard, and wheeling away garden-rubbish and such like," replied Michael.

"Well, but that's better than nothing, boy. At any rate, you know how to hold a spade, which is a long deal better than having never used your fingers, except for tying bits of thread. D'ye think you should be willing to work for me, my boy, and tend my farm-yard stock, and do a turn of work in the fields when it was wanted?"

"I *should* be willing, sir," replied Michael, while a flush passed over his pale face, "I should be willing and most thankful to work for you."

"That's well," said the old man cheerily, "and as to terms, I don't expect we shall find much difficulty; you will come to me my poor fellow, much in the same condition as you first come into the world, therefore all that you want, I must find, which will be about as much as I can afford to give, I take it, just at first, till you, and I too, find out what you're good for. Will you agree to it, my lad, and give me your time and best endeavours for clothes, food, lodging, and good will?"

"It will be a blessed bargain for me, sir," said Michael, "if you will add to all your goodness the excusing my ignorance. But if *will* was all that was wanting to make a good servant, you should not lose by me."

"And will is all that is wanting, boy. You are no fool, I take it, by your looks; and if you will mind what is said, and do your best, I shall ask no more. What is your name, my good fellow?"

"Michael Armstrong, sir."

"Well, then, Michael Armstrong, I am your master, and you are my man. And now you most eat, and then you must go to sleep again, I think, till I have got some decent clothes for you. Those you wore yesterday have had a good washing to be sure. Nevertheless, I don't justly like the looks of them."

*   *   *   *   *

Within six months from this time, Michael Armstrong, promoted to a place of trust, might have been seen sitting upon the hill-side in one of the most romantic spots in Westmorland, a shepherd's maud wrapped round his person, a sheep-dog at his feet, and his master's flocks nibbling the short grass around him on all sides. Many were the solitary hours he thus passed, and very rich was the harvest they brought him. Had the boy remained a year or two longer in the state that

> "Blocks out the forms of nature, preconsumes
> The reason, famishes the heart, shuts up
> The infant being in itself, and makes
> Its very spring a season of decay;"★

had Michael remained a year or two longer at the Deep Valley factory, in the state thus admirably and accurately described, it would have been too late for any contemplation of God's works to have roused his withered spirit to worship and to hope. But as it was, his mind seemed to awaken day by day from the long and heavy sleep in which it had been plunged. With an intellect naturally vigorous, and covetous of acquirement, and having had his first infant stretch of thought happily and indelibly directed, though with primeval simplicity, to one God and father of all, his transition from a condition in which

> "Scarcely could you fancy that a gleam
> Could break from out those languid eyes,"★

to one

> "Sublime from present purity and joy,"★

was rapid and delightful. His heavy losses were not forgotten; but while he meditated beneath the bright arch of heaven on the mother and the brother he had so fondly loved, there were so many sublime and hope-inspiring thoughts mixed with his sorrow, that it could hardly have been called painful.

★ Wordsworth

The worthy "statesman" to whose service he had vowed himself, though he did not, perhaps, follow Michael through all the improving processes which his mountain occupation led to, nor very clearly comprehend the elevating effect of the "skyey influences" under which he lived, was no way slow in perceiving that the Samaritan feeling he had so opportunely displayed in the township of Ashleigh, had bound to his service one of the most trustworthy, active, and intelligent lads he had ever met with. There is always, moreover, in the human heart a propensity to cherish whatever we have preserved; and this feeling, joined to his more worldly-minded approbation of Michael's good gifts, rendered Muster Thornton exceedingly fond of the boy, and well-inclined at all times to grant him every reasonable indulgence. But Michael rarely taxed his kindness as far as it was ready to go. Once he had asked, and obtained leave to mount to the top of Helvellyn, and once to make a sabbath-day's journey over the mountain-tops to Ulswater; these were the only occasions on which he had expressed any wish to wander beyond the immediate neighbourhood of the farmer's sheep-walks, and, in truth, this immediate neighbourhood included so many mountain torrents, glassy lakes, stupendous crags, and sylvan solitudes, that there was little need to go beyond it, in order to ratify a passion for the picturesque. But when Michael had attained the age of eighteen years, a longing, and somewhat restless desire seized him to revisit the place of his birth, to seek for the graves of his mother and Edward, to learn tidings of the kind-hearted Martha, to discover, if possible, whether his own escape from the Deep Valley had been communicated to Sir Matthew, and to ascertain whether he still stood in any danger of being reclaimed as an apprentice, in case of its being discovered that he was at liberty. As to any danger of being personally recognised at Ashleigh, he feared it not; conscious that from his remarkably tall stature and florid health, he was too unlike the factory-child of former days, to run any risk of being known.

It was, however, some months after this wish first suggested itself, before he took courage to name it to his indulgent master. When at length, however, he did so, the good man not only gave his free consent, but declared himself well pleased that such a project had entered his favourite's head.

"It will do thee a power of good, Mike," said he. "The only fault I have to find with thee is, that thee beest too steady for a lad of thy years, and that looks as if, with all our care and coaxing, we had not yet been able to make thee forget thy sorrowful childhood. Set off, in God's name, my boy; stay as long as thou wilt, but only promise to come back at last, for I think it would be heart-aching work to part with thee."

Michael gratefully promised a speedy return, and dressed in his best attire, he set forth upon his much wished-for pilgrimage to his early home. "It was the pride, the spring tide of the year;" every leaf was opened, yet every leaf retained the new-born freshness of its lovely green. The birds saluted him from every bush; the herds lowed from amidst their dewy banquet, in a note that spoke their measureless content; and every object on which his bright young eye fixed itself, seemed to echo the abounding gladness of his own heart. How elastic was the step with which he passed along! How proudly and thankfully did he feel conscious of his own high place amidst this wondrous creation! and how perfectly was he convinced, despite all he had read during his lone hours on the mountain-side, of the splendour of the cities of the earth, that nothing on its whole surface could exceed in grace and glory the majesty of the gorgeous sun, as he rose triumphantly from out his bed of gold ! Had every thought of the boy's heart been chronicled, a very poetical sort of hymn would have been the result; but as it was, all the glowing thankfulness, the heavenward rapture, and the joy supreme, was but for himself alone—yet was it not thrown away, for Michael enjoyed his own existence during these early hours with an intensity that made him feel all his former sufferings most benignantly overpaid by his present happiness. Yet in the midst of this, tears more than once started to his eyes, as he thought of his mother, and the brother he had so entirely loved. His very soul longed to have Edward by his side, as various fancies chased each other through his fertile brain; and the image of little Fanny, too, with her soft reasoning eyes, as she used to look at him when preaching patience at the Deep Valley Mill, as he fondly laboured to recall it, made him sigh in the midst of his pleasure and his freedom, to think how sad it was that all he had ever loved should have passed away from his eyes for ever.

But amidst the million proofs of tender commiseration for the sufferings, incident of necessity, to our place in creation (which those who run may read, if they are not very great dunces indeed), there is, perhaps, none more remarkable than the gradual softening of the agony which all who survive what they love, are doomed to feel. The state which follows, though as sad as the darkness of the lonely night, made visible by the pale backward glances of the parting moon, has the same soothing stillness too. Passion is over, anxiety at rest, and we feel more than consoled, we feel joyful, as we remember that we too shall pass away, and follow them.

The journey to Ashleigh cost Michael three days' smart walking, but his pockets were no longer in the condition they had been at the time of his never-to-be-forgotten escape from the Deep Valley. He had proved himself a good and faithful servant, and the worthy yeoman paid him accordingly, so that he had wherewithal to recruit his spirits and his strength as he jogged along, and reached the hospitable Nag's Head in his native town on the third evening, rather the better than the worse for his pleasant toil.

His first walk on the following morning was to Ashleigh churchyard; but here he was obliged to content himself by knowing that the dear relics of those he wished to honour were near him; for, of course, the only indication by which he could guess whereabouts these precious relics lay, was to be found in the want of all memorial. On the sunny side of Ashleigh churchyard, a number of handsome tombstones may be seen; many a massive monument is there, protected by its strong and stately rail; and thereon may be read, by those who list, the important fact that some one who bore a Christian appellation, lies below. To time north, where the grass grows strongest, though the sun never comes to cheer it, are a multitude of little nameless, unclaimed hillocks, closely wedged together, and rarely showing even a withy-band across the swelling sod, to testify that some one has cared far what lay hidden under it. To this green republic Michael turned himself and knew full surely that it was there his mother lay. Another, though even as humble as himself, might, under similar feelings, have addressed inquiries to the parish-sexton, and endeavoured to set his memory to work as to the exact spot where he had buried her—but this Michael dared not do; for it would be at once losing the advantage of his incognito, and laying himself very needlessly open to the danger of being reclaimed by his old enemy, Sir Matthew, as a bound apprentice who had run away. So he contented himself with walking carefully, and with reverential tread, through and amongst the many grassy mounds, permitting his tears to flow freely as he thought of Teddy, and the dear gentle mother who had so equally loved them both; and then turned slowly away, following a path that brought him at the distance of a mile or so to Brookford factory.

The sensation which he felt when the great many-eyed monster first met his sight, was one of unmixed pleasure. He literally hugged himself, and blessed the freedom of his limbs, the firm and healthy action of his pulse, and the delicious consciousness that he was no man's slave.

For many minutes he stood still to enjoy this; and as his eyes perused line after line of the dusky smoke-stained windows, and recalled the early sufferings he had endured within them, his very heart swelled with gratitude for the change, and he blessed God aloud. But as he approached nearer, and perceived the dim shadowy figures slowly moving here and there, and thought upon the condition of each of them, he almost repented of his selfish joy, and blamed the ecstasy that for a while had made him so utterly forget that thousands were imprisoned still, though he was free.

On, and on, he walked with his eyes immovably fixed upon the hideous fabric till, sooner than he expected it, he stood before the gates. He had conceived no previous plan by which to enter it, and knew that without some specific business, real or feigned, it would be impossible, but while he stood weighing the danger of possible discovery against very strong inclination to see what alteration time had made in the troop within—whether he should recognise any among them—and whether his old tyrant, Parsons, was still their chief,—the gates opened and one of the engine-men, a grizzly fellow, whom he well remembered when his sable hair was somewhat less silvered, came forth.

He gave Michael a look, that very plainly said, "What do *you* want?" and in truth, his neat appearance, unstained skin, and free unshrinking eye, very naturally suggested the idea that he could have no business there.

"Is Mr Parsons within?" said Michael boldly, and daring the inquiry as much because he knew not what to say, as from any deliberate resolution to do so.

"Yes," replied the man; "he is about the place somewhere, I seed him not more than ten minutes ago."

Michael nodded his head, and walked through the gate into the court, across which he had passed in trembling a thousand times. Nor was he now quite free from a slight feeling of alarm at the idea of meeting the sharp eyes of his former terrible taskmaster, and felt much inclined to blame himself for the curious temerity which had brought him so nearly within his gripe. But it was too late to retreat, for at the distance of a dozen yards he saw Parsons before him, coming forth from the building into the court. On seeing the stranger he immediately approached him; Michael touched his hat.

"What may your business here be, young man?" said Parsons eyeing him from top to toe.

"I called in, sir, to inquire whether you happened to want a spinner, and what the wages may be," said Michael.

"Is it for yourself?" demanded Parsons, knitting his brows, and looking at him with a sort of incredulous sneer.

"Why, no sir, it is for a kinsman who happens to be out of employ," replied Michael, colouring from the unusual consciousness of deceit, and from the same cause casting his eyes upon the ground, thereby displaying the remarkable length of his black eyelashes, and giving to his whole countenance a look much more resembling that of former days, than he had worn when he first entered.

Parsons looked at him with a sort of vague idea that he had seen him before.

"Where do you come from?" said he.

"From Westmorland, sir. I have been living in service there for these four years past."

"And pray what may your name be?"

"Robert Thornton, sir," replied Michael, blushing again, as he thus unceremoniously borrowed the appellation of his worthy master.

"Have you ever worked in a factory yourself?"

"Yes, sir, I have, when I was a boy," said Michael, from mere want of skill and hardihood in the art of lying.

"And you think you have bettered yourself, I suppose, with your fine buff waistcoat, and the rest of it. No we don't want no spinners here."

Michael by no means unwillingly obeyed this dismissal, and walked away, more than half ashamed of his achievement.

"If I didn't know that Michael Armstrong was dead, I should say as that there chap was him," said a girl somewhat older than our imprudent masquerader, and who had been watching him very earnestly during the foregoing conversation. The observation was not addressed to the overlooker, but to another girl, who had brought the speaker her dinner to prevent her leaving some particular work on which she was employed.

"What's that you say, Sykes?" said Parsons, turning quickly towards her.

"I was saying, sir, as that boy was unaccountable like Michael Armstrong as used to live in mother's back-kitchen. He wasn't about a year or two younger than me, and I knowed him as well as I did my own brothers."

"Stuff and nonsense, girl! All the world knows that young rascal died years ago; and fuss enough there was made about it by that mad miss at Milford, who I suppose, found out that she was their cousin or something of the sort, for she took it so to heart, that she sold her house and lands, and ran away with another of 'em to some foreign country, for fear he should die too. Sure you must mind all that queer story?"

"Yes, sir," replied the girl; "I remember it right well, and that's the reason why I says that I know it can't be him,"

"Yet upon my soul, now you mention it, he was the very image of him. I fancied as I looked at him that surely I had seen him some where before, But it can't be—a dead dog is dead, all the world over."

"Yes sure, sir," responded Kitty Sykes, who being what is called a very sightly girl, was not unfrequently indulged with a little condescending notice from Mr Parsons. "But 'twas his queer curly black hair, and his particular-looking eyes as put it into my head."

"And if you go on talking of it, Sykes, in that way, you will be putting it into my head too. And after all, there is nothing so very impossible in it. Nobody in these parts could really know much about it, you see, and there's no reason, as I can tell, why the scamp might not have run away from the Deep — that is, the stocking-weaver's manufactory as he was sent 'printice to, and they as ought to have stopped him, might have given out that he was dead," replied the overlooker.

"Then if it *was* possible," resumed Kitty Sykes, "I wouldn't mind taking my bodily oath that that there young fellow was Michael Armstrong, and nobody else."

"Egad, I wish I hadn't let him go!" cried Parsons, running to the gates. "He was 'prenticed till twenty-one, and if he has run away, he's liable to be taken up and put in prison, by the first as catches him."

Kitty Sykes took the liberty of running to the gates also; but to say the truth, she had no wish at all that Mr Parsons should catch him up, and put him into prison. The girl, though she had prudence enough not to communicate the opinion to her friend Mr Parsons, thought the stranger by far the handsomest young fellow she had ever seen, and secretly determined, if she could catch sight of him again, that she would give him a hint to keep clear of his old acquaintance.

"There he goes," cried Parsons, watching Michael, as with upright gait, and rapid strides, he was pursuing his way by the well-remembered path, which led from the factory to Dowling Lodge. "There he goes! He don't look like one of the mill-people any way—and yet the fellow said that he had worked in a factory. Didn't you hear him, Kitty?"

"Yes, sir," replied the girl, "and it was just then as I felt so unaccountable sure that, unless it was out and out impossible, it must be Michael Armstrong as was speaking. I never did see such eyes as Michael's, nor such hair neither."

"And there he goes, I'll bet a sovereign," rejoined the overlooker, "to take a look at his old quarters at the Lodge. Kitty, I'll give you a glass of gin and a shilling, if you'll run after him—you can run like a hare, I know—run and bring him back, Kitty, there's a darling, and say as I have got some good news to tell him."

Off started the girl with right good-will, having her own reasons for wishing to do the errand, as well as a very sufficient inclination to gain the promised reward.

Mr Parsons by no means over-rated her running powers; and had she been less fleet, she would have failed in her object, for Michael walked briskly, and without any inclination to remain longer in the vicinity of the mill, though by no means conscious that he had been recognised.

He had just turned the corner of a hedge when the girl overtook him, so that their colloquy did not take place within sight of the overlooker.

Michael heard the fair Kitty's approach, and turned to see who it was that thus came galloping and panting after him.

"Do you want me, young woman?" said he, civilly stopping for her.

"Well then, you are no changeling!" replied the girl, laying her hand on his arm; "you were always out-and-out, the civilest boy in the mill."

A very bright suffusion dyed the clear brown of Michael's cheek as he heard this.

"I do not know what you mean!" he replied.

"Come, come, Michael Armstrong," rejoined Kitty, "you needn't be afraid of me. Don't you remember Kitty Sykes, as have gone to and from the mill with you and Teddy, a hundred and a hundred times?"

"Is it indeed Kitty Sykes, grown into such a handsome young woman?" said Michael, holding out his hand to her, and feeling quite incapable of preserving his incognito, in the presence of so old an acquaintance. "And to think of your knowing me, Kitty! But you must not betray me, my dear girl. If I was found out for Michael Armstrong, I might get into a scrape."

"And that's true, and no lie," answered the faithless ambassadress, "for I am sent after you by that old beast Parsons, to tell you to come back, because he had good news for you. But his news would just be to give you notice to march into prison for having run away; and I agreed to carry his message for him. He thinks that I delight in him, the old monster! but I'd rather walk a mile to do a kindness to you, Michael, than stir an inch, to please him."

"God bless you, my dear girl! I hope you have done me a great service now; for I think I could show him leg bail, that he would find it difficult to refuse, Kitty. So now good by, old friend; I am sorry to part so soon, but it won't do to stay here to be caught, will it?"

"And God bless you too, you
nice boy!"

"No, truly, Mike! I'd be loath to see any friend of mine at his mercy,
or at that of his master either. But you won't go clear away out of the
country without seeing me again, will you? You needn't be feared of
him, 'twill be easy enough to put him off the scent. I'll back, and tell
that we was both of us altogether deceived, and that you bean't no more
Michael Armstrong than he be."

"I don't think I ought to stay in Ashleigh now, Kitty; there's others
may know me as well as you and he, and 'twould be a terrible change,
I can tell you, my dear girl, to come down from the hills where I am
tending a good master's sheep, and often feel so high and so happy that
I think I am halfway to heaven—it would be a terrible change, Kitty, to
come from that, into the Deep Valley Mill again, which is as much worse
than our old factory here, as hanging is worse than whipping!"

"Lord have mercy upon 'em, then!" ejaculated the poor girl. "But I say, Michael, you needn't run no risk at all, if I go back and say as it isn't you, and then you might meet me after nightfall, in the town."

"It will not be very long, Kitty, before I am one-and-twenty, and a free man, and it's then, please Heaven, that I'll come back again, and pay the old place a visit. You have been kind enough to remember me so long, that I don't think you'll have forgotten me by that time, and it shall go hard with me but I'll bring you a token from some of our north-country fairs." So saying, he gave the damsel a kiss, and she wrung his hand without making any further effort to detain him.

"God bless you!" said the retreating Michael, over his shoulder.

"And God bless you, too, you nice boy!" muttered poor Kitty. "I wouldn't ask no better luck, than just to follow you, and keep sheep too."

Either from wishing to look after him as long as he was in sight, or for the purpose of giving him law, in case Mr Parsons should determine on pursuit, Kitty Sykes remained stationary on the spot where Michael left her, till, abandoning his hardy project of a visit to Dowling Lodge, he had stretched far away over the fields towards the road he was to pursue northwards to his peaceful home; and then she walk leisurely back to the factory, where, after a sharp reproof for staying so long, and a pert reply to it, she informed the overlooker that they had both been wrong, but that the young lad said he might be found if he was wanted, at the sign of the Magpie, that was about a mile the road towards London.

Warned by this unexpected recognition, Michael determined to run no more risks among his townfolks; but not being disposed to lose the little bundle he had deposited at the Nag's Head, he ensconced himself within the shelter of a small public-house, on the road-side, resolved to wait there till the evening set in, and then to venture back to his last night's lodging, pay his bill, reclaim his bundle, and set forth upon a night-march, which he hoped would take him beyond all danger of Mr Parsons, before the following morning.

Having secured his welcome by the usual ceremony of ordering a meal, Michael looked about him for some means of occupation during the hours which he had doomed himself to pass there, and in despair of finding any better literary amusement, seized upon a heap of handbills, of a vast variety of external forms, but having, as he found upon examination, one and all the same object, namely, the calling together a general meeting of the whole county of York (then undivided), for the purpose of signing a petition to parliament for a law, limiting the hours of labour in factories to ten hours a day. Michael Armstrong was no longer a factory operative; free as the air he breathed upon his beloved mountain-tops, he no longer trembled at the omnipotent frown of an overlooker, nor sickened as he watched the rising sun that was to set again long hours before his stifling labour ceased. All this was over and ended with him for ever. Yet did his heart throb, and his eye kindle as he perused page after page of the arousing call which summoned tens of thousands, nay hundreds of thousands to use the right their country vested in them, of imploring mercy and justice from the august tripartite power that ruled the land.

Very powerful was the male and simple eloquence with which many of these unpretending compositions appealed to the paternal feelings of those they addressed; and such terribly true representations were found among them of the well-remembered agonies of his boyhood, that Michael was fain to put his spread hand before his face to conceal the emotions they produced.

He had sat in this situation for some minutes, revolving both his former sufferings, and the blessedness of his present release from them, when a man, who had been quietly sitting writing at a distant window, but had nevertheless found leisure to watch Michael's countenance as he proceeded with his examination of the handbills, rose from his place, and gently approaching him said, in deep, yet very gentle voice, "You seem moved by the perusal of these papers, my good friend. Is it the first time you have met with them?"

"Yes, indeed, sir, it is," replied Michael, starting from his revery.

"Then I presume you are a stranger in this part of the country?"

"Why, yes, sir; the master I serve is a Westmorland statesman, and I am only come this way upon a holiday trip."

"Then maybe you don't care enough for the poor factory operatives to join their meeting, and put your name to their petition?"

"If caring for them could do them any good, master," replied Michael, warmly, "they would be in no want of help, as long as I was near them. But I don't think the name of a poor servant-boy like me, could do them either honour or service."

"Then what sort of names, my good lad, do you suppose will support this petition. Do you think the great mill-owners will sign it?—Do you think such men as Sir Matthew Dowling for instance, whom you may have heard spoken of, down at Ashleigh, maybe, do you think it will be such as he, whose first object in life is to get as many hours of labour out of the little creatures that work for him, as stripes can make them give, do you think it will be such as he, that will sign the ten hours bill?"

"Not if that bill is either to hurt himself, or better the children, I should think," said Michael.

"True enough," replied his new acquaintance, "and not only is that true, but he and the like of him will do all that mortal men can, to prevent all others from signing it. But Heaven forbid they should succeed, young man—for if they do, the best hope of many thousand suffering, and most helpless human beings, will fall to the ground!"

"Then, indeed, may Heaven forbid that they should have their will!" returned Michael, fervently. "When is this meeting to take place?" he added, turning his eyes again to the papers he still held in his hand. "But three days hence!—truly I should like to witness it!"

"Is there any reason against your doing it?" demanded the stranger. "Will your services be wanted by your master before that time?"

"He won't expect me, till two or three days after it," replied Michael; "I have done all I wanted—at least I have stayed as long as I wished at Ashleigh, and I don't see any great harm there would be in witnessing the meeting."

"Do see it, my good lad!" said the stranger; "I predict that it will offer a spectacle such as never was witnessed before, and most likely never will, or can be seen, again. A multitude, probably amounting to above a hundred thousand overworked operatives, will meet in peace and good order, to petition for legal relief from the oppression of a system which has brought them to a lower state of degradation and misery than any to which human beings have ever been brought before. Were

THE LIFE & ADVENTURES OF MICHAEL ARMSTRONG   443

those in whom these poor people have confidence, less deeply anxious to preserve the public peace than they are, a different mode of redress might be sought for. But as it is, an honest man may venture to advise such a respectable young fellow as you seem to be, to stretch your good master's leave a little, in order to be present at this great spectacle."

A good deal more conversation followed on the same the and ere Michael had ceased to listen to his companion, he felt convinced that as well as inclination would lead him to do all that a loyal subject and peaceable citizen could, in aid of the suffering class from who ranks he had so miraculously escaped. In a word, Michael Armstrong determined to attend the great Yorkshire meeting, and hold up his hand for the ten hours bill.

The extraordinary circumstances attending that enormous meeting; the *unaccountable* disappointments which at every halting-place attended all the precautionary efforts of the committee to procure bread for the multitude, while beer was every where found ready, and in the greatest abundance; the terror felt by those most interested, lest heat, fatigue, exhaustion, and beer, together, might lead to some disturbance of the peace; and the triumphant influence of reason and kindness joined, in inducing the hungry multitude to separate peaceably, are already matters of history, and the narrative must therefore adhere to the fortunes of its hero, without dwelling upon nobler themes.

In returning to Ashleigh for his bundle, Michael took good care to be as little seen as possible; he was in fact more than ever anxious to avoid detection, as the more he meditated on his recollections of Sir Matthew Dowling and Parsons, the more did he feel convinced that should he fall into their power before the age of twenty-one, matters would go very hard with him.

At the great assembling of the people at York, he feared not that he should encounter any enemy; the only human beings whom he could so designate being likely to show themselves at the most distant part of the kingdom, rather than before the face of the multitude to be expected there. No feelings of distrust or alarm, therefore, arose to check the pleasurable excitement which this expedition was calculated to inspire; and Michael, with his stout staff over his shoulder, and the cotton handkerchief, containing a change of linen, suspended from it, set out with a light heart and active step upon a walk in which he soon found himself joined by many thousand companions.

The assurance given him by his unknown acquaintance; that he should see a wonderful and spirit-stirring spectacle, was fully verified. The very sight of the road along which he travelled, which looked like a dark and mighty current moving irresistibly along, while tributary streams flowed into it on all sides, so thick and serried was the mass that moved along it, was of itself well worth the toil it cost him, to behold its peaceful tumult. From time to time Michael indulged in a little questioning of the various individuals beside whom he found himself; but for the most part the men were too intent upon the object of their expedition, to converse idly respecting it—and by degrees our hero grew as silent as the rest, and trudged on without any other communion than that of his own thoughts.

It was at about twenty miles distance from York, when the multitude were on their return, that a circumstance occured, which, being of considerable importance to Michael, must be detailed somewhat at length. He had entered an inn by the road-side, which, being one of the largest post-houses on the north road, had an air of pretension and costliness about it, that caused the great majority of the host to walk on, without venturing to approach precincts so dangerous.

But Michael was much exhausted, and having already discovered, when passing before the humbler houses of public entertainment, that no rest could be hoped from entering them, every inch of space being occupied, he deemed it wisest to disburse a splendid shilling, rather than fag on till he had no strength to go further.

In pursuance of this reasoning, he entered the kitchen of the Royal Oak, and called for bread, cheese, and a pint of beer. Though there were not many of his fellow-travellers either rich or extravagant enough to share these splendid quarters with him, there were, nevertheless, three or four men taking refreshment in the apartment. One of these, an elderly respectable-looking personage, who had, as it seemed, exclusive possession of a snug little round-table in a corner, made a sign to Michael to share it with him. This was gratefully accepted, the loaf and cheese were already there, and the foaming tankard quickly followed.

"I marked you at the meeting," said his sociable companion. "It did my heart good to see a sprinkling here and there of them that come out of pure love and kindness to their poor fellow-creatures, having nothing themselves to gain. 'Tis a pity and a sin too, that so many Englishmen stand idly by, when such a business as this is afoot, just as if they had nothing to do with it. But they are one and all mistaken, and that they may chance to find out, too, one of these days."

"You give me credit for more than I deserve, perhaps," replied Michael; "that is, if you think my heart was enough with the poor factory-folks to make me take a long roundabout to sign with them, without having had some knowledge of their sufferings myself. You are right in thinking that I am not one of them now; but I have been, and Heaven forbid I should ever forget it! for the keeping that time in mind, ss quite enough to make every thing that comes to me now seem light and easy."

"You have worked in a factory?" said the other in an accent of surprise; "I should never have guessed as much—but you are very right to be thankful for the present, instead of ashamed for the past. But I don't think," he added, eyeing the fine person of Michael from head to foot, "I don't think I ever saw a lad who showed so little signs of having suffered in health and limb from it. Some lucky accident must have taken you away early?"

"I have seen many a boy and girl crippled for life," replied Michael, "before they were as old as I was when I ran away."

"My good fellow," whispered his companion, "don't you use them words. You are safe with me, I promise you; but if you ran from indentures, you won't do wisely to tell of it."

"You must blame your own kind and friendly looks," said Michael, smiling; "I know well enough that what you say is true, and it isn't a thing I should have told to many. But excepting just now that I took a fancy to come back, and take a look about the old place where I was born, I have got so clear and clean away from mills and mill-owner that I have grown rather bolder, maybe, than I ought to be. My business now, thank Heaven! is sheep-tending upon the beautiful free hills of Westmorland."

"You may well be thankful for such a change," replied his friendly companion. "It must have been some unaccountable good luck; for in

general, a runaway factory 'prentice is hunted down and caught long
before he has get among the good hill-folks."

"It was, indeed, a blessed chance for me!" said Michael, with deep
feeling. "I fell into the hands of the best man and the best master that
ever a wretched runaway hit upon."

"I almost wonder at you then venturing to come within sight of
your own place again. You can't be one-and-twenty yet by your looks,
and you would not over-well like to work out your time in a factory, I
should think," said the other.

"I don't think I should," replied Michael, laughing; "and I have run
some risk, I promise you, already, of the very thing you talk of, since
I left my master's house. Nothing would content my foolish fancy for
calling back old times, but going to look at the very factory where I first
worked, and talking to the identical tyrant who tortured me there."

"But he did not know you, I hope?" said the old man.

"I can hardly say that he did not," replied Michael; "for some notion
or other came into his head, and after I left him he sent for me to come
back again. It was, however, by a friendly messenger who knew well
enough who I was, and gave me pretty plainly to understand which way
I had better walk—and that was good luck again. But I was sorry, too,
to have to turn away from the old place without learning any news of
my former acquaintance. I found the same overlooker at Sir Matthew
Dowling's mill, and that was all I could find out."

"Sir Matthew Dowling's mill at Ashleigh? that's my country, too. My
wife keeps a school at Milford," replied the man, "and we have heard
enough of Sir Matthew."

"Can you tell me any thing about his daughter Martha?" demanded
Michael, with the appearance of being greatly interested in the inquiry.
"She was very kind to me, and I loved her next best, I think, to my own
dear mother and brother. Do you happen to know any thing about
her?"

"Not just at present," replied the man; "though they do say, that all
the family are likely to have a downfal, owing to Sir Matthew's getting
into a scrape about bad bills, or something or other, t'other side of the
water. But I do well remember something particular about Miss Martha

that you talk of, a matter of seven years ago; and if she was good to you, it was more than she was to every body, for it was all along of a cruel piece of treachery of hers, that I lost the best mistress that ever man had. I dare say, if you come from Ashleigh, you must know the name of Miss Brotherton, though it's long since she left Milford. I was her coachman, and if it had not been for Miss Martha Dowling, I believe I might have been so still."

"I was but just turned ten years old, at the time I knew Miss Martha," returned Michael; "but I shouldn't have thought she could be treacherous to any body."

"She was though, for all our people knew the whole story from first to last, and a queer story it was too, when one thinks of the end of it; which was neither more nor less than sending our dear young lady away out of the country."

"I never happened to know any thing about the lady who owned the Park," said Michael; "except that she was one of the fine folks as I have seen at Dowling Lodge, but I should like to hear the story, because of Miss Martha."

"Why the short and the long of it was, that there was a poor widow called Armstrong—"

Michael started so violently, that his companion stopped. "Did you happen to know her, my lad?" he added, after a pause.

"Yes, sir, I remember her very well—but please to go on."

"Well then, this widow Armstrong had two sons, and one of them was had up to the great house, Dowling Lodge, I mean, for some nonsensical reason or other; and Sir Matthew pretended to make the greatest fuss in the world about him, and the whole country was talking about it. But for some offence of the poor boy's, I never rightly heard what, the old sinner determined upon sending him 'prentice to the most infernal place, by all account, that the earth has got to be ashamed of. And how do you think the poor widow was coaxed over to sign the indentures? Why by your friend, Miss Martha, and no one else, and that I know upon the best authority. Well, 'tis a long story, the ins and outs of it, and I can't say that I ever rightly understood the whole, but this I know to be fact: that our young mistress took the whole thing so much to

heart, that she actually set out to look after the boy; but when she got
to the murderous place the poor little fellow was dead! And what did
she do then, dear, tender-hearted lady! but bring back a pretty little girl
instead of him, because, as we all guessed, she was determined to save
somebody."

The emotion of Michael Armstrong on hearing this, was so entirely
beyond his power to conquer, that he lost all capability of utterance,
and in of asking the name of the little girl—an inquiry which he in
vain strove to make—he sat pale and gasping, with his eyes fixed on the
speaker, and every limb trembling.

"The Lord have mercy on us! what is the matter with you, my good
fellow?" Said Miss Brotherton's *ci-devant* coachman. "You look cruel
bad! Is it my tale as turns you so? or is it that you have walked too much
and too fast?"

"No, no, no! *Pray* go on!" murmured Michael, making a strong effort
to articulate.

"'Tis the story, then? and you knowed the poor Armstrongs, beyond
all doubt!" said the kind-hearted coachman. "Well then, you shall hear
the end of it. When my mistress brought back the news of the little
fellow's death, his poor mother, who was but a sickly, cripply sort of
body, just broke her heart and died; whereupon Miss Brotherton took
home the other boy, put him to school to my wife, and then took to
teaching him herself; and treated him for all the world as if he had
been her own brother; and then she began to fancy that he wanted a
doctor—"

"And then," groaned Michael, suddenly interrupting him,—"and
then he died!"

"You don't say so?" said the coachman, in an accent of regret. "Did he
indeed, poor boy? Well now, I'm sorry for that; for it was a pleasure to
see him growing taller and stouter every day, almost, as one may say. And
when was it he died? It's curious that we should never have heard of it."

"Heard of it?" said Michael, while a sort of wild uncertainty took
possession of his mind, that gave him the feeling of one whose reason
threatened to leave him. "Heard it? Why did you want to hear it? Could
you not see it, and know it, if he was living in the same house with you?"

"For certain I could, if he had died while Miss Brotherton remained at the park; but that he did not, for I drove him off the first stage myself, alive and well, and looking as beautiful as he always did, poor lad, for he was to be sure the handsomest-faced boy, that ever I looked upon. But what might have happened to him afterwards, is of course more than I can say; for when the place was sold, and all of us paid off, all we heard was, that our dear young lady was set off to travel in foreign countries, and had left pensions to every one of her servants according to their length of service. So we know nothing since."

"Is there no one can tell me where she is gone, and in what land my brother died?" said Michael, violently agitated.

"Your brother?" said his companion. "Who do you mean by your brother, my lad?"

"Teddy!—my brother Edward!—I am Michael Armstrong!" was the convulsive reply.

"God bless my heart and soul! And you be the boy as Miss Brotherton went to look after? And she got into the wrong box, then, about your being dead? Was there ever any thing like that? But who was it, my boy, that told you as your brother was dead?"

"A woman in Ashleigh—one living in the house where my mother died. She told me that my mother was dead, and my brother too."

"Did she know who she was speaking to? Did she know you was Michael Armstrong?" said the old coachman with quickness.

"No, she knew me not," replied Michael; "but she knew that the widow Armstrong and her boy were dead."

"Then I'll be hanged if I believe as your brother is dead," replied the other eagerly. "When she said the widow's boy, she meant you, I'll lay my life on it; and there is nobody in Ashleigh, if they had told of her death, but would have named that of her boy too; but it would have always been meaning you, because every body knew that one followed close upon the news of the other. And I don't believe that your brother's dead, and that's a fact."

Michael clasped his hands rigidly together, and closing his eyes, remained so long motionless, that his good-natured companion became alarmed, and laying his hand upon the poor lad's arm, shook him gently,

as he said, "Any how, my good fellow, there is no cause for you to break
your heart with thinking about it all. Talking about your poor mother,
and her love of you, has made you turn as pale as a sheet; and natural
enough, too, perhaps. But my notion that your brother is alive and well,
ought to comfort you—oughtn't it?"

Michael opened his eyes, and fixing them on his companion, said,
"The joy of it is more than I can bear!" and then the tears bursting
forth, he wept copiously; a timely relief, for which he had great reason
to be thankful.

"Well well, I don't mind seeing you cry a little—that won't do you no
harm; and thank goodness your colour is coming back again! I declare I
thought I had been the death of you," said his new friend.

"But I'll tell you some more, and that is the name of him as knows
more about Miss Brotherton and your brother too, I'll be bold to say,
than any body in the whole country, and that's Parson Bell, of Fairly."

"And where is Fairly?" said Michael, starting up. "How long shall I
be in getting there? The hope is only hope yet, you know—there is no
certainty. Edward! dear, dear, Edward! Is it God's pleasure that I should
see him again in this world? Is it possible that such a heavenly dream can
ever come true? Oh! how often have I sat upon the hills and watched
the clouds, and thought that he was above them all!"

"Poor boy! But 'twill be better still, for a few years to come, that he
should be upon the earth along with you, won't it?"

"Where is Fairly?" reiterated Michael. "How long shall I be in getting
there?"

"Longer than you'll like, my dear boy," replied the coachman. "It's
a good sixteen miles from this very house; I should not wonder if
they was to charge seventeen, and you must not think of trying to
compass that to-night, for you are not in any wise in a fit condition
for it, changing colour, as you do, every minute. Your best course will
be to rest here for the night, and set off again by times to-morrow
morning, and that will bring you in easy by about the middle of the
day, you know."

"Impossible!" said Michael. "I owe you more than I am able to thank
you for, and I would be willing to show my gratitude by following

your advice—only, sir, I am quite sure I could not sleep a wink. And I don't think it would do me any good to lie tossing from side to side, unknowing, for certain, whether my own dear Teddy was alive or dead! So if you please, I must set off directly, that I may know the best and the worst at once."

"I suppose at your age I should have done the same; therefore I won't pretend to quarrel with you for it," replied the good man; "but I suppose it would be just prudent to call for an ink-horn, and to set down upon a bit of paper the name of the good clergyman that you are to call upon, as well as his place of residence."

"There is no need of that, sir," said Michael; "*Parson Bell, of Fairly*, are the words you said, and they, as well as all the rest you have spoken, seem as if they were stamped upon my very heart. But yet, before I start, I should like to use the ink-horn too, that I might write a line or so to my good master. I know he will be troubled in his mind about me if I don't get back, and I don't know rightly how long it may be. God bless him, good man!" continued Michael; "it was he that had me taught to write, and he shan't be left with any doubts or fears upon his mind for want of a letter from me."

This was a measure that the coachman greatly approved, and observing that he was well known in the house, and sure to be minded, he undertook to order the writing-materials, as well as something substantial by way of a supper; declaring that though he had come into his young friend's wild scheme of walking off straight away for Fairly, instead of putting up for the night, either where they were, or at Leeds, he should not part with him without a quarrel, if he refused to accept, and do justice to the good cheer he should provide. This kindness on the part of the man who had so strongly influenced his destiny, was both kindly intentioned and wisely devised; for greatly did the agitated young man stand in need of recruited strength and tranquillity, before he set off upon a new expedition, which was to lead to information so vitally important to his happiness. Though it was somewhat against his inclination, he accepted the friendly invitation gratefully, and the materials for writing being set before him, he addressed the following epistle to Mr Thornton:

"Honoured Master!

"Your goodness to me, in all ways, would make any abuse of it on my part a heavy crime indeed—too heavy, I think, for me to commit, or you to suspect me of. But I cannot be at the supper-table at Neckerby, on next Saturday night, according to my promise. A very strange thing has happened to me, dear master, which may, perhaps come to nothing, and in that case I know you will hear my story, and pity me too much to think of anger. But if all I hope comes to pass, your generous heart will rejoice with me, and you will bless your own goodness, for bringing me to the knowledge of the very greatest joy that ever fell to the lot of a human being, by giving me this holiday.

"I am, honoured Master,
"Your faithful and grateful servant,
"MICHAEL ARMSTRONG."

Having finished his letter, and committed it to the post, Michael felt somewhat more tranquil, and endeavoured to assume with his new acquaintance an air of greater composure, and self-possession. But his heart beat, his temples throbbed, his thoughts wandered, and when he and his friendly companion sat down to supper, the poor boy felt that he could almost as easily have swallowed the board itself as any portion of the substantial fare which was spread upon it. But he quaffed a long and refreshing draught from a pitcher of cold water, and putting, at the suggestion of the worthy coachman, a crust in his pocket, he sallied forth with the agitating consciousness that on the information of which he was in pursuit, hung all his earthly hopes.

His new friend shook his head as he felt his feverish hand, and marked his heightened colour, and his eager eye.

"God bless you, boy!" said the good man. "Remember, if you fall sick by the way, that my name is Richard Smithson, that I live at Milford, near Ashleigh, and that I'll hold myself ready to come to you at a pinch, if you should happen to have need of me. And here, Michael Armstrong, are three sovereigns, that I give you to keep for two reasons. One is, that you may use them in case you have need. The other, that if you don't want them, I shall be sure to see you, when you bring them back, and that you will do, or I'll never trust a lad's face more; and now good bye. It is but a wildish sort of boy's trick though, setting off this way at night, when you ought to be in bed."

"The air and the walk will do me more good than all the beds in the world!" replied Michael. "God bless you, sir! See me you shall, if I continue to live;" and so saying, he strode forth into the night, with a longing for greater space to breathe in, than could be found in the kitchen of the Royal Oak.

The boy was right as to the effect which this bodily exertion would produce upon him. The very darkness calmed him; he took his hat off that the cool air might bathe his temples with its dewy breath and though his pace was rapid, and scarcely relaxed for a moment during many miles, the action of his pulse became more healthy, and the aching of his throbbing temples passed away.

All he now seemed to fear was that his imagination should cheat him into the persuasion that all he wished was true. Edward! Fanny! (for of her identity with Miss Brotherton's *protégée* he could hardly doubt, when he remembered the history of her departure from the Deep Valley)—these names seemed to ring in his ears, and to be inscribed in starlight on the heavens as he raised his eyes towards them. And thus the sixteen miles were traversed before he had half chewed the cud of all the sweet thoughts that thronged upon his fancy. When he reached Fairly, it was still much too early to find any one stirring, so Michael unceremoniously walked into a cart shed, and clambering up into a vehicle that had the sweet savour of newly-carried hay to recommend it, he placed his bundle under his head, and despite both hopes and fears, fell into a sound sleep, nor waked till cocks, hens, cows, pigs, and ploughboys, all joined in chorus to arouse him.

XXVIII

An important interview—Doubts and fears

Michael's first recollections on opening his eyes were not of the clearest kind, and it required at least a minute's looking about him, after seating himself upright in the cart, before he could perfectly understand where he was, or why and how he got there. But no sooner did all the events of the day before rush back upon his mind, than he felt conscious of being near the most important moment of his life. Again he closed his eyes, but not to sleep, and fervently prayed that whatever might be the tidings which awaited him, he might have strength to receive and bear them as he ought. Then, springing from his resting-place upon the ground, he inquired of a lad near him the way to Mr Bell's, and set off to follow the directions he received with no greater delay than was necessary for a short halt beside a little streamlet on the way, which offered a welcome opportunity of washing his face and hands before he petitioned for admission to the presence of the good clergyman, to whose words he looked forward with an intensity of interest which almost amounted to agony.

Though it was still early, Mr Bell was already in his garden, and when the gate opened, it was himself who turned towards it to learn the errand of the young stranger. Michael felt at the first glance that the gentleman who stood before him was the person from whom he was to learn whether the brother he had so long mourned as dead was still alive, and he trembled so violently from head to foot that he could not articulate a word.

"What ails you, my lad?" said Mr Bell, gently laying a hand upon his shoulder, and looking earnestly in his face. "You have not the look of one who has done mischief, or else I could fancy that you had some terrible tale to tell. Come into the house and sit down, my boy, for it is very clear you are not quite able to stand."

Michael, still silent, followed his considerate host into the house, and thankfully received from his hands a glass of water, which did him good service, for in a minute or two he was able to say, "I want you to tell me, sir—may God give me strength to hear your answer, let it be which way it may!—I want to know—if Edward—if my brother, Edward Armstrong, is alive or dead?" But notwithstanding Michael's torturing eagerness to hear the answer, he put his hand before his eyes, because he had not courage to bear the look that might forestal it.

"Your brother? Edward Armstrong your brother? Who then are you, boy, in the name of Heaven?" said Mr Bell, eagerly.

"I am Michael, sir, Michael Armstrong. But oh! for pity's sake, tell me what I ask!"

"Yes, boy, yes. But compose yourself, my dear fellow! Edward is alive, and your friend Fanny Fletcher too."

Michael sunk from his chair upon his knees, and lifting his clasped hands towards Heaven, seemed breathing thanksgivings for this assured confirmation of tidings which, till now, he had not dared to believe true. But, startled as he was, the anxiety, the excitement, and the fatigue of the preceding night and day, had been more than enough for him, and at the moment when every thought would have been joy, and every sensation delight, he ceased to think or feel at all,—the colour forsook his lips, his eyes closed, and, greatly to the dismay of Mr Bell, he sunk prostrate on the floor.

No time was lost before the usual means of restoring suspended life were administered; and the uncared-for factory-boy, the mountain-braced Westmorland shepherd, lay extended on a sofa, with essences at his nose, and the opening of his dark eyes watched for, as tenderly as if he had been a delicate young lady.

A deep-drawn sigh announced to Mr Bell, who stood by, anxiously watching him, that his remedies had been successful, that the boy so long mourned as dead, was really and truly alive, and a very handsome well-grown fellow into the bargain.

"This is a strange history, Michael, as ever I chanced to hear," said he, taking the boy's hand, and ascertaining that his pulse again made 'healthful music.' "Why we have all been mourning for you as dead for this many a year, and now you drop down, as if from the clouds, and by what I can make out, have been fancying on your side that Edward was dead too. The first thing to do, must, I think, be to give you some breakfast, and then, if you are strong enough, you shall tell me how all this has come to pass."

Full as his heart was, and eagerly as he longed for the conversation in which he had so much to learn, as well as to tell, Michael gratefully submitted to this arrangement, till having received from the hand of the deeply-interested Mrs Bell herself the refreshment he so greatly needed, he felt his young strength return, and if he trembled as he turned his eyes towards his kind host, with a look that seemed to say, "Now, sir, I can talk to you," it was from eagerness, not weakness.

Mr Bell understood the appeal, and well inclined to answer it, said, "Having told you that Edward is alive and well, my dear boy, and only wants the sight that I see now to make him perfectly happy, I think you ought to be satisfied, and not expect me to tell you any more till my curiosity is gratified by hearing your own history. How in the world did it happen, Michael, that when Miss Brotherton went to the Deep Valley Mitls, on purpose to look for you, she should come back persuaded that you were dead, though the charming little girl she brought away with her had seen you there, and seemed to know you well?"

Michael Armstrong told his own story more succinctly than I have been able to do it, and probably much better too; for he beguiled Mrs Bell of many tears as she listened to him; and bare as the sad narrative was of events, her husband also hung upon every word of it, as if, contrary to the theory which seemed to be pretty generally established in his neighbourhood, he thought the feelings and the sufferings of a factory-child might be capable of exciting interest.

When the history had reached its conclusion, and Michael had fairly brought himself into Mr Bell's breakfast-parlour, he paused, and with a very eloquent look of entreaty said, "Now, sir, may I not listen to you?"

"Yes, my dear boy," replied his new friend, in the happy tone with which a kind heart inspires words calculated to give pleasure. "Yes, you have much to hear, and a wonderful story it is, I promise you. But it shall be all true Michael, so don't fancy that I am telling you a false tale, and that Miss Brotherton is the fairy. But first tell me, before I go any further, what sort of a boy was your brother Edward when you saw him last?"

"Oh, sir! He was the dearest, kindest fellow that ever lived!" replied Michael, his fine eyes beaming with tenderness and well-remembered love.

"But what sort of a boy was be to look at?" demanded the clergyman.

Michael closed his eyes as if the better to contemplate the inward picture engraven on his memory.

"His face was a sweet face," said he, "but his dear limbs were crippled. He was a slighter boy than me, and could not stand the labour of the mill; and I fear—I fear," he added, shuddering, "that my poor Edward must live and die a cripple."

"What is your opinion about that, my dear?" said Mr Bell, turning to his laughing wife.

"Why, I am inclined to think that Michael will have some difficulty in identifying his brother when he gets to him," she replied.

"Instead of being a cripple," resumed Mr Bell, "I suspect that your brother is a handsomer fellow than you are, Michael. Every thing promised well for it when he took leave of us, and since then my wife has had letters from Miss Brotherton, which do not speak of any falling off in his improvement."

"Nay," said the lady, "I have had more than letters to speak for it. Shall I show him Miss Brotherton's drawing, George?"

"Most certainly, my dear; it will save me a vast deal of description, and you may trust to Miss Brotherton's pencil, Michael, as impitcitly as to my words, for there never was a more faithful limner."

Mrs Bell then opened a little portfolio, secured by a key, and drew thence a drawing in water-colours, the composition and finish of which would have done no discredit to a professional artist. How the stout

nerves of the young and athletic Michael trembled as he received it! At
first his eyes seemed to fail him, the outline, the colouring, the whole
group was indistinct. "I am a fool, sir!" he said, letting the hand that held
it drop beside him; "I positively cannot see."

"I don't much wonder at it," replied Mr Bell; "but try again, Michael,
it is worth looking at."

And so thought Michael, as he once more placed it before him, and
gazed upon it with an eye as eager as that of Surrey might have been,
when contemplating the magic mirror that was to show him what he
loved "in life and limb." The drawing represented a terrace-walk, along
which ran a handsome stone balustrade partially covered by vine-leaves;
while beneath it in the distance, stretched to a far horizon a glorious
river, careering through a rich and varied landscape. All this was fair to
look upon, but the boy's eyes saw it not—they were riveted upon two
figures that occupied the foreground of the terrace. One of these was a
slender girl, whose bright curls seemed just released from the restraint of
a straw-hat which she held in her hand. But though the head was thus
uncovered, the features were not visible, for the other hand was placed
upon the balustrade, over which she hung, as if in earnest contemplation
of some object below. But the head of the other figure, a young man of
some twenty years or so, was so turned as fully to meet the spectator's
eye; and if the pencil that drew it flattered not, it was one of the
handsomest that nature ever formed. The large expressive eyes, beaming
with mingled softnes and animation, were directed to some object out
of the picture, but at no great distance; for the sweet smile that played
about the mouth seemed to indicate that he was listening to pleasant
words from some well-loved companion. The figure of the young man
thus represepted was tall and graceful. His dress was the light summer
garb of a southern climate—an open book was in his hand, his straw hat
lay at his feet, beside which stood a basket of newly-gathered grapes, and
a small Italian greyhound, its bright eye looking in the same direction as
his own, completed the group, which spoke in every part of it a sort of
graceful ease and enjoyment, that it was very pleasant to look upon.

"Can this indeed be my Edward?" said Michael at length, after a long
silent examination of the drawing. "How beautiful!—how noble!—how

happy—how healthful—how intelligent he looks! *Is* it my own dear, pale, sickly brother? Can this be true?"

"As true as that you stand there to look at it," replied Mr Bell. "Is there nothing in the face, Michael, that recalls your brother to you?"

"Yes, sir," he replied quickly; "the eyes and the sweet smile are so like my own Edward, that strange as it is to see him so healthy, tall, and graceful as he is represented here, and looking, too, so greatly like a gentleman, I do quite believe that this was never drawn for any one but him; for never, never since I saw him last, have I seen such eyes, or such a smile as that."

"You are quite right there, Michael. The face is one not easily forgotten, and I can trace it here, notwithstanding all the change of age and circumstance. But who do you think that slender girl may be? It seems a pity not to see her face; the form, the pretty attitude, the bright waving locks, all plainly tell that it must be worth looking at. Can you guess who it is ?"

"I suppose it is Fanny Fletcher," replied Michael, colouring.

"And there, too, you are quite right. But does it not puzzle you to think how all this has been brought about? How does it happen, think you, that those whom you remember in a state so different, should now be living as you see them here, looking as if their existence was made up of sunshine and sweet air?"

"And now again I shall answer, as they say the fortune-tellers do," replied Michael, smiling, "by telling you, sir, what you have before told me. It is Miss Brotherton, whose name I well remember at Dowling Lodge, it is she who has done all this, and may God bless her for it! But yet, truly, it still seems a mystery. How did it happen, sir, that this rich young lady should have left her grand house, and all her fine acquaintance here, to go into foreign countries with two poor factory-children?"

"You may well marvel at it, Michael, for it is no common act. But will you not think it something stranger still, if I declare, as I can do with all truth, that you are yourself the primal cause of it?" said Mr Bell. "You look incredulous, yet so it is. Do you remember the play, Michael?"

"Sir Matthew's play?" cried Michael, burying his face in his hands. "Oh, sir! can I ever forget it?"

"It was a vastly gay thing, too," returned Mr Bell, smiling, "and all the performers were exceedingly admired; but you do not seem to remember it with any great pleasure?"

"Pleasure, Mr Bell?" returned Michael, with something like a groan; "I have suffered a good deal, considering how few years I had lived before my sufferings were over; but, excepting the coming home to mother's, and finding her and Teddy gone, and, as they told me, dead—both dead! excepting then, I never was so very, very wretched as while Sir Matthew was making me practise for that play!"

"Do you remember the very night it was acted, when you, and he, and Dr Crockley were in a room by yourselves, somewhere behind the scenes; do you remember, Michael, his beating and abusing you because you had cried upon the stage?"

"As well as if it had happened yesterday," replied the young man. "I had to utter false and lying praise about him, and something I am sure there was about loving him as well as my dear mother. That I could not bear—and then it was that the tears burst out, though well I knew what I should pay for shedding them."

"They were the luckiest tears that ever a boy wept, so pray do not quarrel with them," replied Mr Bell. "While you were paying for them, as you call it, in the green-room, Miss Brotherton by accident heard and saw every thing that passed; and from that hour she has never forgotten you, Michael, though more than seven long years have passed, if I mistake not, during which you have never profited by it in your own person. I will not enter now into any description of what her feelings were. An accident prevented her seeing your mother immediately, and when she did, my poor boy, you were already beyond the reach of any help. But she never ceased to inquire, by every means in her power, whither you had been conveyed, and it was then she came to me, so that it is to you I owe the pleasure of knowing one of the purest and noblest-hearted human beings it has ever been my lot to meet with. It was in consequence of—not information, for I had none to give—but of a hint I gave her as to the nature of the place, that she set off on her exploring expedition to that horrid den of sin and suffering, the Deep Valley Mills, in Derbyshire. There she met the pretty creature whom she has since adopted. Little Fanny believed that you were dead, and this was the dismal news they brought to Hoxley-lane.—Your poor mother, Michael! But let it comfort you to know that every want and every hardship were relieved from the first hour that Miss Brotherton saw her—and she died with the comfort of knowing that her poor Edward would never have to labour more. Soon after her death, Miss Brotherton took your brother to London for the purpose of consulting the most able surgeons about his lameness. Their science did not fail them; for they predicted that with proper treatment he would outgrow it—and so he has, completely; being at this time not only the graceful well-made personage you see him represented there, but healthy, active, and gifted, as I hear, with a most rare intelligence. For reasons which it is not very difficulty to guess, Miss Brotherton thought that she and her young *protégées* would find themselves better off on the continent than in Lancashire; and from the time she first left Milford Park to visit London, she has never returned to it. The place is now sold, and Miss Brotherton has no longer any possessions in this neighbourhood. And now my dear boy I think I have told you all, excepting the exact spot where they are now; and this I cannot do, because our last letter from her informed us that they were just setting off upon a tour through Italy. She resided some time ago, for one year, at Paris, that the young people might acquire the language; but for the most part, Germany has been their home. It is there your brother has received his education, and I think it very probable that it is there they will finally settle for it is in the far-famed valley of the Rhingau that Miss Brotherton has purchased a spacious mansion, large enough, as she tells me, to accommodate half-a-dozen rich English families, with extensive and very beautiful grounds around it, and all capabilities for being converted into a delicious residence."

Here he ceased, and it was several minutes before poor Michael was capable of uttering a single word in return. The mention of his mother—the hint that she had not long survived the hearing he was dead, wrung his heart anew, with grief as fresh as if he had lost her yesterday; and spite of his manly stature, the tears flowed silently, but plenteously, down his cheeks. Yet, even when he had conquered this, there was something so surprising in the present situation of his brother, something, that notwithstanding all the fond yearnings of his own heart, seemed to place them so widely asunder, that the joy which Mr Bell looked for, was less obvious, than an expression of almost timid embarrassment, as he said,

"Alas, sir! what shall I seem like amongst them? You speak of my dear Edward's education in Germany—of his learning a foreign language in France—while I!—my best, and truly my only education has been looking at nature from the mountain's side as I kept sheep, and all my learning, what I have gathered from a few strangely mixed volumes that I have bought or borrowed during the last four years. How can I present myself before them? How they can welcome me?'

"Be so kind, my dear," said Mr Bell to his wife, without immediately replying to Michael's question,—"Be so kind, my dear, as to find Miss Brotherton's last letter for me. I think you took possession of it, and I doubt not have preserved it among other treasures of the same kind."

Mrs Bell immediately left the room, and presently returned with the letter in her hand.

"Take that letter, Michael," said Mr Bell; "take it into the garden, my dear boy, and read it alone, and without interruption. You will find a shady seat where you may be very comfortable, and when you have finished the perusal come into my study, and tell me what you think of it."

Michael's hand trembled as he took the letter, and silently obeying the instructions he received, he walked out to an embowered spot where he could not be seen from the house, and seating himself on a garden-bench perused the following letter with a mixture of trepidation and eagerness which may easily be imagined.

"Have you thought it long since last you heard from me, dear friends? I hope you have, for it has seemed very long to me since last I wrote to you. But what a thief of time is occupation! I have been so very busy in drawing plans for the repairing and beautifying my old castle—you would certainly call it a castle in England—and so constantly called upon by Edward, to give my approval to his *carte du voyage* for our Italian tour, and by Fanny, to sanction her plans for our future flower-garden, and by Mrs

Tremlett to settle some point of enormous difficulty respecting the packing up of the things to be left, and the things to be taken, that though day by day I have told myself, for at least a month past, that I was behaving most abominably in not writing, I have never before found a leisure hour to set about it. But if I have not written, I have drawn for you—witness the view from my beautiful terrace which I shall send with this letter. I wish I could have put my own phiz in it to show you how healthy and well I look; but unfortunately, you know, there is no point of sight from which an artist can catch a peep at himself without the aid of a looking-glass, and though I pretty nearly live upon my terrace, I have not yet taken either to sleeping or dressing there, so no mirror was at hand. But instead of myself I have given you Edward; sometimes I do feel a little glorious as I look at him, and remember the delicate pale face and feeble limbs that greeted my first sight of him in Hoxley-lane. He is now—but you will laugh at me if I attempt to describe him in words—the sketch I send is no bad likeness, and may give you a tolerably correct idea of the alteration that has taken place. As to my sweet Fanny, though the attempt would have been a bold one, I meant to have given you a likeness of her too, but her attitude was so picturesquely pretty as she stood, unconscious of what I was about, that I contented myself with the back of her curly head—you shall have her face another time.

"How can I be sufficiently thankful to Providence for having redeemed my isolated existence from the state of uselessness in which I vegetated before I met Edward Armstrong and Fanny Fletcher! Not an hour now passes by me, without leaving behind it some trace of my having advanced in the precious labour of making these two beloved beings happier. Were they merely ordinary young people, with average hearts and average capacities, I should still bless Heaven with a grateful heart, for having permitted me to be the means of changing their condition, from one of great suffering to a life of innocent enjoyment. But as it is, I know not how to be thankful enough!

"It seems to me, dear friends, however much I increase my acquaintance with other human beings, that Edward and Fanny are the noblest creatures in the world. Is it that suffering, being of necessity a part of our earthly nature, we cannot arrive at the perfect development of all our faculties without it? Where it arrives in later life, perhaps the effect, though inwardly healthful, may not show fruits so beautiful. There is in the minds of both of them, a brightness of intelligence and a delicious calm of temper that I have never met elsewhere. It is as if a heavy weight that had been painfully crushing them, was suddenly removed, causing all the ordinary sensations of human existence to be felt as a luxury. Young as they are, they are full of instruction, right thinking, pure feeling, and a firmness of integrity which it is the best joy of my life to contemplate— and all this built on so firm a foundation of religious principle, that I can have no fears for its endurance. After this, it would be very weak and womanish folly to dwell much on their personal advantages, or even on the peculiar charm of their manners and conversation—yet they are gifts which bring a charm, to which it is difficult to be quite insensible.

"Is it not strange, dear friends, that being such as I describe them, and having passed so large a portion of their lives together in the mutual contemplation of each other's excellence, is it not strange that they should not by this time be lovers, instead of friends? Yet such is not the case. That they love each other sincerely is most true, and I could give a thousand proofs that either would at all times gladly renounce amousement or pleasure of any kind, for the sake of the other; but they are not in love. If I did not believe it impossible, considering the age of the parties when they parted, I should think that Fanny's little heart had been buried in the grave of Michael, the poor little fellow, whose sufferings under the tender patronage of Sir Matthew Dowling first roused my sleepy existence into action. She cannot yet hear his name mentioned, without betraying a degree of emotion that it is painful to witness; and when, as sometimes happens, Edward is taken for her brother, it seems to delight her. 'Yes, yes, indeed he is my brother! I love him as such; and if you ask him, he will tell you that I am to him a dear and loving sister,' I have heard her say and if Edward had been asked, I do believe he would have answered and truly too, in the same strain.

"Edward is now twenty-one, and my pretty Fanny nineteen; but, notwithstanding the variety of captivating young people with whom they are perpetually associating, I cannot believe that the heart of either has as yet received any tender impression—though in more cases than one, I have had reason to know that they have not been looked at with indifference. Yet, sometimes I am puzzled about Edward! I think he is less gay and joyous than he used to be. At any time, indeed, the name of Michael has ever been sufficient to bring an expression of profound and hopeless sorrow upon his fine countenance, which it wrings my heart to see; for, alas! how vain must be all my affection, all sisterly love, to help him there! But, incontestably of late, his spirits have been less gay than formerly. This, to tell you the truth, is the only drawback to the happiness I enjoy. Could Fanny and Edward learn to forget poor Michael, I should hardly have a wish left; but I have little hope of this—his memory, I truly believe is too deeply engraven on their hearts, for any subsequent events to efface it. Sometimes, when I meditate on this sadly-enduring sorrow, I fancy that I should rejoice if they were both of them to fall in love, as a cure for it. But, alas! whenever that happens, what a breaking up of happiness it will be! for I can hardly hope to find a continental wife or husband for my adopted children, sufficiently English in habits and character, to permit my inviting them to make a part of my family. Yet marry abroad they must, I think, if they marry at all—for I will never by my own free will expose them to the mortification likely to ensue upon such an explanation respecting their origin, as must be the consequence of any matrimonial negotiation in England. On the continent, the ample fortunes they will possess, with their good education, and great natural advantages, will suffice to make them very desirable alliances to almost any one. But these are anxieties, which though they must come upon me sooner or later, I suppose, I shall endeavour to push from me, and forget as long as I can.

"And now I must bid you farewell; for during the next month, or perhaps longer, our course will be directed by circumstances that we are not fully acquainted with as yet. But I will write as soon as I can tell you with certainty where your letters can reach us.

Mrs Tremlett, Edward, and Fanny, send affectionate greetings to you all. And should it fall in your way to see, or convey a message to poor Martha Dowling, I will beg you to tell her that I shall ever remember her with great affection and esteem. Adieu!

"Ever dear Mr and Mrs Bell,
"Your grateful and affectionate,
"MARY BROTHERTON."

Did one reading of this epistle suffice for Michael? did two? did three? It is difficult to say, for he remained in his shady and obscure retreat so long, that Mr Bell, notwithstanding his previous determination not to disturb him, began to think that it was time to see whether all the good news it contained had not killed him with joy. And when he reached the bench, Michael still sat with the precious letter in his hand, and his eyes fixed upon it, so that it appeared as if he had not yet finished the perusal of it. Michael looked up as Mr Bell approached him, and immediately rising, stepped forward to receive him. It was not, however, any wild excess of joy that his features expressed but there were traces of very strong emotion on his countenance, and his hand trembled as he stretched it forth to receive that which was kindly extended towards him.

"You have remained too long alone, my dear boy, in this cold nook," said Mr Bell, taking the young man's arm within his own, and leading him towards the house. "What makes you look so pale, Michael? You are not ill, I hope?"

"No, sir, I think not," was the reply, "but I can hardly tell you how I feel. At one moment the idea that my dear brother still lives, and that it is possible I may again see him, hear him, hold him in my arms, seems to make me too happy to breathe—and then again, a sort of doubt and sadness takes hold upon me, and I do not feel as if it were possible I could ever make one in the happy party on the terrace."

"And why not, Michael?" demanded Mr Bell somewhat reproachfully; "after reading that letter, can you find it in your heart to doubt that the party on the terrace would receive you joyfully?"

"Will not the happiness be too great?" cried Michael. "Oh! how can I deserve it?"

"Not by doubting the goodness or the affection of those who love you," replied Mr Bell. "But come, I must not preach to you now, I believe, for I suspect that you are not in a condition to profit by it. Come into the house, sit down, and grow reasonable as fast as you can, and then we will talk of the time and the mode in which you must set off to join your family—for your family they are, and will be, Michael, you may depend upon it."

"Can I throw myself upon Miss Brotherton, sir, without her permission?" demanded Michael, while his paleness was changed for a moment into a glow of the deepest red.

"I am afraid you have a very proud heart, Michael," said Mr Bell, looking at him; "and that is not right, it is not christianlike."

"Oh, Mr Bell!" replied Michael, with strong feeling, "have I not already eaten the bitter bread of dependence, and can I, at my age, and with my power to labour, submit to it again?"

"You have a notion then, young man, that benefits conferred by a Sir Matthew Dowling, and a Miss Brotherton, are the same thing?" said Mr Bell.

"Not so, sir," replied Michael, "I cannot doubt that she who wrote this letter, must be both great and good, and I well know that Sir Matthew Dowling was neither. But I only know Miss Brotherton as one of the fine folks visiting at his house, and I cannot feel that I should like to start out suddenly upon her, from the tomb, as it would seem, appearing to expect that she should adopt me too, as she has done my brother Edward."

"Well, Michael, I must not blame you for this, because I believe it is very natural; yet, nevertheless, I feel quite sure that you will forget all such notions when you see Miss Brotherton," returned Mr Bell, smiling. Michael shook his head, but he returned the smile, though rather languidly; and when they had reached the house, and were again seated in the study, he said, "What does Miss Brotherton mean, sir, by calling Miss Martha Dowling 'poor Martha?' I trust that no misfortune has befallen her? she was very kind to me, and I shall always love her, although her name *is* Dowling."

"I believe she deserves it, Michael," returned Mr Bell, "and, by the by, you have it in your power to show your love, and do her a great kindness by the very simple process of letting her know that you are alive. Poor girl! She has suffered dreadfully from believing that she caused your death by the advice she gave to your mother about signing your indentures, and I fancy that letting her know that you did not perish in consequence, would be conferring a real blessing on her."

"Dear, good Miss Martha!" exclaimed Michael, "how well do I remember the walk we took together when she went to Hoxley-lane, to give my dearest mother that advice. She did it for my good, and for my good it would have been, if what she advised had been the thing she thought it! I owe her still, notwithstanding the misery she brought me to, the deepest gratitude; for her kind and careful teaching during the short time I was in her father's house first gave me the ambition and the hope to learn, and, spite of my degraded condition, I have never lost sight of it—and this it is, which, if any thing can, may reconcile me to presenting myself as a poor shepherd-boy before my well-taught brother."

"You are right there, Michael," replied Mr Bell; "it is very clear to me that you have profited greatly by the feelings so inspired, notwithstanding the adverse circumstances in which you were placed during the four terrible years passed in the Deep Valley; and such feelings I can tell you, will make a vast difference in the degree of happiness you are likely to enjoy in a reunion with your brother."

"And to Fanny Fletcher too!" said Michael, with the eagerness of reviving hope heightening his colour, and darting its brightness from his eye,—"to Fanny Fletcher too, I owe the suggestion of thoughts which have saved me from being too utterly degraded to meet her again with pleasure. It is to Martha Dowling, surely, that I owe all the little book learning I have been able to acquire, as well as the power of writing down the thoughts and meditations to which it has given rise; but it was Fanny who made me feel that however lowly our condition and state on earth, we may yet retain as good a right as any of the kings of it, to open our hearts before God, and ask for His Spirit to help us. How many mornings have I watched the sun rise, how many evenings have I seen him set in glory behind the mountain-tops, and thought as I lay amidst the heather, and worshipped his Almighty Maker, that, but for her, I should never have known the comfort of loving and trusting, as well as of adoring Him. It was that dear patient little girl who taught me this, and perhaps I may yet live to thank her for it."

"I trust you will, my dear boy," replied Mr Bell, touched with the earnest energy of the boy's manner; "I trust you will, Michael: and if I mistake her not, she will receive such thanks as a very welcome reward for all the pains she took to comfort you. Such kindness as she showed you is, indeed,

— —'twice blest,
   It blesseth him that gives, and him that takes:'

and I doubt not that she, as well as yourself, has been the better for it, from that time to this."

"May I look once more at that drawing, sir?" said Michael, with some little embarrassment.

"There it is, Michael," said the clergyman smiling, and once more laying it before him. "Were it not that I think you will so soon see the dear originals, and that we shall not, I would ask my wife to give it you."

"I think I shall learn every line, and every shade of it by rote," said Michael, "if I do but look at it a few minutes longer. There, sir," he added, after an earnest gaze, and resigning it into his hands; "I feel as if it were my own now." Then, after one deep sigh, he seemed to rouse himself; and, as if endeavouring to shake off some feeling that oppressed him, he said, "But, you have not told me yet, sir, the reason why Miss Brotherton calls my first benefactress 'poor Martha!'"

"I am sorry to say," replied Mr Bell, "that there are more reasons than one, for applying that pitying epithet to Miss Martha Dowling. In the first place, she is greatly out of health, poor girl; and in the next, her father's affairs are said to be in a very tottering condition, in consequence of his having overloaded himself with a greater quantity of spun cotton than he can get any sale for. He is said to have lent out money, too, on some speculation which has not answered: and, in short, that it is rather a nice question, whether he will be able to get through his difficulties or not. Another misfortune is, that Sir Matthew, as soon as he possibly could after the death of his first wife, thought proper to marry the Lady Clarissa Shrimpton, who, strange to say, thought proper also to marry him; and it is said also, that poor Miss Martha, who is the eldest of the daughters unmarried, is not permitted to enjoy much peace under the rule of her noble step-mother."

"Lady Clarissa Shrimpton?" said Michael, with the air of one to whom some long-lost image is brought back—"Lady Clarissa Shrimpton? Why, surely, that was the name of the tall, thin woman who had to practise the laying her bony hand upon my unfortunate little head, when the terrible play was about?"

"I dare say it was," said Mr Bell. "But, at any rate, Lady Clarissa Shrimpton is now Lady Clarissa Dowling."

"Poor Miss Martha!—and she is out of health too? How can I manage to pay my duty to her, Mr Bell, without running the risk of being recognised by Sir Matthew, as the unfortunate boy who escaped from the Deep Valley? He would be able, I suppose, to make me serve out my time?"

"I do not think he would attempt it just now, Michael?" was the consoling reply. "Thank God!" continued Mr Bell, "there has been a good deal said of late concerning the abominations of the Deep Valley Factory, and I don't much think Sir Matthew Dowling would run the risk of having it proved that he had kidnapped a boy away to it, in the style he managed you. I should have no fear whatever, of your presenting yourself at Dowling Lodge; only I think it is ten to one her ladyship will not let you get a sight of Miss Martha without her being present,—unless you were to write a line to the young lady first, and then perhaps she might contrive it."

Michael now rose to take his leave, offering with a fervour that was very touching, his earnest thanks for the generous kindness with which he had been received but he resisted all the hospitable efforts made to retain him as a guest. He had need, he said, to be alone, that he might bring his mind to such a state as should enable him to sustain the wonderful change in his prospects with something like fortitude and rational composure. There was more real kindness, and true sympathy, in the manner of accepting this excuse, than the most pressing offers of hospitality could have shown; and Michael, after involuntarily kissing the hand stretched out to bid him farewell took his departure from the clergyman's house, with a heart full of thankfulness to God and man.

XXIX

Michael calls his wisdom to council, and the points to be discussed puzzle them—An early walk—An old friend with a changed face

To DESCRIBE MICHAEL ARMSTRONG'S FEELING as he took his solitary way along what seemed to him the most unfrequented fields he could find, would be both a difficult and an unnecessary task. That his heart swelled with thankfulness and joy cannot be doubted; yet there was a vagueness and uncertainty as to what he ought immediately to do, which made him anxious and sad, even in the midst of hope and joy. The small sum he had been able to save from his wages had been spent, or very nearly so, since he set out upon his eventful expedition. He had already accepted a loan from the friendly old coachman of Miss Brotherton, and he shrunk from the idea of contracting more debts, while unable to say with certainty when they should be paid. How then was he to reach his brother in his happy distant home? And where and how was he to pass the anxious interval that must of necessity intervene before he could even know to what point he should direct his pilgrim steps, even had he the means of setting forth?

The path he had taken proved to be a short cut leading into the high road from Fairly to Ashleigh, and on quitting the fields he found himself close to the door of a public-house which he was tempted to select for his shelter as long as he remained in the neighbourhood, both because it was lonely, and because it was humble. Having entered there, bespoken a bed, and made a very frugal repast, he inquired the distance to Dowling Lodge, and finding it was greater than he could traverse on foot with any hope of returning in decent time to occupy his newly-taken lodging, he resolved to wait till the following morning, when, by setting off at daybreak, he might be able to make his visit to Martha, and perhaps report the result of it to Mr Bell, before he slept.

His mind had too much on which to employ itself for him to feel the afternoon a long one: an orchard close behind the little inn, afforded him shade and soft turf whereon to sit or lie, or to pace backwards and forwards, with unequal steps, as he meditated on the chances for and against his ever being one in the happy, thrice happy party described by Miss Brotherton. Nor had he wearied of these exciting but most anxious thoughts, when the moon, and the stars, and the heavy dew warned him at length that the day was gone, and night come. And then he remembered that, in order to follow Mr Bell's advice, he must prepare himself with a letter to Miss Martha, which it would be necessary to write before he went to bed. Fortunately his *hotel* was able to furnish the needful implements, and after a little reflection, he penned the following note:

"A poor lad, to whom Miss Martha Dowling once showed much charitable kindness, is now waiting at the park-gates, to know if he may pay his duty to her. He takes the freedom of asking for this favour because he has been told that she would be pleased to hear he was alive and well."

Having directed this to Miss Martha Dowling, and sealed it in the best manner he could, he retired to his little bed in a state of mind that hovered between inexpressible felicity, and anxiety that he was hardly able to bear.

He was afoot in time to hear the lark's first overture on the following morning and his spirits, cheered by the bracing influence of the delicious hour, and by the sound sleep which had preceded it, enabled him to breakfast on a slice of brown bread, bespoken the night before, and laid ready for him, with a draught of icy-cold water from a neighbouring well, without any mixture of melancholy, though he tlhought the while of all the dangers and difficulties he might have to encounter ere he stood beside his Edward on the beautiful terrace to which his dreams had transported him so easily.

Michael was a stout walker, and had reached the well-remembered precincts of Dowling Lodge soon after the earliest servants were stirring. He had made up his mind to be the bearer of his own letter, and accordingly, having shown the address to the woman at the lodge as a reason for being permitted to enter, he approached the stately mansion by the road which led to the offices, and intrusting his epistle to the first female he encountered, requested her to deliver it to Miss Martha without delay.

"Why she bean't up yet," said the girl, looking at him, however, with the good-humoured smile with which light-hearted young damsels are wont to greet such very handsome lads as our Michael.

"But perhaps you will be so good as to let her have it as soon as she is awake?" he replied, returning the smile.

"Well, poor thing, and that may be now, most likely," returned turned the girl, "for her cough often wakes her before this time. Will you wait for an answer?"

"I won't trouble the servants by staying here," replied Michael, "but if you please you may tell the young lady that I will walk up and down the road till she can let me have it. Does Miss Martha walk out early in the mornings, as she used to do?" he added.

"That's just what she likes best, poor thing," replied the girl. "But you needn't be afeard that she's gone out already; for if she had, I should have been sure to have seed her; for she never has the great door opened for her at this time of day, for fear of disturbing my lady, who always lies unaccountable late."

"And does Sir Matthew rise early now?" demanded Michael with some anxiety.

"He!—not he! He eats and sleeps like a pig, they say; but he is grumpier than ever he was, both to men and maids too, since he married the new lady. I wonder as I never happened to see you before, as you seem to know 'em all so well."

"It is several years since I was last here," returned Michael; "but run up stairs with it, there's a dear girl, will you? because I want to get my answer and be off."

"You had better stop here till I come down again," replied his good-natured messenger, "instead of walking up and down the road, without knowing whether there's an answer or no—sit down in the kitchen, and I'll be back in no time."

And into the kitchen he went—the selfsame kitchen which just eight years before had been the scene of his painful examination by Sir Matthew Dowling's servants. He remembered the room perfectly; could have pointed out the exact spot where the awful housekeeper sat, and the place where he had himself stood, with no better champion to sustain his courage than the greasy kitchen-maid, whose pitying broad face, bent over him, he recollected as perfectly as if it had beamed upon him but the day before. He was still deeply revolving these interesting reminiscences, and the strange contrast they offered to his present hopes, when his envoy returned—"Miss Martha wants to know your name, young man," she said, "but she is getting up, and will be walking in the park as usual, she says, presently, so it is likely enough that she will give you the answer herself."

"Very well," replied Michael, perfectly satisfied—"good morning!—I am very much obliged to you."

"But you haven't told me your name, and Miss Martha says that she should like to know it."

"My name isn't one that would make any difference," he replied, "so I won't trouble you to go up again about that—good bye!" And without waiting for any further discussion, he walked off, exceedingly well pleased at having arranged the wished for *tête-à-tête* so satisfactorily. The noble dimensions of the park enabled Michael to select a space amply sufficient for his promenade which was neither within sight of the mansion nor the lodge, and ere he had made many turns upon it, he peceived the lady he wished to see, approaching him.

He could not doubt that it was Martha, for at that hour of the morning none other was at all likely to be there; but she was too much altered for him to recognise her in any degree. He thought she was taller than he had expected to see her, but at any rate she was greatly thinner, and so delicately pale, that her appearance was rather a contrast, than a resemblance to what he had expected to meet. She was already near him when he turned upon the path, and met her. He stopped, took off his hat, and bowed respectfully.

"You are Miss Martha Dowling, ma'am?" he said interrogatively

"Yes," replied Martha, "that is my name, but when did I see you before, young man? I do not know you."

"It is a great many years, Miss Martha —but I can never forget your kindness."

The pale cheek of Martha was tinted with a vivid blush, as she exclaimed, "If it were possible—if I did not know that he was dead— But this is nonsense," she added, recovering her composure. "I quite forget your person, young man," she continued after a pause: "But if I have ever done you any service, I am glad of it. Perhaps if you tell me your name I may remember the circumstances to which you allude."

"Oh! Miss Martha!" replied Michael, "I am afraid my name will startle you, and therefore I do not like to speak it. But I think it came into your head just now, only you stopped short, and said it was impossible."

"Can it be Michael Armstrong that I see?" demanded Martha, in an agitated voice.

"It is indeed, Miss Martha!" he replied. "It is Michael Armstrong come back to thank you for all your great kindness to him."

"My kindness to Michael Armstrong?" she exclaimed. "Alas! it was I who ocasioned all his sufferings, and, as I have thought for many years, his death. How is it you have been saved, Michael? How is it you have escaped from the horrid place to which I was the cause of your being sent?"

"My dear Miss Martha!" returned Michael greatly affected by her look of ill-health and by the agitation she displayed—for tears were trickling fast down her pale cheeks. "My dear Miss Martha" he said, "*I* know, if nobody else does, the kind motive that you had for every word you spoke—and was it not I myself that said I wanted to go, Miss Martha, when we walked together from here, down to poor mother's house? Never, never can I thank you enough for all your goodness then, as well as at all other times, from the very first moment that ever I saw you?"

"Thank God!" cried poor Martha, fervently clasping her hands, and raising her eyes to heaven, "you know not, Michael, what a load you have taken from my heart! I have for years lived under the dreadful weight of believing myself to be your murderer. The thought has haunted me by night, and rarely quitted me by day. And my poor father, too! This crime at least he has not to answer for!"

Michael could not help thinking—though for worlds he would not have lessened her pious satisfaction by uttering the thought—that though he had escaped with life from the terrible sufferings to which he had been exposed, he owed Sir Matthew but little gratitude for it. Fortunately, however, for his veracity, he was not called upon to answer this observation, for Martha immediately added,

"Does Miss Brotherton know that you are alive, Michael?"

"No, Miss Martha, she does not," he replied; "my brother Edward is living with her in some place abroad, and till yesterday I have existed in the dismal belief that he was dead, and that I had not a single relation in the whole world."

"And where are you living, Michael? What is your home now? And how did you escape from the dismal place to which you were sent as an apprentice?"

In answer to this, Michael related, as briefly as he could contrive to do it, all that had happened to him, confessing freely that he had run away, and that he supposed he was liable to be sent back again to work out his time, if Sir Matthew discovered that he was alive, and if it were his pleasure to do it.

"We will not talk of any thing of that kind, Michael," said Martha, a bright blush again visiting her cheek. "It would not be prudent, certainly, for you to make yourself known here—and I particularly desire that you will not do it. I am grateful, oh! most grateful, for your coming to tell me that the dismal news of your death was not true, but now that you have set my heart at rest on that score, do not come here again, Michael—Lady Clarissa is very particular about every body that comes to the house—and—in short—though I shall always have the greatest regard for you, Michael—I would a great deal rather that you did not come to Dowling Lodge again."

Michael perfectly understood, though it was evident she would not avow it, that poor Martha had fears for his safety, should Sir Matthew discover him; and without giving her the slightest reason to suppose that he saw this, he assured her that he was going immediately from Ashleigh without any intention of returning to it. Martha then looked at her watch, and seeing that there was still above an hour to spare before the usual time at which the family came down stairs, ventured to seat herself on the trunk of a newly-felled tree, while she questioned the youth, for whom she still felt the strongest interest, as to what his projects were, and when, and how he thought of leaving England to join his brother. With frank and touching simplicity, Michael entered freely into all his harassing doubts and difficulties—confessed that he had not a shilling in the world that he could call his own, and, worse still, that he could not help feeling a strong repugnance to throwing himself wholly on the charity of Miss Brotherton, for no other reason in the world than because she had nobly provided for his brother. "To know that Edward is alive, and not endeavour to see him is impossible," he continued. "But I would fain earn money enough, if it were possible, to enable me to get to him without being chargeable to her, and once within reach of him—once near enough to his dwelling-place to know that we need never be many days asunder, I should not fear but that I might earn my living, without being indebted to charity for it. I was always stronger than Edward, you know, Miss Martha, and there is no reason because he lives an idle life, dear fellow, that I should do so too."

"Michael!" she replied, her whole countenance lighted up with the most animated expression of pleasure, "my dear Michael Armstrong! your coming here is certainly the greatest blessing that Heaven could have sent me. I cannot tell you, and you can never know, all I have suffered from believing you were dead, and from *knowing* that I had been the cause of great and terrible suffering to you. And that, too, wholly owing to the trust which you, and your poor mother reposed in me! May you never, my dear boy, know what it is to have a conscience burdened as mine has been. Be very sure that it is worse than any thing you could have suffered at the Deep Valley, Michael! When you see Mary Brotherton tell her that I owned this to you—and perhaps she may think, at last, that she judged me rather more harshly than I deserved."

"If she judged you harshly at all, she was very wrong," replied

Michael, warmly. "People should know, before they judge. Nobody who really knew you, *could* judge you harshly."

"I had rather that kind sentence came from your lips, Michael, than from those of any other human being. If *you* can say it, and mean it to as I am sure you do, who is there living that can have a right to say the contrary? Yet this is not my only pleasure—I happen to have the power—and I bless my poor father for it—of making some little atonement for the years of suffering that I so unwittingly caused you. From the day we were each of us fifteen, we have received an allowance of sixty pounds a year for dress, and though I really never wanted one so much as my sisters, my father, who has ever been a kind father to me, has always insisted upon my having the same, and at the marriage of my two elder sisters, he gave me a hundred pounds each time, that I might be smart. But I have no taste for finery, Michael, it always made me melancholy; so I am very rich—I really do not know how rich, for I have always kept on laying the bank notes that I did not want in a drawer, and I have never counted them. Think if it will not be a pleasure for one now to open that drawer, and give you all that is in it? Oh! with what different feelings shall I go to bed to-night from any I have felt for years past! I am sure there is enough to take you to Italy, or wherever else Miss Brotherton may be gone, and to set you up in some little business into the bargain. Wait here only ten minutes, my dear Michael, and I will return with my treasure—a real treasure now, and for the first time that I ever thought it so!"

Martha had risen from her seat as she spoke, and literally before Michael could recover from his atonishment sufficiently to answer her, she was already at some distance from him. He had by no means settled to his satisfaction the question of whether he ought, or ought nor, to strip the generous Martha of her little hoard when she again appeared. But she looked hurried and out of breath.

"Make haste, Michael, dear Michael!" she said, with much agitation. "For pity's sake let me not be again plunged in all the misery of self-reproach from which I have so recently escaped. Take this parcel, Michael! Nay, never stay to count them! My father has left his room—may have inquired for me—and even now be following me. Bless you,

Michael! Bless you! Go, go, for goodness sake, and leave the country as quickly as possible."

With these words she turned from him, and with a step too rapid for her state of health, and plainly showing her extreme anxiety, she hastily retreated towards the house.

Though after hearing Mr Bell's decided opinion that no further danger was to be feared from Sir Matthew Dowling, Michael would himself have felt not the least desire to run away from him, yet it was impossible not to perceive that Martha was of a different mind, and that for some reason or other she was exceedingly anxious that he should not remain near Dowling Lodge, or, in other words, within her father's reach. Whether she were right, or wrong, in fancying that it was necessary for his safety that he should keep out of the way, he felt that it would be cruel to oppose her; and with the unexamined roll of bank-notes thrust into his coat-pocket, he gave but one farewell look at the retreating drapery of poor Martha, and then with rapid strides, and thoughts so full of the scene which had just passed, that he followed the right path rather mechanically than from judgment, he set off upon his return to the humble lodging he had secured for the night.

XXX

Michael grows rich, and takes a very delightful walk back to Westmorland—His preparations for a longer journey are suddenly stopped—He makes a painful visit, but meets many old acquaintances

THE MORNING'S WALK HAD BEEN a long one, even for Michael Armstrong, and right glad was he to find himself again in the neatly-sanded kitchen of his little inn, with a loaf and cheese before him, of sufficient dimensions to resist any attacks he could make upon them. A moderate proportion of beer, in addition to the solid meal these afforded, refreshed him so effectually that he determined to take his leave of Mr Bell that night, preparatory to setting off on his return to Westmorland on the following morning, in order to bid farewell to his good old master there. On the subject of Martha's bank-notes he meant to be entirely guided by the advice of the clergyman, being equally fearful of offending, or rather of paining their generous owner by refusing to accept them, or of depriving her of what might be hereafter useful, by agreeing to do so.

"I have seen Miss Martha, sir!" were his first words on entering Mr Bell's parlour and both look and accent showed that the interview had been an interesting one. "But, alas! she is greatly altered," he added, restraining with difficulty the tears that rose to his eyes. "I fear she is very ill;—but she was glad—oh! so glad to see me, sir! She has been fretting, poor dear young lady, under the false notion that she had been to blame about me; but, thank Heaven! I think she knows better now, and perhaps when her mind is at ease again she may recover her health. I can't bear to think how pale and thin she is grown, and all about me, to whom she was the best and kindest friend that ever a poor boy had. And see, sir, what she has done now!" continued Michael, drawing forth the roll of notes his pocket. "Here is a large sum of money, I believe. She did not rightly know how much it was herself, she told me, because she had kept on putting by what she did not want, and had never counted how much it came to—and I'm sure I have not counted it either; but whether it is little or much, I don't feel quite certain whether I ought to take it."

Mr Bell smiled at the unusual manner in which the rich-looking, but carelessly-packed roll of paper had passed from one hand to the other. Before he examined the contents he questioned Michael as to what the girl had said to him, on bestowing it, and the young man's faithful answers soon convinced him that there would be little kindness to the self-reproaching Martha in refusing a donation which she evidently considered as an atonement and which would, he doubted not, by its application to Michael's necessities, do more towards healing her wounded mind than any other thing whatever.

"You must not refuse the gift, Michael," said Mr Bell, after hearing his narrative to the end. "I do not wonder, little as she has been to blame in the matter, at her having suffered greatly for all that she innocently made you suffer; nor am I at all surprised since it was in her power to do so, that she should wish to make you this atonement. It comes at a lucky moment, my dear boy, for not only will it enable you to present yourself before Miss Brotherton, without throwing yourself, as you said yesterday, upon her charity but I suspect it may go far in assisting your hopes of entering into some business, which may enable you to support yourself."

Mr Bell then opened the bundle of notes, and found that they amounted to rather more than five hundred pounds; a sum which to Michael, appeared so enormous that he uttered something like a remonstrance against the opinion which advised his appropriating the whole.

"Did you not tell me, sir," he said, "that Sir Matthew Dowling's affairs were not considered to be in so flourishing a state as they had been? And may not this money be wanted by Miss Martha in case she should really become involved in difficulties?"

"I think there is no danger of her wanting it, Michael," returned Mr Bell. "Let what will happen, I have no doubt that Sir Matthew will be able to secure sufficient from the relics of his enormous wealth to maintain his family in easy circumstances. A sum like this, my dear boy, is but a drop in such an ocean."

Michael resisted no longer, and this point being settled, his plan of operations was soon arranged. In deference to Martha's fears for his safety, he decided not to visit his good friend Richard Smithson, at Milford, Mr Bell undertaking to settle the matter of the loan, and moreover to convey to the kind-hearted man the assurances of Michael's well-doing, of his gratitude, and hearty good wishes. The letter from the travellers, which was to settle the happy Michael's road, would probably arrive within a week or two, and Mr Bell recommended that, having paid his farewell visit to Westmorland he should return to Fairly, and there equip himself in such a manner as would be suitable for presenting himself before Miss Brotherton. Mr Bell agreed to take the custody of his treasure, till his return, and with his bundle again on his shoulder, and five pounds in his pocket, Michael set off to walk over the fells and moors he had to traverse, with a lightness of spirit that seemed to strew the deserts with flowers, and made every blast that blew upon him as soft and sweet as the gales of Araby. It was not the least, perhaps, of his pleasures, as he strode sturdily along, to compare his present walk with that which had conducted him from the Deep Valley to Ashleigh, four years before.

The suffering, the terror, and the final agony of that expedition could not come over his mind, however, without throwing a shade over his gladness; but it chastened without obscuring the bright combination of objects that glowed in the prospect before him; and, altogether, it would be difficult to find any walk on record more replete with enjoyment than this of Michael to the humble mountain-home that had so kindly sheltered him.

It was with a very flattering mixture of joy and sorrow that the good statesman and his family accepted Michael's farewell, and listened to his happy hopes; and it was amidst blessings and hearty good wishes that once again he sallied forth to wend his way for the last time over the mountains, and bid a fond and lingering *adieu* to his beloved lakes and tarns. He felt that those had been to him as teachers and preachers, elevating his heart and imagination, and preparing him, more effectually perhaps than any other school could have done, for the different sphere of life in which he now hoped to move.

On reaching Fairly, he found that a letter had arrived from Miss Brotherton, enclosing one to Martha Dowling, which had been forwarded immediately; and which, by what the kind-hearted heiress said to her Fairly friends, seemed to have been written in consequence of the reports which had reached her respecting the failing fortunes of Sir Matthew. Miss Brotherton was at Nice, where it was her purpose to remain for some months. To Nice, then, the thrice happy Michael prepared to go; a respectable wardrobe, and all other necessary equipments were easily procured in the neighbourhood, his place to London taken, and all things ready for his setting off save that he still expected an answer to a very cautiously-worded epistle which he had ventured to address to Martha, informing her that he was setting off for Nice, and that any letter or message she might wish to convey to Miss Brotherton, should be carefully delivered by her faithful humble servant, M. A.

Michael was at breakfast with his kind and hospitable friends, when a lad, bearing great marks of hasty travelling in his appearance, made his way into the room, and with a look that seemed to prophesy eventful tidings if he were but asked for them, delivered a letter to Mr Bell. This proved, however, to be only a blank cover, enclosing one to Michael which was handed to him, while the eyes of his host and hostess fixed themselves with some anxiety on his face. Michael tore open the despatch, and changed colour as he read it. Then, giving an intelligible glance at the messenger who ceased not to wipe his forehead with one arm, while he held his hat squeezed to his side with th other, he said, "I should like to speak to you about this, Mr Bell."

"Go into the kitchen, my lad," said the clergyman, "and get some bread. You shall know when the answer is ready."

Though evidently disappointed at being thus dismissed unquestioned, the boy consoled himself with the hope of a kitchen audience, and making his reverence, retired.

"What in the world have you got there, Michael?" demanded Mr Bell. "Not good news, I am afraid?"

"No, indeed, sir," replied Michael, "very far front it. It is from Miss Martha Dowling, who seems to be in great distress."

"Read it to us, my good fellow, will you? If there is no reason to the contrary."

"What is written here, sir, cannot long be a secret from any body. This is what she says:

"'Dear Michael,

"'Pray come to me at Dowling Lodge directly. There is no longer any danger to be feared from my poor dear father, for he is very, very ill—and I think you can be useful to me, which I am sure you will be if you can. Alas! Michael, you will witness a dreadful scene! My poor father has kept every thing secret to the very last; meaning, I am sure, to prepare his family for it as well as he could. I could not think what it was made him send all my sisters away to Arabella and Harriet. The two little ones, indeed, as well as the three youngest boys, are all at school, so that I am the only child he has left with him, my elder brothers being all away in their different professions. I tell you all this now, Michael, because I shall, I suppose, have no time to say any thing but on necessary business when you come here. Do not delay, I am sure you can be useful to me.

"'In great sorrow, your friend,
"'MARTHA DOWLING.'"

"Poor girl! This is sad indeed!" cried Mr Bell. "I imagine, though she does not explain herself, that her father's affairs are fallen into confusion. Yet I cannot guess what you can do for her. However, you must go immediately, of course; and you had better hire a chaise that no time may be lost. And I would advise you, Michael, to take with you the pocket-book which Mrs Bell packed up for you so carefully last night. I fear that it is but too likely your prediction will be fulfilled already, and that the poor young lady may be glad to have some of her notes returned."

"Thank God! that I was not gone," replied Michael, fervently.

"It will be the greatest pleasure of my life, if I can be useful to her!"

Little time was lost in setting off; and certainly much before his arrival had been hoped for by Martha, Michael, who left his post-chaise at a public-house near the lodge, was walking towards the mansion by the same path in which he had so lately parted from her.

On entering the kitchen, the scene which met his eyes, explained at the very first glance the nature of the business carrying on upon the premises. A number of men were standing about, some few occupied in sticking slips of paper inscribed "Lot No —," upon a variety of articles which appeared to have been collected there for the purpose. Others, with black canvass aprons and paper caps, were coming and going with no very apparent purpose; while another set, with cold meat and beer-flagons before them, sat round a small table in a corner, discoursing upon themes which appeared to occasion them much merriment.

But among all these, there was not one that looked like a servant of the house and taking advantage of the coufusion which seemed to license the freedom, he walked on without speaking to any of them, and determined to trust to his memory for finding the small morning parlour which used to contain all poor Martha's little literary personalties, and in which all his reading and writing lessons had been received.

Neither his recollection nor his conjecture deceived him; he found the apartment he sought, and on opening the door, discovered Martha sitting there. But she was not, as he had hoped to find her, alone. On a sofa placed opposite the windows sat a figure, bolt upright in the middle of it, with a sofa-table before her entirely covered with trinkets, delicate Sèvre china, miniature bronzes, and other valuable nick-nacks. A quantity of cotton-wool lay on the sofa beside her, and her long lean fingers were actively employed in selecting the most precious articles, enveloping them in the wool, and then cramming them into a large basket that stood before her,—sometimes selecting one, either smaller or more precious than the rest, and thrusting it into her pocket or up her sleeve. A large Indian screen was spread before the door, which induced Michael, on hearing a voice that certainly was not that of his friend Martha, to remain unseen long enough to decide whether his entrance would be likely to occasion her any embarrassment.

"I tell you, Martha, that you talk
like a fool."

"I tell you, Martha, that you talk like a fool, and that is what you
always were, and always will be!" said the upright lady, in a shrill voice,
but in a tone that she was endeavouring to reduce to a whisper. "What
can any one of these horrid dirty fellows have with what is mine, I
should like to know? I am not going to be made bankrupt, or sent
to jail, or have my property seized, because your abominable, wicked,
low-born, brutal, treacherous, false father, has been found out, and is
going to be treated as he deserves. As for you, and all the rest of your
family, there is nothing to be said or done, I suppose, but to sit and
just do what you can to get your bread. With such blood as you have
got in your veins, there will be no great harm done if you were all
to go out as housemaids and footmen. The thing happens among low
people continually, if the father gets into distress but I should like to
know who ever heard of a woman of quality, the daughter of an earl,
being treated in the same sort of unceremonious way?"

"But indeed, Lady Clarissa, it will be a great deal worse for my father, if it is found out that his wife has been endeavouring to secrete property." said Martha.

"His wife, indeed! A pretty sort of husband he has made me, hasn't he? Having my noble arms painted on his paltry carriages, and engraven on his plate, not a single ounce of which had been twenty years in his possession; and then, vulgar wretch insisting upon seeing my housekeeper's account, for fear I should save any thing out of the money he allowed me! Pitiful, cheating, brutal, manufacturing savage! But thank Heaven! my slavery is at an end!—To-morrow will see me many a good mile on my way to Scotland! The monsters say I may take my clothes and my money—and my clothes and my money I will take, I promise you, Miss Martha; so I would really advise you to go and collect your own things, and see them put decently. You may be able to sell some of them perhaps, which might be very useful, and that would be spending your time much more profitably, and decently too, than sitting there lecturing me upon what I may, and what I may not take. I shall take every thing that belongs to me, and there's an end of that; and I wish to my heart you would just go away and leave me in peace."

"Did I not know, Lady Clarissa, that my father would suffer for it," said Martha rising, "I would not have troubled you with my remonstrances; but I am certain that you are now occupied in abstracting things that of right belong to my poor father's creditors, and if it is discovered, it may be the means of their refusing his certificate, and he may be thrown into a jail for life."

"And where could he be better, Miss Martha? I am sure I don't know. My belief is that he is mad, or going to be mad, and I don't see but a jail is as comfortable as a mad-house, and as it must be a great deal cheaper, it will suit his circumstances a great deal better. I wish you would go, child, and see if there is such a thing in the house as a basin of soup for my luncheon. I may ring and ring, but there is not a creature that will answer the bell now."

Martha made no reply, but she rose from her chair, and Michael stepped back into the passage, that she might not meet him within hearing of her selfish step-mother.

"You are come, then!" exclaimed the poor girl, on catching sight of him. "This is very kind of you, Michael! If you will walk this way with me—there is nobody in the great drawing-room now—I will explain my reasons for sending for you."

Michael followed her to the well-remembered drawing-room, which had so often witnessed the display of Sir Matthew's munificent charity, by showing him off to all the neighbourhood. The recollection was very hateful to him, yet the right-hearted lad felt a pang as he accompanied his benefactress into this greatly-altered scene of former splendour. The whole house was under preparation for a sale by auction, and nothing could exceed the speaking state of gilded desolation which this fine room exhibited.

"Never mind the confusion, Michael! Just step over these curtains— we can sit down, up in that corner of the room—take care of the mirrors, my dear boy! Surely they have thrown these costly things about more needlessly than was necessary?" said poor Martha, as she led the way rather over, then through the scattered mass of splendid furniture with which the room was strewed.

"It is strange, Michael," she resumed, as soon as they had seated themselves in a clear space of six feet wide, where two chairs were standing near one of the windows,—"It is strange, most strange, that you should be the only person that I could think of to assist my poor father in his misery! You who have suffered so severely from—from his displeasure. But I found out, Michael, that you had a kind, good heart, when you used to talk to me of your mother and poor Teddy. It was that which made me take notice of you then, and it is that which makes me ask for your assistance now."

"And happy and thankful shall I be if I can do you any good, Miss Martha!" replied Michael, eagerly. "I have brought back the notes, all but about twelve pounds, that has been laid out for me. It is a very large sum, Miss Martha, and I trust it will be useful to you."

"I do not want it, my dear boy!" replied Martha, smiling through her tears, "but I am glad to find that I was not mistaken in you. No, Michael! let me still, under all circumstances, have the unspeakable comfort of believing that I have been able to make you some little atonement for all you have gone through from my ill-judged and ignorant advice. You would make no difficulty about keeping what has been accumulated out of my hatred of silks and satins, Michael, if you could guess the extraordinary good it has done me to know that you are alive and well, and less destitute than you would have been, had you never seen me. I thought I was dying, Michael, before your little note reached me; but now, strange to say, spite of all the calamities which have fallen upon my family since, I feel as if I might still live long enough to be useful to my poor father. Alas! Michael, his condition is very dreadful! For some months past, I have perceived a great alteration in him. His memory has failed him, and at times his temper has been so variable that I have seen him violently angry, and very intemperate in his language, one minute, and enduring the insolence of Lady Clarissa, with the meekness of a child, the next. And now—In short, Michael, I greatly fear that his reason is shaken by the misfortunes that have fallen upon him. He has kept all his commercial disasters so completely to himself, that not even his most confidential agents were at all aware of their extent; and I therefore hope that if I can contrive to remove him from this melancholy scene, his mind will be relieved by feeling that the worst is over, and that I may have the exceeding happiness of seeing him restored to reason and to health."

"And in what way then can I be useful to you, my dear Miss Martha? I dare not combat your will, but it seems to me that if his creditors are stripping his house in this way, such a sum as you have put into my hands might he very useful to him," said Michael.

"And so it would, certainly, my good friend, if he had not provided for the exigences of this terrible moment, by having a large sum of ready money in the house, a fact which he has confided to me only," replied Martha. "His marriage with Lady Clarissa," she continued, "has been a greater misfortune to him, Michael, than any losses in his business could possibly be. She has led him a most wretched life—constantly keeping his high spirit in subjection by threatening to bring her brother upon him, if he treated her with any want of respect, and my poor father's reverence for rank and title is such, that he has submitted to her in every thing. But during the terrible fortnight that has passed since the disclosure of his ruin, her conduct has been perfectly frightful—and I feel quite certain that when she has taken herself off to Scotland, which she intends to do to-morrow, my father will feel so greatly relieved, that the very best effects upon his mind may be hoped for from it. What I want you to do for me, Michael, is this: You must procure a post-chaise to be at the Lodge-gates to-night at twelve. The men who are left in charge of the house, get both tired and tipsy before that hour, and will be in bed and asleep; and then I think I shall be able to get my poor father away from all the irritating objects which surround him here. He has been very ill with violent spasms, and confined to his bed for a day or two, which one of the maids tells me is the reason why he has not been more strictly watched. They think he is too ill to get away. But he is greatly better to-day, and though I have persuaded him to remain in bed, I think he has quite lost the complaint, nd will be able to get off if you will do what I desire of you. I know not another being that I could trust. My poor father has spent a great deal of money, and been very liberal to many, but I do not know one whom I do not suspect would be more ready to betray, than to help him, if they saw him endeavouring to get away. His physician, Dr Crockley, a man on whom he has heaped innumerable favours, is, I strongly suspect, acting as a spy upon him and it is because I expect his daily visit presently, that I will not let my father get up. Therefore you see, Michael, there are some difficulties to be encountered. Do you think you could manage to get a chaise to the gates without its being known that it was for him?"

"I am quite sure of it," replied Michael; "for to save time I came hither in a chaise myself, which is now waiting at the public-house to take me back to Fairly. I have only to go and tell the boy that I shall not be able to return before night, in order to have him ready to start at any hour you please."

"To Fairly?" said Martha, musingly. "But it is no matter—he may sleep at the inn there as well as at any other, and the next morning we must make our way to the nearest port where there is a chance of our finding a steam-boat going to France. It will not do at present for my father to remain in the country. When he has got his certificate, he will be safe; but I greatly fear some difficulty about it."

While Martha was thus explaining her hopes and fears, the sound of carriage-wheels was heard slowly approaching by the road which led to the chief entrance, and which passed at no great distance from the window at which they were sitting.

"Here comes Dr Crockley!" she exclaimed; "I am very glad his visit will be over so early. This will give me time for preparation."

But she was mistaken; the equipage she heard approaching was not the recently set-up cab of Dr Crockley, but the donkey-chair of the ever active Mrs Gabberly. Nothing could be much farther from poor Martha's inclination than encountering the prying old woman at this moment; but having hastily told Michael to appear as if he were employed in taking a catalogue of the furniture, for which purpose, paper, pens, and ink lay conveniently ready on one of the marble-slabs, she hurried out into the hall for the purpose of meeting the physician, and attending him as usual to her father—so that the avoiding Mrs Gabberly was impossible.

"Oh, my poor dear Martha! that's you, is it! Well now! you were just the person I wanted to see. But I do wonder you did not get off with your father, poor man! when he made his escape, this morning," said the unchanged little lady.

"I know not what you mean, Mrs Gabberly," replied Martha gravely. "My poor father has been extremely ill, and is at this moment confined to his bed." The old lady gave a wink with one of her little cunning black eyes, and nodding her head very expressively, replied, "Old birds are not caught with chaff, my dear."

"What is it that you mean, Mrs Gabberly—that you do not believe me?" said Martha, indignantly.

"You are very foolish to bawl out in that manner, my dear, with that young fellow that's cataloguing in there, close within hearing. Mind, it is your fault and not mine, if he suspects any thing from your violence."

"You are taking an account of all the looking-glasses, are you not!" said Martha, approaching the drawing-room door and addressing Michael. "You may come into Sir Matthew's room now, if you please. He was asleep when I sent you away just now." Then, turning to Mrs Gabberly, she added—"Perhaps you would be so good as to see my poor

father, Mrs Gabberly? I would not wish you to stay long with him, for
he is very feverish; but I dare say he would take it very kindly if you will
just come in to inquire for him."

Looking a good deal surprised, but accepting the invitation with great
alacrity, Mrs Gabberly began to mount the stairs; exceedingly well pleased
to have an opportunity of procuring so excellent a ticket of admission
to every house in the neighbourhood, as this ocular demonstration of
the actual condition of the fallen knight would furnish. Michael, in
compliance with the order he had received, followed after; and in a few
minutes, found himself once more in the presence of the man under
whose tyranny he had suffered so terribly. But a harder heart than
Michael's might have been softened into forgiveness and forgetfulness
of all former injuries, by the miserable aspect of the wretched man who
lay stretched upon the splendid bed that he could no longer call his
own. His steadfast-minded and affectionate daughter—the only earthly
good that avenging Heaven had left him—entered first, intending to
announce the visit of Mrs Gabberly; but Sir Matthew started up in bed,
and before she could speak, cried out,

"Do not let that devil Crockley come to me, Martha! I will not
see him, I tell you. I have got no pain now; and if I had, don't I know
he would rather give me poison than physic? He is going to lose his
annuity, you know."

"It is Mrs Gabberly, dear papa, just come to ask you how you are," said
Martha, leading the old lady to the bedside. "She will not stay because
you are not well enough to talk; but you will be glad to see her, will
you not?"

"Glad?" said the miserable man, knitting his brows, and throwing
upon her a look of deep aversion. "Don't I know her? Is she not the
town-crier of all the country round? Have I not paid her for it a
hundred times? And do you think I don't know what she is come for
now? Somebody else will pay her now, for bringing them word how the
poor bankrupt Dowling looks."

"Well now, that *is* terrible, to be sure!" exclaimed Mrs Gabberiy. "He
is quite shook in his mind. Do you think he would be outrageous if
I was to feel his pulse, my dear? I should like to prescribe for him—I

should indeed. Poor dear man! His talking about paying me is comical to be sure. Let me feel your pulse, Sir Matthew, shall I?"

Sir Matthew looked so very much as if he would have liked to take her up in his enormous hand and throw her to the further end of the room, that Martha thought it prudent to prevent her nearer approach.

"You have now *seen* my father, Mrs Gabberly," she said with emphasis, "and that, I think, is all that can be necessary for your satisfaction."

"Oh! certainly—it is very satisfactory," she replied, but without appearing to have the slightest intention of leaving the room: for, in truth, it was at that moment the place where, beyond all others, she best liked to be. The downfall of Sir Matthew Dowling was the subject that employed every tongue, and nobody could be so welcome to every drawing-room, and every dining-room too, throughout the neighbourhood, as one who could testify to having seen him, listened to him, and ascertained how he seemed to bear it. It was impossible that any person could have been better qualified for the service than Mrs Gabberly. Willingly would the still brisk little lady have crept under the toilet-table, or the bed itself, rather than have lost so glorious an opportunity; and instead of attending to Martha's repeated assurance that she "had better go now," she began opening sundry physic-vials that stood on a table at the bottom of the bed, smelling some, tasting others, and pronouncing judgment upon all.

"It is quite a mystery to me, my dear, what Dr Crockley can be thinking of, giving such medicines as these to your father," said she. "I see, plainly enough, that he is in a very inflammable and irritable state, and he ought to be put altogether upon the depleting plan." Then putting her finger on her lip, in sign of secrecy, she whispered, "I'll just stay here, Martha, behind the bed-curtains, till Dr Crockley comes, and I think it may be very useful for us to have a little conversation together. I know my poor dear father's method in these cases as well as he did himself, and he was regular bred you know, which is more than we can say of poor dear Dr Crockley."

Exceedingly provoked, Martha now addressed her father, saying, "Mrs Gabberly wishes to stay, papa, till Dr Crockley comes, in order that they may have a consultation about you; but you won't like that, shall you?"

"Like it?" replied the prostrate man, with bitterness, "Oh! dear yes, I shall like it vastly! They are exactly a fitting pair to come together, glowering and gloating round the bed of a ruined neighbour. Let her stay, by all means, Martha, let her stay and watch it all. See, Mrs Gabberly, there is a young auctioneering gentleman come to take an account of the furniture. Isn't it pleasant? I am sure it must do your heart good to see it. Don't go away, young man!" he continued, addressing Michael, who, shocked and disgusted, was making his way towards the door. "Don't go away. Go on, never mind losing a little time, I dare say you will be paid for it all the same, and my dear good neighbour would not enjoy it half so much if she did not see something of the kind going on."

"Oh, dear oh, dear! quite wild and wandering! Isn't he?—Calling Crockley and me a pair, too! As if we ever thought of such a thing! I am sure, for one, I can answer for it that I never did.—His doll of a wife, you know, hasn't been dead above a year, and I've no notion of such quick work, it is quite indecent, I think. Good gracious me, now!" she continued, catching Sir Matthew's fierce eye fixed upon her with a mixture of hatred and bitter irony; "what have I said!—I'll bet a guinea he fancies I mean something about his marrying himself up, all in such a hurry with Lady Clarissa."

"Lady Clarissa!" cried the knight in a loud voice. "That's right! I had very nearly forgotten her ladyship. Go to her this moment, Martha—tell her to come here. Is she not my wife—bone of my bone—of my flesh? Is she not, Mrs Gabberly? And shall she not come hither and share with me the delight of seeing a broker taking of my furniture, and a dear good soul like you looking on? Go, Martha, go when I tell you, and bring the right honourable Lady Clarissa Dowling here."

"I am quite certain she won't come, papa," said Martha, leaning down, and whispering in his ear. "So don't make me go to her."

"But she *shall*, though!" shouted Sir Matthew, "even if I go down, and fetch her myself. My dear Mrs Gabberly, my sweet Mrs Gabberly—will you have the great condescension to go for her? You used to run about, if I did but hold up my finger, you know—and you would not be so ungenerous as to refuse now, merely because I am a bankrupt! Go to my Lady Clarissa, if you please, sweet Mrs Gabberly, and tell her that as she is a daughter of the noble house of Highlandloch, I wish, before we part, to give her a parting token of remembrance. She knows that I wear a magnificent diamond ring, Mrs Gabberly, and you may just hint to her, if you please, that nothing has been taken off my body yet. I do assure you it will be a very pretty touching scene for you to witness, and talk about. It will indeed. I am quite determined to have a sentimental parting; and as she has told me that she means to set off to-morrow, this will be just the right time for it—won't it, Mrs Gabberly?"

Perfectly well disposed to execute the commission, and quite as desirous as Sir Matthew could be that the proud poor lady who had ever treated her with haughty coldness, should be properly humbled, she darted towards the door, in order to perform her errand; but Martha remembering the manner in which she had left her step-mother engaged, stepped forward to prevent her, quietly saying, "If my father wishes to see his wife, Mrs Gabberly, I can go for her, without troubling you—and I really wish you would permit me to lead you down stairs to your donkey-chair, at the same time—I am sure you must be aware that papa is not in a state to bear seeing company."

"You are quite right, my dear, quite right, indeed—Sir Matthew is looking sadly wild and feverish, and I should say that nobody whatever but the doctor and his own family ought to see him. Of course I suppose it would not be very convenient to hire attendants now, for these sort of people, I am sorry to say, always insist upon ready money, which is a cruel thing under such circumstances. But so it is, and therefore it follows that you and Lady Clarissa must be the chief nurses."

"Cetainly, ma'am, it will be his own family who will wish to attend to him. And therefore, if you please, I will take you down stairs, and see you to your carriage."

"Me! my dear!" cried Mrs Gabberly, in the shrillest possible tone. "Surely, you cannot mean to call such an old friend as I am, company? No, no, my dear Martha. Don't think me such a brute! I would not leave you just yet, for the whole world! You shall go yourself, my dear, if you will, and bring her ladyship up. I will stay here as quiet as a mouse, and watch by your poor papa. But perhaps it might be as well to desire that young man to finish with his scribbling, and get out of the room. He must have gone over every thing by this time, mustn't he?"

"I will have her right honourable ladyship here before that fellow stirs a step, Martha. Do you hear me? That's more than half the fun," cried Sir Matthew, bursting into a shout of laughter. "Doesn't she know our kind, clever, observing, neighbour, who is come here so thoughtfully, just to look about her a little? Doesn't she know her, almost as well as I do? And won't she enjoy thinking what a pleasant description dear Mrs Gabberly will be able to give of my Lord Highlandloch's sweet daughter watching the broker, and seeing that he sets every thing down fair?"

Thankful was Martha that the supposed broker was one who could not in reality add to the horror of the scene. She turned to him as she left the room, saying, "You had better remain here, if you please, till I return," upon which he modestly ensconced himself in a distant corner of the room, and resting his paper upon acommode, continued, as he stood, to scribble upon it.

Quite certain that it would be impossible to get rid of Mrs Gabberly till her father's summons to his proud wife had been obeyed, and greatly more anxious to clear his room of this troublesome guest, than to spare the feelings of her ladyship, Martha entered the little sitting-room, determined to deliver the message concerning the diamond-ring, if she could not prevail without it. She found Lady Clarissa in the act of finishing the packing of her basket, by laying on the top of it sundry light articles of female attire, very cleverly calculated to make the whole pass under the general description of wearing-apparel, which the courtesy of the law permits to be removed by all persons in the unfortunate situation of her ladyship.

"Now I hope you will cease your impertinent preaching, Miss Martha," she said, as the pale and agitated young woman entered the room. "Unless every separate nightcap and frill are to be examined one by one by these brutes, I conceive no objection can be made to this package. Gather up the cotton-wool, and poke it somewhere out of sight directly." Martha obediently set herself to collect the scattered fragments of the suspicious-looking wool, but as she did so, said, "My father wishes to see you, Lady Clarissa."

"Insolent wretch!" exclaimed her ladyship, pausing in the act of collecting various little articles for which she had not found room in the basket, "have you the audacity to bring me this as a message?"

"My father says, Lady Clarissa, that as you are going to leave him to-morrow, he should wish to see you once more," replied Martha.

"Monster!" screamed Lady Clarissa stamping her foot upon the floor, "he, see me again? he, dare to lift his bankrupt eyes upon the noble woman he has so basely injured?—Tell him, you bold messenger, who fear not to face the descendant of a dozen earls to convey to her the words of a bankrupt cotton-spinner, tell him, that the only atonement he can make, is TO DIE. Tell him this from me!—and may the ostentatious settlement his unprincipled pride made on me, excuse me in some degree in the eyes of my noble brother, for the degradation I brought upon him by accepting it!" These last words were uttered with clasped hands, raised eyes, fervent accents, and all other indications of uttering a prayer.

Indignant and disgusted, Martha felt no scruple in employing the means her father had given her for obtaining the interview he desired, and quietly said in reply to this burst, "My father stated that his motive for asking to see you, Lady Clarissa, proceeded from his wish to present to you, as a parting gift, the diamond ring which he wears on his ring hand."

The effect of these words was as sudden as that produced by the magic touch of a hand employed in turning off gas.

"That indeed is a most natural wish! Unhappy, guilty man! I can well believe that had he the crown jewels at command, he would deem them all too poor an offering to atone for the offence he has committed against me! I thank God, Martha Dowling, that my noble blood never taught me to forget that I am a Christian! There are many women, believe me there are, of less exalted rank than myself, who would not deign to obey such a summons. But I feel what my duties are, and I shall nerve my courage to perform them. Come with me to my dressing-room, Martha, carry that basket for me, and then I will go with you to the bedside of Sir Matthew."

Martha then attempted to obey, but the basket was too heavy for her to carry, and she set it down again, declaring that the task was beyond her strength.

"A tolerably good joke that," said Lady Clarissa, endeavouring to laugh, "considering your origin; but this is the last day of such pleasant jestings, and therefore I must bear it with good humour, I suppose. Then applying her own much stronger hand, she lifted her treasure, and was stalking off with it; but stopped short ere she reached the door, saying, "No, I will stay here while you go and fetch my faithful Mistress Saunderson. She enters into all my feelings! thank God! and is as strong as a Highland pony into the bargain." Having obediently performed this commission, and brought back the faithful Scotch waiting-woman, who had adhered very steadfastly to her mistress through all the vicissitudes of her fortune, Martha at length succeeded in marshalling the Lady Clarissa Dowling into the bedroom of her husband.

No signet-ring ever made a deeper impression on wax, than the diamond one of Sir Matthew had done on the memory of his noble wife; and her first glance, as she entered the room, was directed to the hand which lay on the bedclothes, that she might see if it had been already removed; but no! there it sparkled still, and with a gentler aspect than she had been seen to wear since the tremendous hour when the declension of Sir Matthew, from the richest commoner in the county into a bankrupt, had been announced to her, she said,

"You wish to see me. Sir Matthew—Martha says you wish to see me."

"Yes, my beloved!" replied the knight. "I do wish to see you. Angelic sweetness! How can I do otherwise? Look at yourself in the mirror, most beautiful Clarissa? Look in the mirror before that broker there carries it off, and tell me if you think it possible that any man could bear to part with so much beauty, without having one final gaze upon it? And see, my dear, here is your amiable neighbour, Mrs Gabberly! Is it not kind of her to leave all other visitings, that she may come to nestle herself here, among the very brokers, in the very centre of our misery? It is so heavenly-minded of her, isn't it? I guessed indeed that one great reason for her making such a tremendous sacrifice was the hope of edification from beholding the christian spirit with which your ladyship bears your ladyship's overthrow; and besides her own improvement from it, she wishes to have it in her power to describe it to the whole neighbourhood. Very right of her, isn't it, my dear? And that is the reason why I sent for you."

In general the nose of Lady Clarissa greatly outblushed her cheeks, which had more of the jonquil than the rose in them; but now, from the tip of her high forehead, to that of her long chin, she became crimson; and but from the remarkable length of her throat, which seemed to rear itself in defiance of such danger, a fit of apoplexy might have been expected.

"Begone! you vulgar gossip-picker!" she cried, turning in uncontrollable rage upon the terrified little woman, "and tell the contemptible neighbourhood through which you are going to crawl in your donkey-cart, like a snail in his shell, leaving your slime as you go, tell them all, from me, that the best consolation under my remorse at having forgotten my own dignity by condescending to hold a place among them, arises from being released from the degradation of associating with so contemptible a being as yourself, and all who are capable of listening to you!" And having uttered these words in a piercing voice, she rushed to the door, threw it with great violence wide open, and so left it, as she paced, with rapid but tragic strides, to the shelter of her own boudoir, and the sympathy of Mistress Saunderson.

It was, perhaps, because the door was open, and that he knew the sound would follow her, that Sir Matthew burst into the most violent shout of laughter that ever made itself heard from mortal lungs; it terrified Martha, made Michael Armstrong shudder, and caused Mrs Gabberly herself to wish she were any where else, notwithstanding the very valuable information this extraordinary scene would enable her to communicate. Long did this frightful laugh continue, and when strength seemed to fail, and the boisterous merriment could be sustained no longer, a vehement and reiterated hissing followed, which at length ended in such complete exhaustion that Sir Matthew fell back pale, and apparently motionless, upon his pillow

"Mrs Gabberly," said Martha, "I must beg you to leave us now. You must perceive that my poor father ought to be alone. It is very important—fearfully important, I am afraid—that he should be kept perfectly quiet! Give me leave to wish you good morning."

"Begone, you vulgar gossip-picker!"

"I must say that it does seem very odd in you, Miss Martha, to persist in calling me *company*. Good gracious! To think of the terms on which I have always been in this house before your poor papa's unfortunate marriage! I cannot and I will not leave you in such a condition. It would be perfectly monstrous, and every body would call me a brute for it. Till Dr Crockley has been here, I really neither can nor will go. I am quite determined that I will hear what he says about him."

"Let her stay," said Sir Matthew, in a hollow whisper, which proved that he was neither asleep nor dead, though his closed eyes, and ghastly countenance, might have been mistaken for one state or the other

Martha went to him, took his hand, wiped the profuse perspiration from his brow, and then placing herself in a chair beside him, continued to his altered countenance, alike unmindful as it seemed of the presence of Mrs Gabberly, or that of Michael either.

The lady, perfectly contented to be thus quietly established as a looker-on determined, for the present, neither to move nor speak, lest she might lose the valued privilege thereby; but Michael became so conscious of the awkwardness of his situation, and so fearful lest Martha, from forgetting him, might get into a scrape likewise, that he ventured to approach the foot of the bed on tiptoe, merely for the purpose of recalling himself to her recollection, and then, on seeing her start at the sight of him, he said in a whisper, "I suppose I had better go down stairs now, Miss Martha?"

Martha, in reply to this, nodded affirmatively, and in the same low tone added, "I shall have other business to speak to you about. Do not go away till you have seen me."

Michael's eyes were naturally turned to Martha while this passed but when he withdrew them, and was about to make his retreat, he caught the large, wide open, wild-looking eyes of Sir Matthew fixed earnestly upon him. The young man involuntarily dropped his eyelids, for the gaze was a frightful one, and turned to leave the room.

"Stay!" roared a hoarse but loud and stunning voice from the bed. "Stay! devil! demon! hell-bird! what do you come here for? Cowardly blackguard! Do you think I do not know you? You never dared to come till it was too late for me to hold you! I have heard of you purring round the place weeks ago. But you escaped me then, base runaway! What do you come spying here for? Did you think I should not know ye? Did you think I should forget those d—d hypocritical eyes, and that hateful curly hair, of the devil's own colour? No, my pretty 'prentice, I have not forgotten your crocodile looks, and never shall. I suppose you thought you should bring me to repentance by sending home word that you were dead. Was that it, eh?"

"I am able now, Sir Matthew, to pay for leaving the mill before my time, and I am quite ready to do it, if you please," replied Michael, gently. But he spoke to one who heard him not. Sir Matthew had a neck as short and thick as that of his lady was long and thin. His last interview with her had not been a salutary one for a man in his state of mind and body; and the subsequent discovery of Michael, of whose visit to the factory he had heard from Parsons, and at whose escape he expressed the most unbridled rage, accelerated symptoms which had before threatened him, and sent such a rush of blood to the brain as instantly produced apoplexy, and left him totally deprived of sense and motion.

Martha, whose eyes were fixed upon him, uttered a fearful shriek, and threw herself on the body, believing that he was dead. But Mrs Gabberly knew better. She had practised too long as an amateur not to know a fit of apoplexy when she saw it, and promptly exclaimed, "Get away, Martha! Get off of him, child! He is not dead, I tell you, and, if we could but bleed him, he would open his eyes again fast enough."

With the rapidity of lightning poor Martha obeyed. She with drew herself from the bed, endeavoured to raise her father in her arms, and, by the help of Michael, succeeded. She then bared his arm, bound her own waist-belt tightly round it, and with unshrinking courage had thrust a sharp penknife which she drew from her pocket into a vein, before the skilful lady who had prescribed the measure had half recovered her astonishment on perceiving that the poor girl had conceived the project of putting it into immediate execution.

The old adage that "where there is a will, there is a way," was never better illustrated than by this act of the tender-hearted and invalided Martha. She felt that her father's life hung on the promptness with which the operation was performed; she felt too, that if she shrunk from it, there was no one else who would perform it, and totally forgetful of herself and her own feelings conquered the rebellious weakness that would have held her hand, and did what two minutes before she would have believed it utterly impossible she could have done. The result did honour to the skill of Mrs Gabberly. The lazy current flowed, though reluctantly. Sir Matthew opened his large eyes, rolled them from side to side, heaved a deep and heavy sigh, and presently attempted to speak, but this was beyond his power.

"What more should be done?" said the pale, and now trembling Martha, turning towards Mrs Gabberly.

"Why now, my dear, you must just let him alone for a little bit," replied the physician by hereditary right. "Well now!" she added, "Wasn't it a blessing that I was here? If I had not staid, he would have been as dead as mutton by this time."

XXXI

*A friendly consultation—A dangerous embassy—Lady
Clarissa receives some disagreeable intelligence—An awkward
contest—Unpleasant visions—A fitting termination to
the confidential union between master and man*

SUCH WAS THE STATE OF affairs in the bedroom of Sir Matthew
Dowling when Dr Crockley entered it. Were all the words which
Mrs Gabberly then uttered in explanation of what she had done, why
she had done it, and how her doings had answered, to be written
down here, my waning pages would hardly suffice to contain them. Dr
Crockley nodded, winked, approved, and applauded a great deal, joked a
little, and finally felt the patient's pulse, observing at the same time that
it was necessary at any rate to bring him round sufficiently to get a little
talk on business out of him, before he popped off for good and all.

"Very right and proper if you can manage it, doctor," sagaciously
observed Mrs Gabberly. "But you may depend upon it, that—" and here
she whispered something, that it was especially intended Martha should
be neither the better nor the worse for. The doctor nodded and winked,
and nodded again; and then turning to the poor girl who was not only
the one who alone in that presence cared any thing for the prostrate
millocrat, but the one of all created beings who would alone have felt
his death to be a cause of mourning. Dr Crockley turned to her, and
with very little of even the external decency of sympathy said, "Do you
think you can manage to get some mustard, my dear, out of the clutches
of the bailiffs?—beeause that is what we want here."

Without answering, Martha moved towards the door; and Michael,
not conceiving that the physician's words were but a brutal jest, and

fancying that Martha might really have to petition those who now held authority in the household for the article wanted, stepped after her, to request that he might execute the commission in her place.

"You shall come down with me, Michael," she replied, "and I doubt not you will be able to procure what we want without difficulty. But alas! Michael, it will avail nothing—I am sure by their whispering, that they both know it will avail nothing! Nevertheless it shall be tried. But is it not dreadful that of all his numerous family there should be only one to receive his dying breath? O God!" she added with clasped hands and streaming eyes, "if it be a jadgment, let it atone for all that has been wrong! For surely it is a heavy one!"

On reaching the hall, the pitying Michael, who in the sufferings of his friend forgot all the cruelty of his enemy, insisted upon going alone into the thronged and noisy offices, while she sat down to wait for his return. He did his errand promptly, and was by her side again in a minute or two; but he found that she had left the chair on which he had placed her, and was now pacing up and down the hall in violent agitation.

"I am overpowered, I am borne down by all this horror—this deep and bitter grief!" she exclaimed. "And there is not a single human being near me, but your ill-used self, Michael, from whom I am likely to find any real kindness! The conduct of all with whom I have had intercourse since my poor father's distresses came upon him, has been such as to make me wish rather to shun, than seek them at this awful moment, yet I want some one to tell me how I ought to act. I know that fearful man Parsons, who is greatly in his confidence, had business of importance to settle with him; for again and again my father has said to me, since the execution has been in the house, that let what would happen, he must find time to speak to him. Ought I not then to send to him in this extremity?"

"Would to Heaven I were fitter to advise you, my dear Miss Martha!" replied Michael, with equal respect and tenderness. "Certainly if such were your father's words, it is very right to remember them. Shall I go to the factory and summon Mr Parsons hither?"

"Oh! It is hateful to me," replied poor Martha, "to call such a being to his deathbed! But it may be that the interests of others are at stake, and when I recall my father's earnestness as he spoke of the necessity of seeing him, I tremble at the idea of disobeying him. Go then, Michael! hasten to the factory, and tell this man that his master is very ill, but that if he recovers his senses and his speech, it is probable he may wish to speak to him."

Michael lost no time in obeying her; and on reaching the mills found the superintendent, as usual, at his post. At the first glance he did not recognise the messenger, for the appearance of the young man was greatly changed by the style of equipment which, under the advice of Mr Bell, had been provided for him. No sooner did Michael speak, however, than the man started, as if he had been shot.

"Sir Matthew send *you*?" he exclaimed, "what mountebank tricks are you got at now, you young villain? What! did you think that this fine toggery could bamboozle me? Has it really bamboozled him? Have you, faith and troth, contrived to pass yourself off upon your dearly-beloved benefactor as a gentleman of fashion and fortune who was come to make him a visit of condolence upon his misfortunes? A capital fellow, ain't you? or, perhaps, my nice young grandee, you fancy his grinders are drawn, and that he can't, or won't, maybe, have any thing to do, now that he has fallen into trouble, with putting such an elegant young gentleman to inconvenience? Is that it? But it is just possible that other people may be more at leisure. Who knows?"

"Never mind me now, Mr Parsons," replied Michael, utterly indifferent, at that moment, to any thing, and every thing, that his old enemy might attempt for the purpose of annoying him. "Never think of me or my affairs at such a time as this. You have given me no opportunity to speak, or you would have understood that it was not Sir Matthew who sent me here, but his daughter. Sir Matthew was too ill when I left the house, to know any thing about it; but Miss Martha thinks that, if he recovers his speech and senses, he may wish to see to you."

"Like enough!" replied the superintendent with a sneer. "Sir Matthew's troubles have nowise changed his nature. The young lady is quite right: but I shouldn't have thought as he'd have told her any thing about it, either. Not but what she might approve the job, too, if she had got any spirit in her. But she is but a poor, puling sort of a cretur, much as she was when she used to cosset you, my beautiful master runaway apprentice. However, never mind that now, as you say, my pretty master; there's a time for all things. You may just step in here while I change my coat. It bean't the first time as you have entered this pleasant building, Master Mike, is it?"

Michael was going to obey him; but, at the moment he was about to pass the threshold, something in the eye of the superintendent made him pause. He recollected full well the ready lock of that once hated door; and it struck him, as by no means impossible, that his old acquaintance might turn it upon him, if he put it in his power to do so.

Fears for his own personal safety, he certainly had none, being quite aware that he was no longer in danger of being kidnapped as heretofore; but the idea of Martha being left, at this her utmost need, in want of any little service he could afford, was quite enough to make him cautious, and with something of an involuntary smile, he stepped back, saying, "There is no occasion for me to wait for you, Mr Parsons; I have delivered my message, and you may obey it or not, as you please. At any rate, you cannot want me to show you the way to Dowling Lodge." And so saying, he turned round, and walked out of the yard.

"Pestilent young viper!" muttered the superintendent between his closed teeth. "That I should live to see him strut off before me in that fashion! But I'll have a try if I can't plague him yet. Fool that I was, when I had him snug by myself on Ridgetop Moor, not to give him one farewell thrashing with the horsewhip! If I had put out a joint two, it would have been no great matter; and then I should have been spared the d—d sight of him now, marching off—hang him! like a peacock before me! As to changing my coat, that's fudge. People don't trouble themselves to change their coats, when they are going to pay their compliments to an apoplectic bankrupt."

Having fairly got beyond all the bolts and bars immediately within the jurisdiction of Mr Parsons, Michael slackened his pace, being rather inclined to have the society of his former tyrant, than not. "Sir Matthew appears to be in a very dangerous state, Mr Parsons," said he, as soon as the sulky superintendent came up to him.

"Perhaps your right honourable greatness has been studying medicine, since I had the pleasure of taking that little drive with you into Derbyshire?"

"I have studied many things since that time, Mr Parsons," replied Michael, laughing; "and one is the nature and use of locks."

The tone in which this was answered was so brutal, that the young man, rather from disgust than anger, walked on faster than his foe could follow him; and reaching the house some minutes before him, made his way again without ceremony—for it was no time for it—into the apartment of Sir Matthew. A considerable change had taken place in the condition of the patient since he left it. The cataplasms had so far succeeded as to restore animation and consciousness: Sir Matthew, still surrounded by Martha, Mrs Gabberly, and the doctor, was gazing upon them with widely-opened eyes, which, though wild and wandering in expression, were evidently not devoid of speculation. Michael had entered very gently, but not without being heard by the sick man; for he turned his eyes full upon him as he approached. The sight of him, however, no longer seemed to produce any emotion; for after looking quietly at him for a moment, Sir Matthew turned his gaze upon Mrs Gabberly, who from being in the act of leaning over him, brought herself particularly within his sight.

"Is Parsons come?" said Martha in a whisper.

"He must be in the hall by this time," replied Michael: "shall I tell him to come up?"

"My dear father has not yet spoken," she said; "but, perhaps, he may understand me.—Parsons is here, papa," she added, taking her father's hand, and leaning over him— "should you like to see him?"

"He is in London, my dear," replied the knight very distinctly.

"Thank God!" exclaimed Martha, tenderly kissing him—"Thank God! His speech is not in the least affected!"

"Rather wandering, though," said Dr Crockley, winking his eye at Mrs Gabberly.

"I should say, bleed him again, if you want to get any thing out of him;" observed Mrs Gabberly, looking sagaciously at the doctor.

"Perhaps I may, in an hour or two," he replied, applying his finger to the patient's pulse.

Sir Matthew fixed his eyes upon him, and laughed a horrid, rattling, ghastly sort of laugh, that seemed to come from his throat. "You haven't quite done with me yet, have you, Crockley?" said he.

"Done with you, my dear friend? God forbid!" replied the physician, rather startled at the apparently healthy state of his patient's intellect, and affectionately smoothing his pillows, and settling the bedclothes about him.

"Would you like to see Parsons, dear papa?" said Martha, gently, and again bending over him.

"Oh, yes!" he replied eagerly; "I'll see Parsons now, directly—I should be very sorry not to see Parsons. I may live, or I may die, you know; but I must see Parsons."

Martha immediately left the room, intending to explain to the superintendent, before she brought him into it, the state in which her father lay, and the necessity of receiving any orders he might wish to give, with as little disturbance to him as possible. On reaching the hill, however, she saw him not, and was on the point of returning up stairs to inquire of Michael where he had left him, when she caught the sound of his voice from Sir Matthew's study. On entering this ropm she perceived not only Mr Parsons but Lady Clarissa, who, standing before the commode in which, as she happened to know, her husband was accustomed to keep papers of importance, as well as money, appeared to have been very assiduously examining its contents; for every recess had evidently been visited, and, as one of her hands was tightly clutched over a pocket-book, it seemed that her researchs had not been wholly in vain, and that she had not privately obtained possession of his keys for nothing.

"I was sent for, my lady," said Parsons, apparently replying to some question of her ladyship's, which, to judge by her angry frown, and the vexed expression of her countenance, had not been a civil one.

"My father wishes to see Mr Parsons directly," said Martha.

"And by your ladyship's leave I must take that green pocket-book with me," said Parsons.

"What pocket-book, you rude fellow?" replied Lady Clarissa, indignantly.

"That one as your ladyship now holds in your left hand," replied the confidential superintendent.

"I wonder, sirrah, that you do not ask me to give you the rings off my fingers!" cried the angry mistress of the mansion. "Go to your master, fellow, if has has sent for you, and I shall go too. So you need not trouble yourself about the pocket-book."

And with these words she pushed past both Martha and Mr Parsons, preceding them to the sick man's chamber. By the time they entered it his eyes were again closed, but he appeared to breathe without difficulty, though rather more audibly than usual, and Martha fancied that he was asleep.

"Hush!" said she. "Do not disturb him. He is sleeping."

Dr Crockley and Mrs Gabberly had withdrawn to a window, and were evidently in consultation; but whether on the symptoms of apoplexy, or bankruptcy, might be doubtful. Michael, however, was still close beside the bed, and in answer to Martha's observation shook his head, saying, "No! not asleep."

"Then he'll manage to hear what I've got to say to him," said Parsons, advancing, and throwing a glance of spiteful vengeance at Lady Clarissa, "because it is just what he wants to know."

At the sound of Parsons's voice Sir Matthew opened his eyes, and made an effort to raise himself, but this was beyond his power, and it was only by being lifted with as little effort as possible on his own pillow, as if he were already dead, that he was placed in the attitude he seemed to desire, and in which he was supported by pillows, aud by the arms of poor Martha, who had placed herself on the bolster behind him.

It was a frightful and awful expression which then took possession of his sunken features, nevertheless a hateful sort of smile made part of it.

"Parsons! that's you, isn't it? That's Parsons that stands there?" he said, directing his misty eyes full upon the superintendent.

"Yes, Sir Matthew, 'tis me," replied the man.

"Have you done my bidding, Parsons?" demanded the knight, with a sort of gasping which seemed to threaten that his breath was about to leave him.

"Yes, Sir Matthew, it's all regularly made out," replied Parsons, "nobody can mistake now about times or dates in any way."

"And isn't that the Honourable Lady Clarissa?" said the sick man, directing his eyes towards her.

"Yes, Sir Matthew," replied Parsons, with something like a titter.

"Then—then—then," panted the dying man, "let her ladyship know what was the last business that I gave you instructions about."

"A very fitting business for an honourable gentleman to attend to, when his affairs are in confusion, and he not in an over good state of health," replied the confidential servant, turning himself round, so as exactly to face her ladyship. "No less a matter than restoring three good thousand pounds a year, for ever, towards clearing scores with his creditors."

Now three thousand pounds a year was exactly the sum, for the settlement of which upon herself, a daughter of the noble house of Highlandloch had condescended to assume the name of Dowling, and the mention of the often-meditated sum roused her ladyship's attention so effectually that her face involuntarily protruded itself beyond her body, till her nose very nearly reached that of the individual who was addressing her.

"Go on!" said Sir Matthew, positively chuckling, though his chin dropped on his chest as he spoke.

"Well then," resumed Parsons, leering aside at Dr Crockley, who with Mrs Gabberly had drawn near to listen to this very interesting disclosure,—"well then, justice is justice; and Sir Matthew, let him die when he will, won't have it upon his conscience that he defrauded his creditors to make a settlement upon any lady in the land, gentle or simple; because you see he has left proof, plain and clear, that he had committed more than one act of bankruptcy before he made the settlement upon her ladyship, and for that good and excellent reason her ladyship will have no right to one single penny that he leaves behind him; and that is a comfort to an honest man like me, who likes to see justice done to high and low."

"Villain!" screamed Lady Clarissa, "it is false!"

"No, no, no, no!" issued from the pillows, in a voice that shook with ghastly laughter. "True, all true; and now she may go to Scotland."

"Just ask her to give you your green pocket-book, Sir Matthew, before she goes," said Parsons, grinning. "I saw her ladyship take it out of your bureau, and if she will be pleased to open her hand, I think it will tumble out of it."

With a look of inexpressible rage, Lady Clarissa turned away from him and made towards the door.

"Stop her, Crockley!" cried Sir Matthew, feebly, adding with panting difficulty, "and—you—shall—have—it."

Dr Crockley had a great respect for the peerage, and would, beyond all question, have preferred snatching a pocket-book from nine hundred and ninety-nine untitled ladies in succession, rather than from Lady Clarissa; but he felt that this was no moment for ceremony, and obeying what was very likely to be the last behest of his patron, he rolled his fat person after her with extraordinary muscular exertion, and grasping the lady's robe with one hand, seized on her rigidly clenched fist with the other, in such a sort, that, according to the prophecy of Mr Parsons, the green pocket-book dropped out of it.

Unfortunately, however, the attitude in which this feat was performed, was one which could not be retained by the ill-balanced person of the doctor, after the supporting form of the lady on whom he had thrown himself had escaped from his grasp, and, struggling with as much anxious care as Cæsar to fall well (*i.e.* upon the pocket-book), he measured his length upon the ground.

Parsons, though certainly not hoping for so lucky an accident, had, with the same sort of instinct which brings the crow beside a sickly sheep, followed closely the retreating steps of her ladyship, and adroitly jerking the coveted pocket-book with his foot, so that it should escape the being buried under the stumbling physician, prepared himself to dip and catch it. But the success of the manœuvre was less perfect than its ingenuity deserved; for ere his tall rigid person had bent itself sufficiently for him to reach the ground, Mrs Gabberly, who had become one of the group at the same instant with Dr Crockley, was in possession of it, and ere the prostrate Crockley or the stooping Parsons could raise their eyes, the prize had dropped into the deepest recesses of a prodigious pocket, which reached nearly to the bottom of her little petticoat.

It is probable that both inquiry and search might have been instituted in consequence of this, had not the condition of the patient at that moment rendered it impossible. Sir Matthew's ghastly eyes had fixed themselves on Lady Clarissa during the foregoing scene, but as if though they had still the power of discerning objects, they had lost that of moving after them, he appeared to lose sight of her as she approached the door, and the heavy orbs seemed seeking for something on which to rest themselves without any change of position. It chanced that Michael, who, quite aware that the last moments of Sir Matthew were approaching, determined not to leave the premises till he had learned the wishes and intentions of Martha, was at that moment moving from the corner he had occupied near a window, not within sight of the bed, to a table exactly at the foot of it, on which was placed a *flacon* of Cologne water, which poor Martha, almost exhausted by the painful attitude necessary to sustain the pillows, had made him a sign to get for her. This movement brought him within the range of Sir Matthew eyes, and something in his aspect as he cautiously bent to take the bottle, or else the thick-coming fancies of a brain diseased, though not paralyzed, suddenly produced a terrible effect upon the dying man, and he uttered a cry so harsh and terrible as to constrain the attention even of the preoccupied group at the door.

"There's a dead body walking about the room!" he ejaculated in an unnatural and frightful accent. "He is come for me! and I must go!" The shriek which followed these words was terrible. In a minute or two he spoke again, but almost in a whisper. "One? No!—it is not one, it is five hundred! Take them!—take them away from me, I tell you! They are all dirty, beastly factory-children. Their arms and legs are all broken and smashed, and hanging by bits of skin. Take them away, I tell you, Crockley! Their horrid joints will drop upon me! They are dangling and loose, I tell you!" and then again he shouted with so fearful a cry, that even Parsons pressed him hands upon his ears to save them from the sound.

"Calm him! Calm him!" cried the trembling Martha. "Can you not give him something that may still this dreadful agony, Doctor Crockley?"

"It is not a very easy symptom to master, Miss Martha," replied the physician drily. "However, it is not likely that it will last long. All the life that's left is just about the heart and brain, which is always unlucky if there happens to be any thing particular upon the mind."

"Parsons!" cried the dying man, again raising his voice, but without looking towards the person he addressed. "Parsons! are you not ashamed of yourself to turn the whole set of them out upon me at once in this way? You that have paid, and bribed, and tipped so often! Rascal! Take them off me, I tell you! Do you mean that they shall stifle me? They will stifle me!—they will, they will. I cannot breathe for them! Parsons!—I tell you they will stifle me!"

"Papa! my dear, dear papa!" cried Martha, bending forward till her cheek touched that of her father. "Compose yourself! It is only that you are unwell and fancy things. There are no children here, papa, but your own Martha."

Her tender caresses, and her gentle voice together, seemed to reach, and quiet for a moment his wandering intellect. He made an effort to turn his head towards her, but that was impossible; and Michael, who had, upon his first frightful cry, removed himself to the head of the bed, where the eye of the wretched man could not reach, silently offered to take Martha's place, that she might station herself where it could. She quickly understood him, and in a moment stood where that dying eye could gaze upon her. His hand, with its glittering ring, still lay upon the bed; she took it in hers, and fondly chafed and kissed it. But it was stiff and cold as marble!

"Father! dearest father!" she said, "speak one word to me!" But was too late; his lips never opened more. For some hours longer he continued to breathe, but, on again feeling his pulse, Dr Crockley declared that its faint pulsations must inevitably cease before night.

"I suppose your old servant Betty Parker is still in the house, Miss Martha?" said he. The poor girl bowed an affirmative, but had no power to speak.

"Well, then," said the doctor, "I should recommend that you should put her to sit here; it is no good for any of us to stay any longer, for it's all over just as much as if he was already in his coffin. You had better go away, and see what you can pack up to get off with, Miss Martha, that's all that is left to be done, as far as I can see. Come, Mrs Gabberly," he added, "I have got a friendly word or two to say to you, so your boy shall mount my pony and I'll drive your donkey for you." And so saying, he took the little woman under his arm and trudged off, without waiting for her to inform him whether she approved his proposal, or not. Mr Parsons, giving one scowling look at the silent bed, followed them, and Martha and Michael were left together beside the dying man.

"There's a dead body walking about
the room! One? No! It is not one;
it is five hundred!"

Upon perceiving the totally unconscious state into which Sir
Matthew had fallen, Michael had gently withdrawn himself from behind
his pillows, and now stood, almost as silent and motionless as himself,
beside the bed, respectfully waiting to receive from the desolate and
weeping Martha some hint or instruction respecting his staying where
he was, or leaving her. Never, when the poor dependant of her family,
had the young heart of Michael been impressed with a feeling of respect
so profound as he at that moment felt for the unhappy girl. In truth the
feeling was so powerful as to interfere with his usefulness, for he shrank
from appearing to put himself forward too presumptuously before
giving her advice, or venturing in any degree to dictate what it might
be best for her to do. But when, after remaining thus bashfully silent
for a quarter of an hour, he perceived that she gave no other sign of life
than by tears that flowed incessantly, and sighs that seemed to heave her
breast "almost to bursting,"—when he saw this, he began to think that

some degree of seeming presumption on his part might be better and more profitable for her, whom he would really have died to serve, than the continuance of a degree of deference which must render him useless. Approaching, therefore, to the chair on which she had thrown herself, he ventured to say, "Miss Martha! where can I find your old servant Betty Parker? I remember her very well—she used to be always in the nursery. If you would tell me where she is likely to be, I will go for her."

Poor Martha for a moment ceased to weep, and looked up at him. "Michael Armstrong!" she replied, "I am not conscious of ever having injured any human being but yourself; and yet you are the only one who is near to support and help me at this dreadful hour. God bless you for your kindness, my good boy! Do not go away, Michael—that is, I mean, do not leave the house till all is over—indeed, I think you may be useful to me!"

"Miss Martha," he returned, "will you trust me to sit here, while you yourself summon whomever you may wish to keep you company. I will keep out of sight in case—" and here he stopped.

"His eyes will never open more, Michael!" she replied, while the tears again burst forth, "and thank God their last look at me was gentle! But I almost fear to leave the room, Michael—I would not that he should breathe his last, and I not by him." But Michael, unskilful as he was, felt that the scene was too awful a one for the poor girl to be left alone in, and he therefore persisted to declare with the authority which such subduing sorrow gives to all around who will take the trouble to exercise it, that he would watch by the bedside of her father while she sought the old woman mentioned by Dr Crockley.

Reluctantly, and unresistingly she consented, and giving a look at the bed that seemed to wring her very heart, she quitted the room, leaving Michael Armstrong alone with the motionless mass of still living clay, before which he had so often trembled.

How strangely eventful had been the interval between those well-remembered days, and the one actually present with him! How extraordinary the change in the circumstances of both parties! it was not triumph, but it was thankfulness, which Michael felt, as the sense of this came fully upon him during these moments of profound stillness; and the result of all the moving thoughts that crowded upon his mind was an earnest prayer to Heaven that he might never be placed in any circumstances likely to harden his heart, and make him the cause of suffering to others,—a fearful and a dreadful crime, which he felt, as he gazed with trembling awe on the sunken features of the living corpse before him, must in the sight of God be held as one of the most daring rebellion to his heavenly will of which man is capable.

Solemn and solitary as was Michael's position in the chamber of Sir Matthew, the interval of Martha's absence did not seem long. She returned accompanied by the old servant who had been nursery attendant, though never raised to the dignity of nurse, from the birth of the eldest child of the family, and who was the only one remaining of all the numerous household who retained the slightest feeling of attachment to any of them. To her, habit stood in the place of preference, and she might perhaps be said to love all the Dowling children, from the eldest to the youngest; a sentiment which led her to conceive, as in duty bound, a most hearty detestation of their step-mother. It was, therefore, with something very like pleasure that she obeyed a summons so solemn and so peremptory as to justify her, even in the judgment of Mrs Saunderson, for laying aside the ironing-box, which she had been plying incessantly for two whole days upon the frills and furbelows of Lady Clarissa, in order to obey it. On perceiving the condition in which her master lay, Betty Parker strongly advised poor Martha to retire, urging the uselessness of her remaining to look upon what was so grievous, when a baby might see at half a glance that the poor gentleman could not tell friend from foe. But Betty Parker knew little of the intensity of Martha's pertinacious love for her unworthy parent, if she fancied that her very reasonable remonstrance would produce any effect. Martha attempted not even to answer it, but placing herself in a chair close beside the bed, remained nearly as motionless as the faintly breathing figure that lay upon it.

Poor Michael knew not too well what he ought to do next. He felt that he was useless there; he knew that he should be stared at, as a very incomprehensible intruder, if he descended to the offices. Yet he remembered that his benefactress had bid him not to go, and he could not have felt himself more strongly bound to remain, had the crime of high treason been involved in his departure. Yet there was something in the stupid puzzled look with which Betty Parker regarded him, that vexed his spirit. He was conscious that he had no business in that room, and therefore at such a moment he ought not to be there. After a few moments of reflection he approached Martha, and making so profound a reverence as to convince Betty, that let him be who he would, he was a very well-behaved young gentleman, he said, "I will now, Miss Martha, go to the inn for an hour or two, and then return to take your orders." A look of gratitude was all her reply, and Michael departed.

It was three o'clock in the afternoon when he entered the little inn, where the postboy, who had driven him from Fairly in the morning, was still waiting his orders. "I cannot tell you yet, my lad, when I shall be ready to return," he replied, in answer to the boy's questionings.

"It's all one to me, master," said the driver. "In course I shall be paid accordingly."

"Certainly you will," returned Michael: and he was then left to eat his solitary dinner with what appetite he might.

For three long melancholy hours he employed himself in pacing backwards and forwards on the high-road before the little inn, and was beginning to think that time enough had elapsed to justify his returning to inquire how matters were going on at Dowling Lodge, when the sound of a carriage approaching as it seemed from the park-gates, caused him to stop abruptly to listen, and to look.

The equipage that drew near was a handsome travelling-carriage, though its appearance was considerably disfigured by the prodigious quantity of luggage, which was fastened by ropes and chains to every part of it. The imperial only formed the foundation for a pyramid of trunks and bandboxes, which were piled upon it. The servant's-seat behind was loaded to its very utmost capacity with more trunks and bandboxes, while, chained below it, was a massive coffer, that looked very like a plate-chest, having suspended round its sides, bundles, baskets and bags innumerable. Nor was the interior by any means reserved for live lumber alone, for although the rigid figures of Lady Clarissa Dowling, and her waiting-woman, Saunderson, were visible in the midst, it appeared to be crammed with every imaginable species of property which such a conveyance could transport.

Michael watched the overloaded vehicle roll by with great satisfaction. "Whatever happens," thought he, "Miss Martha must be better without her." Relieved by knowing that he should not again run the risk of encountering her delectable ladyship, Michael immediately took his way to the magnificent mansion she had forsaken, and perceiving that the hall-doors stood wide open, preferred passing through them to encountering again the motley throng that had taken possession of the offices. But instead of finding this portion of the house as quiet and forsaken as he had left it, he was startled by hearing, as he mounted the steps of the stately portico, a multitude of voices in violent altercation.

At first he felt disposed to turn away and seek another entrance, but the vehemence of the sounds he heard excited his curiosity, and he went on. Instead of one, half-a-dozen strangers might have entered without running any risk of having their right there challenged, so great was the confusion that reigned; and Michael might have passed up the great stairs, and into the chamber which it was his purpose to visit, without any difficulty. But he was prevented from taking immediate advantage of this, by hearing words which excited new fears for the unfortunate Martha; and, ere he had listened many minutes, he became aware that a new creditor had reached the lodge after he left it, who had come, armed with proper authority, to arrest the knight, dead or alive. Nor did the discussion of this event cause all the uproar; for the agents of the parties who had previously sent in the execution were threatening with all sorts of punishment, several of the servants, whom they accused of having been bribed to assist Lady Clarissa in the removal of many valuables which she had no right to take. It was not this part of the tumult, however, that interested him and, having obtained but too clearly the information that Sir Matthew was arrested, he once more sought for the unhappy Martha in the dismal chamber where he had left her. And there he found her; but with such frightful adjuncts to her natural grief, that the state of quiet decent sorrow in which he had left her, seemed a condition positively enviable compared to that in which he found her now.

Sir Matthew had breathed his last, and the corpse was already arranged with decency upon its stately bed; but, on each side of it stood an officer, whose duty it was to violate by their presence the solemn sanctity of that dismal chamber, and to prevent the body's being carried to the grave, till the claims of their employer were satisfied. In front of her father's corpse, with her troubled eyes (no longer bathed in the healing dew of natural sorrow), turning from it to its rude guardians, and back again to all that was left of the sinful being she had so fondly, blindly loved,—stood the wretched daughter, so sad a spectacle of woe, that it was evident the men themselves turned their hard eyes studiously away because they felt a pang of pity as they looked upon her.

"Come with me, Miss Martha!" cried Michael, unceremoniously seizing her arm. "You must not, you cannot remain here. You can do no good, Miss Martha; all is over now! You must come away, you must indeed," The only answer that poor Martha gave, was forcibly shaking off the hand that held her, and then pointing, first to her father's body, and afterwards to the two unseemly attendants who stood beside it.

"It is no use, young man, to strive with her," said Betty, who was still occupied in completing some of her lugubrious operations about the bed: "I know her better than you do. She will stay here watching him till she is as dead as he is, rather than go away and leave his body to be tended by such as those."

For a moment Michael really felt all the enervating effects of despair, and stood perfectly incapable of even imagining any means of help for the agony which it wrung his heart to witness. But, as the old woman pursued her ghastly occupation, she went muttering on, expatiating on the sinful and unchristian outrage that was thus committed.

"And what will the rogue get by it?" she said. "Does he mean to show the corpse for a farthing a head to his factory blackguards? Isn't he as big a fool as he is knave?"

"No, mistress, no, by no means," said the friendly defender of Mr Joseph Parsons:—for it was at his suit that the body of Sir Matthew had been arrested.—"You may call the superintendent rogue, a knave, or what you will of that kind, and I don't suppose that there's many as would contradict you; but, as to his being a fool, especially as to the doing what he has done here, that he is not. 'Twas his only chance."

"And how much do you think he'll make of it?" demanded old Betty with a sneer.

"Why just the four hundred and sixty-seven pounds as is due to him," replied the man.

To all this poor Martha appeared not to pay the slightest attention, and, in truth, neither understood nor heard a word of it; but Michael did, and with sudden animation stepped up to the man who had spoken, and whispered in his ear, "Perhaps we may be able to settle this business without any further difficulty. Step out of the room with me, will you, for a moment: your companion can do all that is necessary without you."— "Neither I nor my employer are people to make difficulties," replied the man; "and I am quite ready to hear you, young man, if you have got any thing to say upon the subject." They accordingly retired together; and in a wondrously short space of time the uninitiated Michael was made to understand all the circumstances of the case, the most important of which was that if, as Mr Parsons hoped and expected, Miss Martha could find ready money enough quietly to pay his little private account with the late Sir Matthew, the arrest would be immediately withdrawn, and the body left for her to dispose of it at her pleasure.

"And the sum," said Michael, "is—how much?"

"Four hundred and sixty-seven pounds," replied the man, "with some little matter, not exceeding four or five pounds more, for costs"

"Withdraw the arrest," said Michael, "and the money shall be instantly forthcoming."

"Let us see the money forthcoming," replied the fellow, grinning, and the arrest shall be instantly withdrawn."

"Here is the money, sir,' said Michael, taking out the pocket-book containing Martha's generous donation, and drawing from it notes to the amount demanded.

"Then the business will be soon settled, young gentleman. May I take the liberty to ask your name?"

"My name is of no consequence whatever, sir," replied Michael. "But lose no time in giving me the discharge. Only first enter that chamber with me once again, withdraw your companion from his frightful watch, and tell the poor young lady that it is over."

The man readily obeyed, and the mourning, but thankful Martha was once more left with her old servant, to watch beside her father's corpse.

XXXII

Mr Augustus Dowling gives his sister Marha notice to quit the premises; which occasions Michael to appear in a new character— A long journey taken by novices; but they do not lose their way, and arrive at the right place at last

THE CIRCUMSTANCES WHICH IMMEDIATELY FOLLOWED are not of sufficient consequence to detain us long. Our old acquaintaince, Mr Augustus, now Major Dowling of the — regiment, quartered at the distance of a day's journey, was sent for to get through the melancholy business going on in his paternal mansion, as well as he could; to give orders respecting the funeral, and to make himself as thoroughly acquainted with the real state of his family affairs as circumstances would permit. Michael, meanwhile, had taken leave of the weeping Martha without having given her the slightest hint as to the means by which Sir Matthew's body had been released. Had he not known that the Mr Augustus, whose kicks and pinches he so well remembered, was expected to arrive for the protection of his sister, and of whatever property they might still call their own, he would hardly have made up his mind to leave her, however conscious he might have been of the doubtful propriety of offering such protection as he could give. But it was evident that the poor girl thought he had better go, though it was equally so that she parted from him with the greatest reluctance.

"You shall hear from me," she said, "my good Michael, and if it should never be my good fortune to see you more, remember me with the same forgiving kindness that you have shown through all the dreadful scenes you have witnessed here. You have a good and generous heart, Michael, and though I know you suffered much by being present at them, you will always like to remember how greatly your presence helped to support your early friend in her great affliction."

But it was not destined that these sad scenes should be the last in which Michael and his early friend were to be thrown together. In little more than a week after the death of Sir Matthew, and while Michael was still anxiously waiting at Fairly for such tidings from her as might put him at liberty to set off without further delay for Nice, a packet reached him from Dowling Lodge, containing two letters. On was from Martha, and contained these words:

"Dear Michael,

"My brother tells mee that all of us, who are old enough, must seek our own living, for that there is nothing left to support us. Myself especially, he says, must, to use his own words, look about me directly as my behaviour to my family has never been such as to justify my looking to any of them for assistance. This amounts to my being actually turned out of doors, an exigency which at this moment leaves me no other resource than what is afforded by the enclosed letter. Read it, Michael, and let me know if you are willing to give me your assistance and protection in reaching the amiable writer of it. I could never have accepted, even for a day, the hospitality she so generously offers, could I not prove to her, by bringing you with me, that the sad subject which interrupted our friendship some seven or eight years ago, could never again be a source of pain to either of us.

"My dear father's last act towards me, which was, as I think I told you, the placing of a few hundred pounds in my hands for the express purpose of my leaving the country, will enable me to undertake this long journey without being a burden upon you. The *green pocket-book*, Michael, so well known to Mr Parsons and Lady Clarissa, as the repository of my father's ready money, and so disgracefully struggled for during his last moments, will prove of no value to its possessors beyond its morocco cover and its silken lining; for the notes which he took from it to give to me, were the last he ever placed in it. My messenger has orders to wait for your reply. If it will suit you immediately to accompany me to Nice—my first stage shall be to the little inn at Fairly, which you mentioned to me. I fear you will find me a weak and troublesome traveller; but I think I have been improving in health ever since I learnt that I had not your death to answer for.

> "Your grateful friend,
> "MARTHA DOWLING."

The other letter was from Miss Brotberton, and ran thus:

> "Need I tell you, my dearest Martha, with what feelings I received the news of your present painful position? Your father's marriage with Lady Clarissa was, for your sake, a source of great sorrow to me, for I was certain that your domestic happiness would be destroyed by it; and this most unexpected event of your father's bankruptcy makes me feel quite sure that you have no longer a comfortable home in England. Come then to me, my dear Martha! The painful estrangement which grew between us, just when I was beginning to know and value your excellent qualities, has long been a source of very painful regret to me, because I am aware that I judged you unfairly, and pronounced that judgment harshly. Be generous, then, and prove that you can forgive this, by immediately giving me the pleasure of receiving you as my guest. When we are together, we will consult about what will be best for the future; but at any rate I have the satisfaction of knowing that the climate to which I am inviting you is likely to be beneficial to your health during the approaching winter: come to me, then, dear friend, without delay. On the other side you will find the route sketched that I recommend you for your journey. My quarters are roomy enough to accommodate either man or maid servant, or both, if it will suit you to be so accompanied.

> "Ever, my dear Martha
> "Affectionately yours,
> "MARY BROTHERTON."

The consequence of this packet was another metamorphosis on the part of Michael, "She shall not think," said he, addressing Mr Bell, "that my respect for her is lessened because her fortune has fallen. I will wait upon her with faithful duty and most grateful affection but she was born in a palace, and I in a cabin; and I will not, especially just now, obtrude myself upon her as a companion. As her servant I hope I may be useful to her, and it is in that capacity that I shall attend her."

There was so much good feeling shown in this project, that Mr Bell could not oppose it, whatever he might think of its necessity; and Michael, therefore, gave the astonished Martha the meeting at the little inn she had named, in the character of a very neat and respectable-looking man-servant. Her faithful Betty Parker, who had consented to be the companion of her journey, was in the room with her when Michael made his appearance at the door, to receive her orders. The cautious manner in which he made her comprehend his purpose, and the nature of the office he had assumed, suggested to her the propriety of not discussing it in the presence of the well-contented Betty, who was exceedingly comforted by discovering that the young man whom her mistress had informed her would travel with them, was to do so as her fellow-servant, as she by no means felt herself capable of becoming "servant of all work" to a young lady travelling through foreign countries, of which she had never even heard the names. But having contrived to dismiss her female attendant on an errand, Martha began to remonstrate with her faithful squire upon the great mistake he had made in fancying that she had ever thought of travelling with him in any other capacity than that of a friend. All she said, however, was in vain. Michael, though in a manner the most humbly respectful, persisted in his purpose; and the almost destitute girl was therefore constrained to set off upon her travels in a style which she felt to be very unfitting to her situation. Her conscience, however, could not reproach her for this, for most assuredly she could not help it.

Many were the letters, and various the mementos of affection, intrusted by Mr and Mrs Bell to the care of Michael for their dearly-beloved Mary Brotberton. Nor was there an individual of whose welfare he thought it would please her to hear, whom he did not visit to receive their loving blessings for the benefactress who, not withstanding her wide wanderings, had never failed to remember the wants of all who had faithfully served her, or in any way become dependent on her bounty.

These duties completed, and a farewell of most grateful affection uttered to the amiable clergyman and his excellent wife, Michael set off upon his long journey with feelings of hope, joy, confidence, fear, diffidence, and trembling affection,—all so strongly mixed together in his bosom that, had his life depended on it, he could not himself have told which it was that most frequently preponderated. Yet, altogether, his state of mind was very delightful: the novelty and excitement of journeying, so pregnant of enjoyment to most of us, was most especially captivating to him, whose education had been little more than the unchecked development of imagination, and of that keen observation of all surrounding objects which his shepherd life had taught him.

The first painful interruption to the state of felicity, arose from his finding himself under the necessity of confessing to Martha that he had no more money wherewith to pay their way. Aware that in the performance of his self-appointed office Michael would have to pay every thing, and keep a regular account of it; and aware also that the money he had received from her would enable him to do this, without giving him the additional trouble of daily settlements with her, she had merely said, a minute or two before they set off, "You will be kind enough to be my banker, Michael, during the journey, and we will settle accounts at the end of it."

For just one week from the day of their leaving Fairly, he was able to do this; but then the little remnant of his treasure failed him, and great as was his repugnance to the measure, he was compelled by dire necessity to confess that nearly the whole of her generous gift had gone to—"to satisfy the rapacity of Mr Parsons."

It would be hardly possible for one human being to be more grateful to another than poor Martha felt to her young attendant after this disclosure. She remembered the agony which he had made to cease; she remembered, too, her state of utter incapacity even to comprehend and still less to avert the horrors that surrounded her; and, spite of all Michael's respectful efforts to induce her to perform her allotted character properly, she never from the hour of this disclosure treated him otherwise than as a dear and valued friend.

As their journey approached its termination, however (to which period Michael had looked with peculiar anxiety, as that most important to the dignity of Martha), there was one argument, and one only which he was able to coax her into letting him make his first appearance before Miss Brotherton in the character of her servant; and this was his very natural wish to ascertain whether Edward and Fanny would recognise him.

It was therefore still in the dress, and with the demeanour of a servant, that the poor factory-boy now become a tall and very handsome young man, armed himself with courage to enter the presence of his brother, and once more to draw near to the dear and gentle little being whom he had so fondly loved during the miserable period they had passed together at the Deep Valley. It had been previously agreed between himself and Martha, that when she sent for him, it should be for the purpose of giving him some long and particular instructions respecting the luggage he was to get from the custom house, in order to give him time to look, and be looked at, before the moment of discovery should arrive.

The young man trembled like an aspen-leaf as he laid his hand upon the lock of the door, the opening of which would bring him face to face with his brother. And perchance he might have indulged in a longer interval of preparation, had not the voice of Martha distinctly pronounced the words "Come in!" Further delay was out of the question; he pushed forward the door, and entered.

The first figure that his eyes fell upon was that of a young lady—small, and of very delicate proportions—whose head, which was hanging over some employment as the door opened, was raised as he entered, displaying to him a very lovely face, and a pair of eyes whose dark brilliance almost made the beholder wink. Could that be Fanny Fletcher? No. Yet that it should be Miss Brotherton seemed more impossible still. Like all young people who have been separated from some one considerably older than themselves, ever since the period when this difference made one of them appear fully grown, while the other was still a child, Michael fancied that in Miss Brotherton he should see an elderly person, no more like a pretty girl, than he was himself. But Mary Brotherton had not fully completed her twenty-ninth year; and happening, moreover, to be very peculiarly young-looking both in face and figure, it was not very wonderful that he should doubt of her identity; nor it was in truth Mary Brotherton, and no other, whose bright and laughing loveliness made him turn his admiring eyes away, in search of something dearer, though not more beautiful.

At the end of the sofa-table, at which Miss Brotherton sat with Martha Dowling beside her, was a young female figure which presented only a profile to his gaze—But that was enough—the delicate oval face, the sweet regular small features, the glossy light brown hair parted Madonna-like upon the ivory brow, and the long eyelash that seemed to rest upon her cheek as she read, all proclaimed that he looked upon the same gentle lovely creature whose soft voice had whispered "patience!" when his spirit, but for her, had died within him. At the sight of this sweet vision, that in shadowy and uncertain outline had so often visited his reveries, Michael's manhood almost forsook him, and large tears gathered in his eyes, which he was fain to hide by turning round again and performing some blundering operation with the lock of the door. Martha played her part admirably, appearing to be the most exceedingly particular young lady, about boxes, bags, and desks, that ever travelled.

"Remember, I beg," she said, "that you see yourself to the opening of every package. Don't let them touch a single article that you do not watch the whole time; and be sure that every thing is locked again—and on no account forget the covers, or mismatch them—and remember particularly—" *et cetera, et cetera*, and so she ran on at the imminent risk of being classed by her clever friend Mary as he veriest fidget that ever arrived to bore a peaceable household, and all in order to give her poor companion time to recover himself, and see distinctly what was before him.

But Michael could not recover himself, nor could he even find courage to look about him. It was a large saloon that Miss Brotherton occupied, and the agitated young man rather felt that there was a gentleman occupied with books and papers at a distant table, than saw him. Yet to see him he was determined, if his life were to be the forfeit; and turning his head with an eye as troubled as that of Hamlet, when tremblingly following his father's spirit, he stood at last with clasped hands, protruded head, and features almost convulsed with emotion, when he had an uninterrupted view of his brother's calm and beautiful countenance.

Edward was very busily employed, and unconsciously submitted himself to this examination without raising his eyes, or moving in any way; but Miss Brotherton's ear caught something like a sob from the silent object of all Martha's eloquence, and suddenly looking up perceived Michael in the attitude described, but stealthily, and perhaps unknowingly approaching Edward's table, while the tears he could no longer check, rolled down his manly cheek.

There are some individuals of the human family gifted with such quickness of perception, and rapidity of inference, that their faculties act with the certainty of instinct, and the brilliancy of inspiration. Miss Brotherton was one of those; and after looking for a minute or two Michael, quite as earnestly as Michael looked at Edward, she sprung from the sofa, pushed the table that stood before it with such violence from her as nearly to overset it, and rushing forward laid her hand upon his arm, exclaiming, "For mercy's sake tell me young man, who you are, and where you come from?"

On hearing these words in a voice unusually loud and agitated, Edward rose hastily from his seat, and approached Miss Brotherton as if to protect her from some threatened danger; but turning towards him, she held up her hand as if to prevent his hostile approach, and said, "Stay Edward, stay! Look at him! Good Heaven! Look at him, dearest Edward, and tell me who he is like!"

Thus addressed, Edward did look at his brother, and for a moment with a countenance that seemed to say Miss Brotherton had lost her wits—but suddenly Michael smiled at him as he caught his puzzled eye, and then he started, and almost gasped for breath—and his distracted eyes fixed themselves on the agitated face before him as if they would read in it the history of years.

"Edward!—Teddy!" cried Michael, opening his arms, and making a step in advance.

In the next instant the brothers were locked in each other's arms, and Miss Brotherton drew back, and gazed upon them from a distance as if the very ground that sustained hearts under the influence of much feelings was holy—while Fanny Fletcher, rose and sat down, and rose again, checking the feeling that would have sent her to stretch forth a hand of welcome to her old friend, by telling herself that no hand, no voice but Edward's could be cared for then. And perhaps she was right; for it is certain that for several minutes, neither Edward nor Michael were fully conscious where they were, nor who they might be that were near them. Once and again each beating heart was strained against the brother heart, and then, their right hands clasped, and the left placed, each on the other's shoulder,

"They fell to such perusal of the face,"

that now, after eight cruel years of absence, was once more beaming with love and sympathy before their eyes, that it must have been a very heartless and soulless being who should have come between them.

Though such a history as Michael's might well have occupied more than one long summer's day in the telling, to ears so greedy of every circumstance connected with it as were those of Edward, yet it is wonderful how very short a time sufficed to point out the keystone of the arch, upon which the whole wonderful fabric hung, and then it was that Fanny Fletcher's voice was heard exclaiming in a burst of uncontrollable emotion,

"Then it was I that caused it all! Oh! Miss Brotherton, it was I who kept him in that horrid place for years! Had I not told you he was dead, it would have been he who would have been the happy object of your bounty, instead of me! Oh! how can he ever forgive me?"

This was uttered with such agitated rapidity, that though there was more than one present, who would have been ready enough to contradict the self-accusing statement, she gave them no time for it. But it sufficed to draw Michael from the side of his brother, and to place him at hers; and though this terrible thought drew a shower of tears from Fanny's eyes, notwithstanding the exceeding happiness which was at the very same moment throbbing at her heart; it may be that there could not have been found a more effectual mode of at once bringing

"Yes! Michael Armstrong is a
hero; he is our hero!"

back the long-parted friends to the same tone of familiar intercourse
in which they had parted, as this sincere self-recrimination on one part,
and the warm pleading against its injustice, on the other. For some
minutes this lasted without being interrupted by a word from any one;
for both Mary and Edward found sufficient occupation in looking at
them both, and then exchanging expressive glances of thanks giving
and happiness with each other. But at length, upon Fanny's saying with
a fresh burst of tears,

"Oh, Michael! Michael! your eloquence is all in vain. You will never,
never teach me to forget that I have been enjoying the blessed destiny
intended for you, and that by means of words uttered by myself."

Upon her saying this, the happy Mary Brotherton pushed a low tabouret before the reunited friends, and seating herself upon it, took Fanny's hand in hers, and said, "If you would not cry about it, my Fanny, I should think it was a mighty pretty exhibition of true feeling and false argument that we were witnessing; but if you really intend to be unhappy, we shall all range ourselves immediately on Michael's side, and laugh you to scorn for your sophistry, and the deplorable confusion you are making between cause and effect. I should like to know, little lady, how much it would have profited our Michael had you refused to answer when I inquired at the Deep Valley factory, if you knew aught about him? had you, while firmly believing he was dead, declared to state your belief, lest you might be mistaken, what would it have availed him, darling? Could he have crept down before us from his sick bed to settle the question? No, dear casuist, you know better. Your looks are much more wise than your words, Fanny; for even now, though you pretend to shake your head, you truth-telling eyes confess that you have not another syllable to say.'

"But is it not singular," said Martha, who had been contemplating the scene with unspeakable delight, "is it not singular that Michael should twice have been the victim of words, uttered by such very friendly lips?"

"Singular, dear Martha?" replied Mary; "is not every event connected with a hero of romance, of necessity and by immutable prescription, singular? And whom did Fate and Fortune ever fix upon more unmistakably to fill that distinguished position in society, than Michael Armstrong? Why are we all here together? Wholly and solely because Michael Armstrong saved Lady Clarissa Shrimpton from the terrors inspired by a cow—is it not so, dear friends? Can any of you deny that all the exceeding happiness that blesses us at this moment, has arisen from that most marvellously silly adventure? And shall we any of us quarrel at the steps (though some of them it must be confessed were rough enough), which have led from that nonsensical beginning, to an end that has made us all so very happy? Yes! Michael Armstrong is a hero; he is our hero; he is the crowning blessing that is come to make us all thank Heaven for having brought us every one from greater and less degrees of misery, to very perfect happiness, and shall we not welcome him with smiles, instead of tears, Fanny?"

Nothing ould have been more admirably suited to the effect which the happy heiress meant to produce, than these words. How, after this, could Michael shrink, as he had expected to do, from the humiliating comparison between Edward and Fanny, with himself? Or how could Fanny persist in weeping, when her own heart, as well as those of all around her, was so cheeringly called upon to rejoice? Nothing of the sort was any longer thought of by either.

Without very well knowing how it came about, Michael, of all the multitude of contending feelings which had been lately so cruelly as sailing him, being as they were, of that most harassing race begotten between fear and hope, was now conscious of only one, and that one was happiness unmixed. His frank and generous nature could no longer harbour any doubts as to the place he held in the affections of those whom he had lately thought of, as almost too high and too happy to remember him. He was with them, he was of them. If a thought of the future glanced athwart the delicious present, it came accompanied by a buoyant consciousness that there was that within him which would enable him to redeem lost time, and that whatever those he loved wished him to be, THAT he should have power to become.

Nor was an answering confidence wanting in those who wearied not of gazing at his bright, expressive features, and his noble form. Fanny thought that he was exactly every thing she would have dreamed he must be, had she ventured to dream that he existed at all. Mary thought that she read capacity which promised power to become all that Edward could wish him to be—and she was not disposed to wish for more—and Edward himself thought and felt that had he power to choose a brother from among all the nations of the earth, and the noblest of them, Michael would have been the one he would have selected.

"And where is my dear, good Tremlett?" said Miss Brotherton.

"In the midst of all this rare felicity she must not be left out. She has shared our mourning for your loss, dear Michael, and shame it were she should not share our joy at finding you."

"Shall I go and call her hither?" cried Fanny, rising.

"No! that you shall not, Fanny," replied Miss Brotherton.

"I will not trust you. It was I who dragged the dear good soul from post to pillar, in order to find you, Michael.—It was I who never let her know rest, night nor day, because you were not, and who but I shall bring her the glad tidings of your restoration?"

But truly delighted as was Mary Brotherton at the idea of the pleasure which she well knew this unlooked-for arrival would cause her old friend, she would not let her taste it without the addition of a little mystification and accordingly she led her into the room which contained the happy party, with no other preparation than telling her that there was a young Englishman in the saloon, to whom she must come and be introduced, because he was a countryman.

To this the tractable old lady agreed, without testifying any very lively emotion; but when she had got into the midst of the group, and witnessed the general exaltation of spirits which seemed to possess them all, after looking and listening for a little while she could not help whispering to Fanny, "Do you know, my dear, who that young man is? I never saw Miss Brotherton—no! nor Mr Armstrong either—seem to he so extraordinarily intimate with any one before, just at first sight."

In reply to this Fanny only hid her face, and laughed, for she dared not trust her voice to give the information required.

"How very odd," murmured the old lady, drawing her knitting from her bag.

"It is very odd, Mrs Tremlett, very odd indeed," said Mary, "there is no denying it. But the fact is, that Mr Armstrong has taken such an extraordinary fancy to this young man, that I really think I shall be obliged to ask him to live with us. There will be plenty of room, you know, in my Rhenish castle."

The old lady said not a word in reply, but she looked puzzled, and vexed, and shook her head, as much as to say that it was not like her young mistress to talk such nonsense as that. So in her own defence Mary was obliged to explain the mystery, and as happy an old woman was nurse Tremlett, as she looked and listened, as ever tasted joy from the contemplation of it in others.

XXXIII

A tête-à-tête—A second—A third—A mysterious result—Conclusion

DELIGHTFUL AS WAS THIS STATE of mind to all that shared it, it could not last. Michael was too much in earnest in his dread of being a burden upon Miss Brotherton to permit many days to pass before he begged her to let him converse with her for a few moments in private; and Mary, who had already seen quite enough to convince her that the affection which Michael and Fanny had conceived for each other, amidst the dreary misery of the Deep Valley Mill, was not likely to be forgotten in the gay happiness of Nice, fully anticipated an humble confession, on the part of Michael, that he could not be happy without her permission to become the acknowledged lover of her charming friend and *protégée,* and very amiable, frank, and noble-minded, did she consider it in him, thus openly to avow the truth at once. But nothing could be further from the thoughts of Michael than making any such confession as this; which, it may be observed, is by no means saying that his heart was either innocent or unconscious of the presumptuous passion she attributed to it.

Greatly, however, did Miss Brotherton underrate the young man's character when she conceived that the gracious favour with which she had received him, could generate in his heart a wish to ask for more.

"It is taking a great liberty, madam," began Michael.

"If you love me, do not call me madam, my dear Michael," she replied. "Do not you perceive that Edward and Fanny both call me Mary?

and till I had taught them to do so I never could feel that they quite understood the true spirit of my attachment towards them, or the mode and manner of existence which I have imagined for myself, and which must have fallen to the ground, if I had found them incapable of being to me, or letting me be to them, all that I wished and desired. You must not, dearest Michael, come and shake this perfect and delightful union, introducing forms and ceremonies, foreign to our manners, and our feelings. Pray do not look so grave, dear friend! Promise to offend thus no more, and I will cease to scold you."

"Dearest Miss Brotherton!" said Michael. But this did not satisfy the *exigeante* lady, who shook her head, and held up her finger in reproof. "Dearest Mary! then —" he resumed, colouring brightly, and with a smile that made her think she could trace a family likeness to Edward, "the greatest wish I have on earth is to become such as you might approve, and if I shrink from the dear and precious familiarity which must make Edward and Fanny so happy, think not that I am incapable of loving you as perfectly as they do; but remember, dearest lady! that however humble their origin, the very circumstance of their having been your honoured companions for years, is of itself sufficient to raise them to such a tone of thinking and of manners, as may, in some sort, justify their using the privilege you so graciously afford. But, alas! You must know too well that the case is far different with me. The overflowing joy of our first meeting, naturally broke down, as it were, all inequalities, all boundaries, and I certainly felt, and perhaps spoke, as if I too were one of the accomplished little circle that might call this earthly paradise their home. But reflection will come, most generous Mary! if not amidst the happy intoxicating moments of the day, it will make itself a voice in the quiet reasoning meditations of the night, and so loudly has this voice been heard by me, that I cannot—no, in spite of all the happiness that surrounds me, I cannot live on thus, an idle, ignorant dependant on your bounty."

The heiress was half vexed, but more than half pleased by this trembling address, the deep sincerity of which was testified by the working features of a countenance more than commonly expressive of all that passed within. She had enjoyed so much genuine happiness since the arrival of Michael, and had watched with pleasure so exquisite the happiness of Edward and Fanny, that she almost trembled at the idea of any change; yet she knew the boy was right; she knew that he ought to apply himself immediately and strenuously to such studies as were most necessary for redeeming the time he had lost, and so well aware was she of this, that, notwithstanding her unwillingness to part with him, she rejoiced heartily to find that she was wrong as to the subject on which she had suspected he wished to speak. Had she been right in her conjecture, all she could have done would have been to endow the boy and girl with such a portion of her wealth as might have sufficed to make them independent; but under such circumstances all notion of essential improvement must of course be abandoned for ever, and for many reasons this would have been a source of lasting regret to her. It was therefore with cordial approbation that after the interval of a few moments, she replied, "Michael, you are right. Nature has done so much for you, my dear friend, that our wish to keep you constantly with us might easily, had you shown less courage, have tempted us to fancy that you wanted nothing which you have not got, or which we could not give you. But you are quite right in refusing to consent to this. We will immediately return to Germany where you shall be placed at the same admirable institution that so rapidly made your brother what you now see him. Two years of well-directed devotion to study, my dear Michael, will perhaps make you feel more at your ease among us, though I doubt, if it can produce any change which will make us love you better."

"Miss Brotherton! dearest Miss Brotherton!" exclaimed Michael— while perhaps the brightest beam of hope that ever yet shot from his eyes, met hers as she affectionately gazed upon him, "that was not what I—what I dared venture to hope and ask for. What you now propose, would be a happiness, the idea of which I think I should have turned from, even in my dreams, from shame at its towering ambition. All I meant to ask was, your kind aid to place me in some business where I might earn a maintenance, that in a year or two might my being a burden to you—and now —."

"And now, Michael, I tell you fairly, that I have not the slightest intention of doing any such thing. Besides my own particular objection to such a mode of proceeding, I have lately heard a little anecdote of you, from your friend Martha, which makes it very doubful whether you deserve that species of independence—for she put it in your possession once, you know—and you could not keep it. I shall manage better, Michael, depend upon it. One week more of idleness in this sweet spot—and then we travel back to Germany. You shall not be left to study in a more forsaken condition than was your brother. We shall be within an easy distance of you, my dear Michael. One corner of my castle must hold us, while another is beautified, and it is likely enough the work will go on all the better for our being there."

"And your visit to Rome given up for my sake?" cried Michael. "Oh! no, no, no!"

"No, no, no, most certainly," replied Mary, laughing, "I would not give up that journey, Michael, for more than I will say,

"All is not lost that is delayed."

"Instead of giving up the plan, I only mean to improve it. Tell me, and tell me honestly, dear Michael, do you not think in your heart that we shall, one and all, enjoy this journey more if you are with us?"

"Mary!" exclaimed the boy, wholly overcome, and seizing and kissing her hand with an emotion that at once and for ever banished all reserve, "Mary! it is your will to be loved, and who can disobey? But my happiness seems greater than I can bear! Where is Edward? Let me walk, and talk with him! He is used to you, Mary, and all this may not seem to him so very much like a dream as it does to me. If he tells me it is all real, I shall believe it;" and with these words, and his fine face glowing with all the best and happiest feelings of our nature, Michael bounded from the presence of his benefactress to seek his brother.

"I might have lived a good while in my fine house, at Milford, and received a prodigious number of complimentary visits from my elegant neighbours, before I should have enjoyed half an hour as I have done this," thought the happy Mary Brotherton, as she strolled out through an open window, that led to a little garden of orange-trees. "How delicious is the air this morning!" But where was the climate, where, at that moment, she would have felt it to be otherwise?

Michael had no difficulty in finding his brother, who in truth was lingering near, on purpose to question him after this interview.

"Come with me, Edward!" cried the agitated boy, seizing his arm; "here are our hats—come with me into that little grove yonder—my heart will burst if I do not instantly tell you what has passed." And arm-in-arm they crossed the road, and a small enclosure opposite, and there found themselves under the shelter of a little wood, thick enough to exclude the peering eyes of mortals, as well as that of the sun.

Notwithstanding their eagerness for the communication which was to follow, and which was pretty equally strong in both, not a word was uttered by either till they reached this covert, and then, Michael, throwing himself upon a bank, and casting his hat away, clasped his hands, and raising his eyes to heaven, exclaimed, "Edward, she is an angel!"

Edward had not followed his brother's example, in lying down, but stood before him in act to listen. But there was something in these words that seemed to shake him, for he turned away without answering.

"Has she ever named to you her plans about me?" resumed Michael.

"Yes!" replied Edward.

"Then you know that it is not her intention to assist me, by enabling me to learn any trade in handicraft?"

"No such idea, Michael, ever entered her head," said Edward, gravely.

"But, my dear fellow! you seem to take all this so very coolly. Do you know that it is her intention to send me to the same place where your education was completed?—Do you know that she gives up—no—that she postpones her journey to Italy, till I am ready to go with her?—Edward, do you know all this?"

"My dear brother," replied Edward, "I only know, that from the moment she learnt you were alive, she determined that she would immediately make you perfectly independent, as she has done me. All the rest, I think, depended upon your own inclination—and had she not found you disposed for this scheme, she would not have insisted upon it."

"Disposed for it, Edward? Oh! what cold, what chilling words! You could not speak so, if you thought there were any hope of my so profiting by it as to become a fit companion for you—for her—for Fanny. But it is too late—you feel that it is too late—is it not so, Edward?"

"No, Michael, no!" returned Edward, with sudden animation. "With your faculties, your eager desire to learn, and the masters you will have to put you in the way of doing so, I KNOW that the result of these two years of study will be all you wish, and all your friends can desire."

"Then how can you receive this glorious news, my Edward, so composedly?"

"First, dear Michael, because it is no news to me. And secondly, because I am a selfish wretch, and was thinking, perhaps, more of my own interest than of yours. Forgive me for it, my own dear Michael! But I would rather have had it decided that we should have both marched off, and taken service under the Emperor of Austria. I know that commissions would have been obtained for us."

Michael, as his brother uttered these words, looked up into his face with an expression of such astonishment and dismay, that the blood rushed to Edward's face, and he turned away to conceal his confusion.

"Edward! you are a mystery to me," exclaimed Michael, springing upon his feet, and taking his brother by the arm. "Can it be possible that you are weary of the life you lead? Oh, heaven! and such a life!"

"Weary? am I weary of it, Michael? weary of rising every day to feel that I am a wretch unworthy to breathe the breath of life any where? And oh! how utterly unworthy to breathe it here!"

It was now poor Michael's turn to change colour, and he did so pretty violently—for first he became very red, and then exceedingly pale. That Edward, such as he had ever remembered him, such as he found him now, that he should so very solemnly declare himself to be a wretch unworthy of life, was a horror and a misery as terrible as it was unexpected. He had no power to utter any soothing in contradiction to this appalling statement, for, alas! it might be true—and Michael's heart sunk within him as he remembered how totally ignorant he was of every thing that might enable him to disbelieve it. Silently the brothers walked on for some paces, side by side. They were both of them either unwilling, or unable to speak. At length a sort of shuddering emotion that passed through Michael's frame, made itself felt by the arm of

Edward, which he still held, and then he stopped, and without raising his eyes from the ground, said,

"Michael! How is it you understand me! Do you suppose that I have been guilty of some criminal act, such as dooms man to the gallows? If not, why do you shudder thus?"

"Would you not shudder, Edward, if you heard me say, that I was a wretch unworthy to live?"

"Poor Michael! perhaps I might; but still I doubt if I should understand the phrase as you do. It is so difficult, so impossible to express temperately and soberly, my own reprobation of the feelings that destroy me! And yet, dear Michael," he continued more tranquilly, "I could have fancied that there was something working in your own heart which might have taught you in some degree to guess the state of mine—I have no strength, no couragge to enter on the guilty subject fully—but—that you may not think me a felon, Michael, I will tell you in one audacious word, I LOVE, and that with a fervour, a vehemence of passion, that often makes me tremble at myself—for did it ever master me so far as to force a confession of it in the presence of its object, I never could look up again, but must and would for ever become an alien from all I love, and a friendless wanderer on the face of the earth."

Though shocked more deeply than he had any wish or power to express, Michael could not resist the belief, which came with terrible strength upon him, that his unhappy brother had conceived a passion for some married woman, and that his best chance of recovering both his virtue and his tranquillity would be by following the wish he had expressed, and by entering on a new and active career, to give himself a chance of obliterating from his mind the feelings which had so unhappily taken possession of it. Such a destination for Edward must of course destroy some of the very brightest of his own beautiful day-dreams but there was a fund of integrity and real goodness in the heart of Michael that permitted him not at that moment to think of himself. "Edward!" said he solemnly, "if this be so, follow the course that your better feelings have suggested—adopt at once the profession of a soldier. It has ever been accounted a noble one—though, under happier circumstances—but that matters not—if your passions have led you wrong, let your principles bring you back again. Confess the truth to your generous benefactress at once."

"Michael!" replied Edward, looking in his face with an expression of suffering that almost amounted to agony—"I would rather die first." These words seemed intended to close the conversation, or at any rate they did so; for the two brothers silently retraced their path to the house, and a fond pressure, expressive of love and pity, which Michael gave to the arm of Edward before he parted from it, was all that passed between them further at that time.

The interview of that morning with Miss Brotherton had awakened in the mind of Michael, feelings towards her which an hour before he would have thought it must have taken years to produce; but being equally sincere, both in his former timidity and his present confidence, he speedily made up his mind to open his heart to her, and do for his guilty, but suffering brother, what it was evident he had not courage to do for himself. In pursuance of this resolution, he again sought the heiress, and whispered in her ear, "Mary!—will you let me talk to you a little more?" She eagerly complied with the implied invitation, and passing her arm through his, accompanied him to the scene of their former *tête-à-tête*.

There was, no shyness on the part of Michael. The familiar appellation he had used was not assumed for the purpose of proving his obedience, but resulted from a genuine feeling of affectionate confidence in every word she had uttered, and which had left on his mind the belief that she was not only his generous patroness, but his loving friend

"I little thought when I was talking to you this morning about my poor self," he said, "that I should so soon have to take you away again from your drawing, to talk about Edward."

"About Edward?" said Mary colouring, "what do you wish to say about him, dear Michael?"

"It is something that he declares he would die rather than say to you himself;" replied Michael, "but I am certain that you ought to know it, for it is quite clear that there is no chance of happiness for him unless you agree to his wishes."

"What wishes?" exclaimed the heiress, terribly agitated, "for goodness
sake, Michael, do not trifle with me! Did Edward commission you to
speak to me?"

"Oh, no! had he felt courage to do *that*, I should have told him at once,
that he had better do it himself," replied Michael. "Indeed, I fear greatly
that he will be displeased with me; but I can't bear to see him so miserable
without mentioning it to the only person capable of helping him."

"Miserable?—Helping him?—Tell me, Michael, tell me at once what
you mean!"

"That is what I wish to do, dear Mary!" replied Michael, looking
with considerable surprise at her varying colour, and agitated features;
"I fear I am doing wrong, and that I have already said something that
vexes you."

"No, no!" cried Mary impatiently, "only, go on!"

"In one word, then," resumed Michael, "our dear Edward wishes
beyond all things to enter the Austrian service."

"And leave us!" returned the heiress, almost gasping. "Does Edward
want to leave me?"

"Do not suspect him of ingratitude, Mary!" cried Michael, eagerly;
"there is reason for it, and without this I am quite sure he would never
think of such a thing—Edward has conceived an unfortunate passion for
an object from whom he ought to fly—and this, of course, will explain
every thing to you."

"Let me see him! Let me hear him! From himself, and from himself
only I can hear this. Let it mean what it may." On uttering these words,
which were spoken with a very agitated and untranquil air, Mary
Brotherton rushed out of the room, much to Michael's astonishment,
for be could by no means comprehend *why* she should testify such
strong emotion, especially as he had so cautiously and delicately avoided
hinting any thing about a married woman's being unhappily the object
of his brother's passion.

In this ignorance of Michael's, the reader, I am very sorry to say, must
share. There are some facts which no wise historian will ever venture to
dilate upon, lest their strangeness should provoke incredulity; and great
wisdom is shown by such forbearance; for it is infinitely better that an

enlightened public should be driven to exclaim, *"How very obscure this passage is!"* than *"How very improbable!"*

Michael Armstrong is the hero of the book that is now drawing rapidly to its conclusion; and every reader has therefore a right to expect that his destiny shall be plainly announced to them, whatever mystery may hang over that of others. Whatever occurred between the heiress and Edward in the conference which they speedily held together, it did not cause any alteration in that lady's purpose of immediately returning to her chateau upon the Rhine. A man of worth and great ability was engaged to take charge of the richly teeming eager mind of Michael, during the two years that it was settled he should remain at a German university, and nothing could be more satisfactory than the result of this arrangement. Never, perhaps, were two years put to greater profit in the development of mind, than upon this occasion; and when they were ended, Michael Armstrong was able to take his station upon the beautiful terrace, without feeling that he was out of his place there.

Less than these two years had sufficed to bring to perfection all Mary Brotherton's plans for improving and beautifying her spacious residence. It was one of those super-terranean quarries which are sometimes seen to spread themselves to such miraculous extent in that region, and would have inspired most ladies with a feeling of dreary vastness, which, notwithstanding the exceeding beauty of its position, would have prevented any hope of rendering it comfortably habitable. But Mary had an ample heart, and an ample purse. Circumstances over which (to use a thoroughly authorized expression) she had no control, for in truth they had preceded her birth, had rendered her own country less dear to her than it is to most others; and she therefore not only determined to plant herself elsewhere, but to do so in such a manner as would enable her to make her new abode her home, in the best sense of the word, and this could only be done by giving

"Ample room, and verge enough,"

to make it the home of others also. Any travellers lucky enough to light upon this widely-spreading, but comfortable and thoroughly well kept-up abode, will find that, notwithstanding its great extent, it has, by no means, the air of being uninhabited. Nobody will be much surprised to hear that Michael Armstrong and Fanny Fletcher became man and wife, or that they proved a loving and very happy pair but, should any curious Rhenish tourist obtain an introduction to this Rhingau paradise, they will probably observe two very loving and happy pairs, to whom it serves as a common yet, in some sort, a separate home, each having its suite of drawing-rooms, boudoirs, nurseries, school-rooms, *et cetera*. But however much a gossiping inclination might lead to a more explicit detail, there is really no room left to enter upon it. All that can be said in addition to this is, that when Sir Matthew Dowling's affairs came to be wound up, there was discovered to be a sufficient surplus to afford a small independence to each of his children, which, being divided according to the proportion dictated by the knight's will, gave something approaching to a Benjamin's mess portion to his daughter Martha. To claim and receive this, as well as occasionally to visit some members of her family, Martha made frequent excursions to England, but her happiest hours were those she passed with her dear friends in Germany, by whom she is ever received with open arms.

Mrs Tremlett is still enjoying an old age of perfect comfort, cheered by warm affection, and is already the darling of many little hearts.

There is no record to be found in any documents relating to the inhabitants of the chateau, showing that Edward Armstrong ever entered the Austrian service. It is, therefore, most reasonable to suppose that this wish was never complied with.